The Birds of Bedfordshire

The Birds
of
Bedfordshire

by

PAUL TRODD
and
DAVID KRAMER

Bird Illustrations by
ANDREW P. CHICK

Castlemead
PUBLICATIONS
WELWYN GARDEN CITY

First published in 1991

CASTLEMEAD PUBLICATIONS
12 Little Mundells
Welwyn Garden City
Hertfordshire AL7 1EW

Proprietors: Ward's Publishing Services

ISBN 0 948555 15 7

© Paul Trodd and David Kramer 1991
Birds Illustrations © Andrew P. Chick 1991
Breeding Bird Maps © B. D. Harding 1979

British Library Cataloguing in Publication Data
Trodd, Paul
    The birds of Bedfordshire.
    I. Title   II. Kramer, David
    598.294256
    ISBN 0–948555–15–7

Phototypeset by Intype, London
Printed in Great Britain
in 10/11pt Century
by The Bath Press, Avon

This Book is Dedicated
to the Memory of
Jannion Steele-Elliott (1871–1942)
and Members Past and Present
of the
Bedfordshire Natural History Society

Foreword

Is is common? Is it rare? Is it here all year, or is it a migrant? When does it occur? Where? How many? Was it formerly more common? Why is it rarer now? When did it colonise Bedfordshire? How can I see it?

That is what a county avifauna is all about. Current local records are placed in geographical and temporal context, not only to satisfy the immediate curiosity of those interested in birdwatching and natural history, but also to provide an historical record of value 20, 50, or 100 years hence.

The interest in birds has grown markedly in recent decades, nowhere more so than in Bedfordshire. Back in the days of the first breeding bird survey (1968–77) there were more 10km squares in Bedfordshire than there were active local birdwatchers to visit them. Nowadays, with a repeat breeding bird atlas in progress, several keen and active local birders can be allocated to cover each square. The information being gathered from such surveys and censuses, and by individual birdwatchers visiting their local birdwatching spots, is the basis for this new book, which also delves into the historical record provided by earlier chroniclers.

I was born in Devon, went to school in Kent, and completed my education in Hampshire, but have lived more of my life in Bedfordshire than in any other county. This book recalls an abundance of memories for me and for countless other Bedfordshire birdwatchers, and will also be a constant source of reference now and for decades to come. Future researchers will have good reason to be grateful to the compilers for their labours.

J. T. R. Sharrock
British Birds
Blunham, Bedfordshire
August 1990

Preface

In a county as small and apparently well recorded as Bedfordshire it was difficult to imagine when our research began for this book in 1986 that we would be opening an ornithological Pandora's Box. How wrong we were! It seemed that the deeper we investigated the county archives the more fascinating the picture became: in one instance a species new to the county was discovered. Consultations with what would seem a straightforward contact often threw up anomalies sending us off pursuing another name, address or telephone number.

Inevitably the majority of material for this book was condensed from two main sources. The works of Jannion Steele-Elliott (1871–1942) were our base reference and it is only now that we can appreciate the importance of his writings when comparing the status of species then with those of today. To him we are greatly indebted.

However, the greatest single source of information came from the Bedfordshire Natural History Society in the form of annual bird reports, notes, and papers published in the *Bedfordshire Naturalist* from 1946. Also published by the Society was the *Bedfordshire Bird Atlas* (Harding 1979) whose tetrad maps are reproduced in Chapter 4. To all recorders and contributors to this estimable Society and its honorary officers both past and present we owe a special gratitude for this commitment over the past half century. Long may it continue so.

Along with other English counties, Bedfordshire suffers from a dearth of records between the Victorian era and the formation of the post-war Natural History Society. To fill this gap in our knowledge relevant information was extracted from the national journal *British Birds*, which is now based in the county at Blunham. Our thanks go to Dr J. T. R. Sharrock for access to a complete set of journals and to Robin Dazley for assistance with record extraction and collation.

The Nature Conservancy Council and the British Trust For Ornithology funded and supplied the ringing data, and the Wildfowl and Wetlands Trust provided details of the monthly wildfowl counts. To representatives of all three organisations we extend our gratitude.

On a more local basis Rosemary Brind at Bedford Museum has ably assisted us with the Steele-Elliott collection of bird skins and with access to the diaries of George North, an early twentieth-century egg-collector. Paul Hyman at Luton Museum has helped similarly and we thank them both for their time and support.

The Public Record Office at Bedford has been a valuable source of information as has the County Library, where we received much help and advice from Barry Stephenson. Brian Sawford at Letchworth Museum commented on historical records relating to the Hitchin area which included records for a part of east Bedfordshire. Thanks are also due to the Manshead Archaeological Society for access to their archives where Barry Horne was most helpful with the interpretation of remains from the second-century Roman cess pit.

In the preparatory stages of this work we received much advice and encouragement from county stalwarts Barry Nightingale, Peter Smith, Peter Wilkinson, Frank Gribble, and Don Green. The text was read by Robin Dazley, Martin Palmer, Barry Nightingale, Bernaud Nau, and Ian Dawson, whom we thank immeasurably; particularly Ian Dawson who commented, corrected, and criticised the entire species text in less than a fortnight.

We are most grateful to our publishers Alan Ward and Susan Lee of Castlemead Publications for their support throughout this venture. How fortunate we are in having a publisher who is so supportive of local natural history writings.

Paul would like to thank his wife Patricia for much early typing and support throughout the entire project, and to Sue Johnson for extensive word-processing at a time of great personal loss.

Our gratitude goes out to our photographers, particularly Mary Sheridan for her habitat photographs, and to Jonathan Palmer for his accurate and professionally produced figures and maps.

Finally, to more than anybody else we are eternally grateful to our artist Andrew Chick for his exquisite illustrations. Each one has been specially produced for this work with painstaking accuracy, and many are set in a familiar Bedfordshire scene. We are privileged indeed for them to grace the pages of this book.

PAUL TRODD AND DAVID KRAMER
September 1990

Contents

List of Figures

List of Colour Plates

List of Tables

1
Introduction

Exactly when birdwatching as a hobby began in Bedfordshire is difficult to establish. The earliest serious attempt to give an account of
the birds in any part of the county is that of Frederick Davis in 1855
with the publication of A *History of Luton* in which a list of 'Birds of
the Neighbourhood' is produced. The status of each species is given
as being common, scarce or rare and some local names are also given.

Most of the interest taken in birds during the nineteenth century
was by country gentlemen who shot them for sport. Some of these not
only took an interest in birds pursued as game but also made
occasional notes in their diaries (alas no longer extant) of other
unusual species or were sufficiently stimulated by their occurrence to
be able to recall details in later years. These would have been useless
to the modern researcher were it not for the efforts of Jannion Steele-
Elliott (1871–1942) who, when gathering material for his *Vertebrate
Fauna of Bedfordshire* (1897–1901), and later the Zoology section for
the Victoria County History (1904), corresponded with many of these
people and collected further information from articles in magazines,
newspapers, and journals. His publications are undoubtedly the first
milestones in a study of the county's avifauna. Steele-Elliott was born
in Midland Road, Bedford and attended Bedford Modern School from
1878 to 1887. He was a great traveller, visiting Lapland in 1896 and
St Kilda in 1894 where he found the first Subalpine Warbler for
Britain. As was the custom at that time he shot it. He was a collector
of eggs and skins which he later gave on trust partly to Luton Museum
and partly to his old school. The collections are now together and
housed in the Bedford Museum. This tall, powerful, athletically-built
man who once walked from London to Bedford with seemingly little
effort, accumulated much interesting information, most of which was
unfortunately lost in a fire at his beautiful home, Dowles Manor, at
Bewdley in Worcestershire.

The interest in shooting birds and in fishing during the second half
of the nineteenth century is reflected by the number of taxidermists
in the county at that time. At least three were present in the town of
Bedford towards the end of the century, one of whom, Mr Arthur
Covington, had a close association with Steele-Elliott and supplied
him with much information concerning specimens shot in the county.
Covington left Bedford Commercial School in 1861 and in 1864 set up
his own shop adjoining the old Coach and Horses in St Paul's Square.
He later moved to Foster Hill Road where he carried out his business
for a further 25 years. He died somewhere between 1921 and 1927
after being the best known local taxidermist for upwards of 50 years.

The Duchess of Bedford, more popularly known as the Flying Duchess, made a significant contribution to knowledge of birds during the
latter part of the nineteenth century and early part of the present

one, being a regular contributor to *British Birds* magazine. She was a keen and accurate observer, not only of plumage details but also of bird behaviour. Even by today's standards she was an enthusiastic birdwatcher and in her steam yacht *Saphire* often made trips up to her cottages at Barra and Fair Isle to watch the sea birds and migrants. She also had time to encourage the younger generation, taking under her wing her 'bird-boys', four local lads whom she more or less adopted. Not only did she provide them with suitable clothing but also took them on trips to her birdwatching haunts in Perthshire, the Tamar Valley, Barra, and Fair Isle. She insisted on them keeping accurate notes which she corrected and in 1912 the boys twice won the shield in the County Naturalists' Competition organised by the RSPB.

Another milestone in the recording of the county's avifauna was the arrival of Henry A. S. Key in 1934. A lively and dynamic personality and not averse to speaking his mind, he was responsible for the setting up of the Bedfordshire Natural History Society in 1946 and served it in various capacities, including that of President, for over 30 years. Full of enthusiasm, he urged its members to higher standards of observation and recording, ever improving the quality of the annual bird reports which appeared in its journal. He was a well-travelled man, having visited Lapland, Greenland, and Iceland all in the company of his wife. Henry Key did a great deal to spread his enthusiasm for birds, giving many talks himself to various societies. He also managed to get Peter Scott and Oliver G. Pike to address packed meetings at Bedford Town Hall. An Ornithological Section of the Natural History Society was constituted in October 1948 and attracted speakers such as James Fisher and Derek Goodwin. In March 1949 he organised the first of six annual Bedfordshire Ornithological Conferences. Looking back at some of the speakers it resembles a veritable Who's Who of ornithology, involving amongst others B. W. Tucker (then editor of *British Birds*), W. B. Alexander, E. M. Nicholson, G. H. Yeates, Dr Bruce Campbell, W. R. P. Bourne, R. A. O. Hickling, R. S. R. Fitter, R. A. Richardson, and R. P. Bagnall-Oakley. It is interesting to note that this type of ornithological conference has recently been introduced in other counties.

The increasing number of keen birdwatchers during the 1960s and 1970s and the initiative of the British Trust for Ornithology made possible major national projects, most important of which was the *Atlas of Breeding Birds in Britain and Ireland* (Sharrock 1976), followed by the *Atlas of Wintering Birds* (Lack 1986). Both these surveys have involved many birdwatchers in useful work and provided a great deal of information concerning the status of birds in the county. The work accumulated during the former project enabled the Bedfordshire Natural History Society to publish their own *Bedfordshire Bird Atlas*. Work on another breeding birds atlas is now in progress. The National Wildfowl Counts organised by the Wildfowl and Wetlands Trust have also provided a significant amount of important information.

The 1980s saw an increase in both the number and standard of birdwatchers in the county, a nucleus of whom are very dedicated.

Such is their enthusiasm that many of the county's major sites are now covered on an almost daily basis.

The increase in birdwatching and other recreational activities has brought its problems. The possibility of some sensitive sites suffering too much disturbance became a reality, but most birdwatchers responded well to this, once it was recognised, and regulated their activities. Making the general public aware of the problems of disturbance has been less easy. Many areas have been opened to the public and access made easier. This is to be welcomed but has resulted in some areas being heavily used by dog walkers and others, some of whom pay little attention to notices and allow dogs to run around in important breeding areas or even send dogs in to chase ducks from water areas in winter. The Bedfordshire and Huntingdonshire Trust (now the Bedfordshire and Cambridgeshire Wildlife Trust) has done much in recent years to improve public awareness. Bedfordshire County Council as well as local councils have improved their awareness of environmental issues and planning is much more sympathetic than it used to be. The creation of country parks such as those at Bedford, Stewartby, and Harrold has proved popular and shown that there is a demand for such areas, but there is still much to learn about their management.

For the ornithologist interested in the wider aspects of natural history in Bedfordshire, *Bedfordshire Wildlife* (Nau *et al.* 1987) is a thoroughly recommended source of information. As well as describing the county's flora and fauna, habitats, too, are discussed, both in an historical context and with consideration of what shape they may take in the future.

2
The Bedfordshire Environment

2.1 Geology

The geology of the county shows a wide variety of rock types arranged in a simple way. It determines to a large extent the flora of the county which in turn affects the variety of bird species. In Bedfordshire the use made of land rather than the geological formations is perhaps of greater influence in determining the species of birds which breed and, to some extent, those which pause in the county whilst they are on passage. The geology can be divided into two types, the solid geology and the drift geology. The solid geology is that which was laid down between 150 and 70 million years ago during which time the land was often covered by the sea.

Solid Geology
The strata follow an approximate north-east/south-west alignment with the south of the county being mainly composed of Chalk. This line of chalk follows two scarps, one along the line of Dunstable Downs, Blows Downs, and Warden Hills, all reaching 180m, the other through Totternhoe and Sundon to Barton Hills and Deacon Hill, reaching around 150m. Further north the Chalk falls to the Gault Clay and then drops further to the Lower Greensand. The Oxford Clay dominates the northern half of the county, only interrupted by a high (90m) area of Great Oolite and Cornbrash Limestone in the north-west.

Drift Geology
The solid geology has been altered by the effects of drift and deposition. The chalk downlands provide the main feature of the southern part of the county, with the Clay-with-Flints covering the highest parts of the chalk in the very south and, like the Greensand, are acidic. The Lower Greensand, along with the Clay-with-Flints, provides the main areas of woodland which are mainly coniferous. Boulder Clay of glacial origin covers some of the Lower Greensand and much of the Oxford Clay. It is very variable but is usually alkaline. The Marston Vale is an area of drift deposits overlaying the Oxford Clay and the extraction of clay for the brick industry dominates this region. The rather desolate landscape created by pits provides habitat for waders and gulls. Disused pits eventually become flooded and in severe winters the deep pits around Stewartby, Brogborough, and Kempston Hardwick are the last to freeze up and thus provide the only refuges for winter wildfowl at this time. The Boulder Clay in the north of the county provides the second main area of woodland.

The alkaline Valley Gravels are present along the Ouse, Ivel, Flit, Ouzel, and Lea Valleys, being more extensive around Bedford and

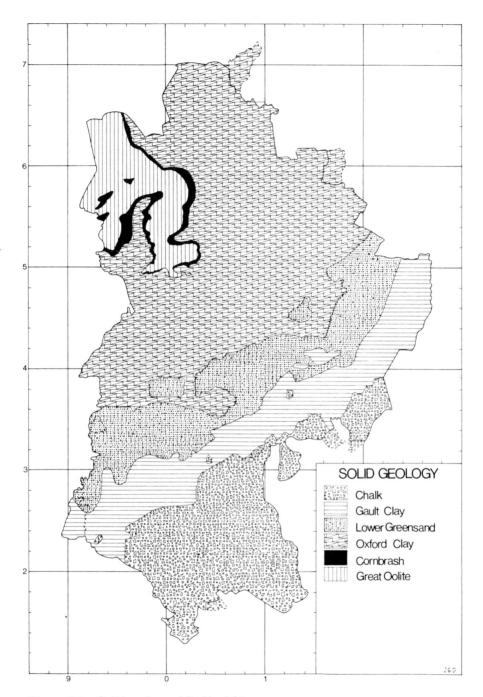

Figure 2.1   *Solid geology of Bedfordshire*

Biggleswade. The abundance of gravel along the Ouse Valley has inevitably lead to its exploitation and the formation of gravel pits at Harrold/Odell, Radwell, Priory Country Park, Willington, Wyboston, South Mills, Blunham, and Langford. As with the clay pit lakes these

5

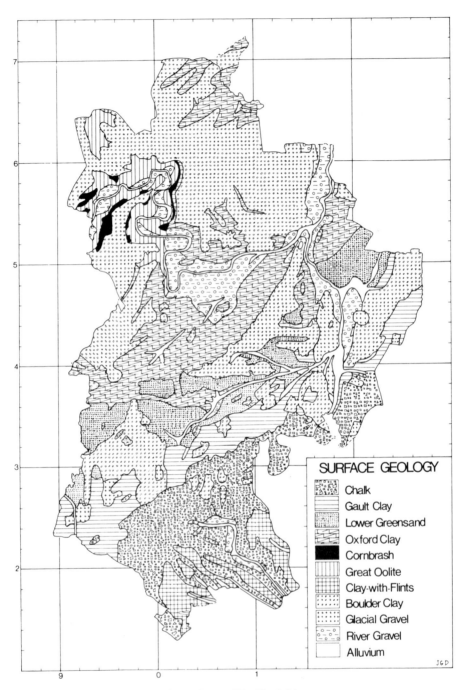

SURFACE GEOLOGY

	Chalk
	Gault Clay
	Lower Greensand
	Oxford Clay
	Cornbrash
	Great Oolite
	Clay-with-Flints
	Boulder Clay
	Glacial Gravel
	River Gravel
	Alluvium

JGD

Figure 2.2   *Surface (drift) geology of Bedfordshire*

areas provide a variety of habitats depending on the amount of inundation and succession of flora and fauna.

The Ivel Valley contains the best farmland in the county, much of it being classified as Grade I by the Ministry of Agriculture and the

6

Figure 2.3 *Bedfordshire: towns, villages, main roads, and railways*

remainder as Grade II, with the exception of the narrow strips of floodplain adjoining the rivers which is Grade IV. The intensification of farming in these high-grade areas has resulted in the removal of many ancient hedgerows and weedy areas leaving them less attractive to birds than they were in former times. The wet meadows can attract such breeding birds as Snipe and Redshank. They tend to be too dry during the summer months but could be improved by suitable management.

Peat-formed fens once occupied a large area in the centre of the county but only a few remnants remain, the largest being Flitwick Moor.

2.2 Climate and Weather

The diversity of animal and plant life in Britain is very much determined by climate as well as physical and geological factors. Temperature tends to be lower further north whilst humidity and rainfall decreases as one goes east. Bedfordshire is characterised by having a low rainfall and wide extremes in temperature, these factors combining to give a more Continental climate.

There is little difference in temperature over the county with the lowest being recorded in January and February (4–5 °C) and the highest in July (16–17 °C). Being inland and very low-lying the annual range of temperature is about 12 °C, greater than in any other part of Britain except East Anglia. Low temperatures can have a severe effect on bird life but it is not so much the low temperature itself nor the number of days in a year when low temperatures occur but the number of *consecutive* days.

Although Bedfordshire is one of the lowest rainfall areas in the country, the south tends to be wetter due to the presence of the Chiltern Hills and the Greensand Ridge. This is related to altitude, the northern part of the county having an average annual rainfall of about 550mm compared with 750mm in the south. The largest proportion of the rain falls in the months of October, November, and December with 30% of the total while February, March, and April are the driest with 20%. There is not much difference in the number of days of snow over the county but that which falls on the higher ground is usually deeper due to lower temperatures and more likely to effect birds.

South-west winds predominate for most of the year but these have little effect unless they are exceptionally strong, as in the hurricane of October 1987 which resulted in the county's first record of Sabine's Gull along with nine Great Skuas and a Grey Phalarope. When sustained easterly or north-easterly winds coincide with the spring or autumn, sea birds are often blown inland. Fulmars, Leach's Petrels, Gannets, Kittiwakes, and Arctic Terns are just some examples of birds which have turned up in the county on these occasions. It is interesting to note that in August 1987 and in September 1989 large flocks of Sandwich Terns arrived after thunderstorms.

In recent years we have had some very mild winters followed by hot periods during the summer months and occasional very strong winds which have been attributed to the 'Greenhouse Effect'. Similar types of weather have occurred before and only time will tell if this will become a permanent feature of our climate.

2.3 Water Areas

The water areas of Bedfordshire are composed of its rivers, parkland lakes, flooded mineral extraction pits, water meadows, and marsh. Sewage lagoons and, more recently, farm irrigation lagoons have also contributed to these water areas. Apart from the rivers there are no natural open areas of water.

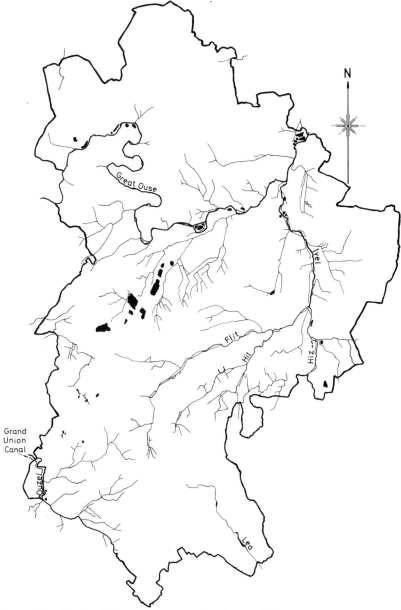

Figure 2.4 *Bedfordshire: rivers, canals, pits, and lakes*

Until the middle of this century the only still water areas of any ornithological significance were the artificial lakes at Southill, Woburn, and Battlesden. Other artificial lakes were to be found at Old Warden Park and Tingrith Manor.

Mineral extraction pits fall into three main types; sand and gravel pits, clay pits, and chalk pits.

The extraction of sand and gravel has been carried out in the county for centuries to provide materials for the building industry but the amount extracted before the end of the nineteenth century was very small. The pits created only fulfilled very local needs and this continued with a relatively small increase in production until the start of the Second World War. Thus mineral extraction pits did not play an important part in the distribution of the county's avifauna until around the middle of this century. During the Second World War gravel was extracted at Felmersham to provide material for the runways at Thurleigh and Cranfield. Since that time relatively local building projects such as the construction of the M1 motorway, the creation of Milton Keynes, and the building expansion taking place in Northampton have resulted in a continued demand for sand and gravel which, in turn, has resulted in the creation of more pits. These building projects are very much influenced by such factors as the mortgage rate and the level of public expenditure and it is interesting that the creation of an important part of the county's habitat is greatly influenced by the country's economy.

Many of the older pits have been filled with refuse, a role for which they are no longer very suitable, being too shallow to accommodate any significant amount of the huge quantities now produced.

The gravel quarries are situated along the county's river systems. The extraction methods in the earlier pits, such as Cople and the two small pits at Priory Country Park, resulted in parallel strips of sand and gravel remaining after extraction was complete. This resulted in what are known as 'finger lakes' which, unless managed, become overgrown to such an extent that little light reaches the water and aquatic life becomes very poor. The more recent lakes are larger, only about 3–4m deep, tend to have steep sides, a narrow shoreline, and regular outline. When the extraction of gravel is complete the pits are very barren, but the presence of a few pools may attract waders. The lack of food results in them soon moving on again. Occasionally vertical faces have provided suitable places for Sand Martins to colonise. As with the clay and chalk pits, piles of earth and rubble are often left at these sites which provide suitable habitat for Wheatears, Whinchats, and occasionally Stonechats on passage.

Figure 2.5 (Top)   *Fullers Earth quarry at Wavendon Heath supporting a large Sand Martin colony*

Figure 2.6 (Centre)   *Willington Gravel Pit, an actively worked pit in the Ouse valley. A classic site for breeding Little Ringed Plover*

Figure 2.7 (Lower)   *South Mills Nature Reserve, a disused gravel pit in the Ivel valley now managed for wildlife and of particular importance to breeding Redshank*

11

In the early stages water accumulates and is retained by the layer of clay underlying the gravel. The pools thus created attract waders on passage and bare gravel areas provide suitable breeding habitat for Common Terns, Little Ringed and Ringed Plovers.

Flooding of these pits may remove this type of habitat but several, such as those at Harrold Country Park, Priory Country Park, and Radwell, have islands which remained after flooding and provided places for Common Terns and Redshank as well as the previous species. Wyboston Gravel Pit however was less fortunate, no islands remained after flooding, and the colony of Common Terns was wiped out.

As vegetation increases these sites become less suitable, but the Common Terns continue to occupy them to a later stage of plant colonisation than the two plovers. Unless these sites are managed, further nesting is prohibited. Thus the populations of these species in the county tend to fluctuate as some sites become unsuitable and new ones are created. Tern rafts have been placed at some of the sites to encourage breeding.

After flooding it is not long before Coot, Great Crested Grebes, and Mute Swans take up residence. Tufted Duck and a few Pochard may also move in to breed. If flooding takes place after vegetation is well established, the initial presence of nutrients in the water encourages aquatic vegetation and a subsequent increase in the invertebrate population. It often results in a very large growth of Canadian water-weed, which floats to the surface in vast rafts and can cover the whole of the water surface. After about three years the nutrients become exhausted and the weed declines to almost nothing. This has been observed at Harrold Country Park and Priory Country Park. Tufted Ducks and Pochard are amongst the several species of wintering ducks at this stage. Many of the flooded gravel pits are connected to a river and fish are able to enter. As the lakes are shallow they soon warm up and provide excellent conditions for fish to breed and develop. As a result, many of these lakes support an abundant fish population and fish-eating birds such as Cormorant, Goosander, Red-breasted Merganser, and the occasional diver may be seen.

Marginal vegetation is often slow to establish itself as the sides are often steep and subject to erosion. Where common reed does develop, either naturally or introduced by man, Reed Warblers begin to colonise whilst the Sedge Warbler often prefers the drier areas of willow.

The hawthorn scrub and hedges associated with many gravel pits has attracted the Great Grey Shrike on several occasions and the

Figure 2.8 (Top) *Rookery Clay Pit, an actively worked pit with shallow lagoons, islands, and marginal growth, an important site for wetland birds including passage waders*

Figure 2.9 (Centre) *Stewartby Lake, a flooded clay pit supporting a wide range of riparian species*

Figure 2.10 (Lower) *Brogborough No. 2 Clay Pit, an exhausted pit now used for waste disposal, attracting thousands of wintering Gulls*

county's only record of Woodchat Shrike was also observed in this habitat.

The clay pits are concentrated in the Marston Vale around Stewartby, Millbrook, Brogborough, Kempston Hardwick, and Elstow. The removal of the Oxford Clay leaves steep-sided pits about 20–30m deep. At first the bottoms of these pits are very uneven, covered with small hummocks and pools. Plant colonisation is fairly slow and at this stage may provide suitable habitat for breeding Redshanks, Lapwings, and Black-headed Gulls, while Lesser Black-backed and Herring Gulls have also bred. Immediately after excavation is completed the invertebrate population is extremely low and, although occasional waders may be attracted down, they usually depart after a short time. After two or three years, visiting waders in spring and autumn become more frequent. Clay pits may flood quite slowly, usually with run-off rain water. They are slow to acquire aquatic vegetation and an invertebrate population as unlike gravel pits they are not adjacent to rivers and do not gain aquatic life when rivers flood. Their steep sides are not very suitable for the establishment of marginal vegetation and the lack of a gradually sloping shoreline after flooding usually makes them unattractive to waders on passage. Being very deep, they are the last to freeze over in severe winters and thus become the last refuge for the county's wildfowl. Both Stewartby and Brogborough Lakes are used for water sports and the disturbance caused by this deters wildfowl. At Brogborough Lake, an area of shallower water at the southern end has more aquatic vegetation. The presence of submerged machinery in this area makes it dangerous and thus out of bounds for sail boarding. This acts as a refuge zone when sailboarding is taking place and large numbers of wildfowl may congregate here in winter.

The completion of deep clay pits in Bedfordshire occurred at the same time as London was experiencing severe problems in finding suitable sites to dispose of its rubbish. London's problem has been solved by transporting many thousands of tons of waste to be dumped in the county's clay pits. This has attracted huge numbers of gulls which feed on the rubbish during the day and most of which roost overnight on the water areas of Stewartby and Brogborough Lakes.

The pit at Houghton Regis is the only chalk pit of any great importance for birds but this is less due to the small flooded area than to the land which surrounds it. Part of this can become quite marshy and has attracted breeding Redshanks in the summer, while it is a good place to find Jack Snipe in the winter. Its 'moonscape' features attract some unusual species. Both Wheatear and Stonechat have bred and the county's first Black-winged Stilt this century was recorded there. Unfortunately this potentially good habitat suffers constant disturbance from motorcycles. Vertical cliff faces have provided suitable nesting sites for several species including Stock Doves and Little Owl.

The River Great Ouse, the River Ivel, and the River Ouzel are the major rivers in the county with the River Flit, the River Lea, and the River Hiz completing the river system. A short length of the Grand

Figure 2.11 *Houghton Regis Chalk Pit, disused, whose shallow marl lake, reed bed, and willow scrub attract a wide range of species all year round*

Union Canal cuts across the south-west of the county. None of the county's rivers are truly natural as all have been altered by man for centuries. This has resulted in the loss of many valuable sites for wildlife and, in particular, reduced the areas of flooded meadow. Until the early 1980s the Anglian Water Authority 'improved' rivers by straightening the water course, making it uniform depth, often removing islands and making rather steep sides thus reducing marginal vegetation. This had a severe effect on breeding birds as is shown in the following tables.

TABLE 2.1 *Survey of breeding pairs on a 650m stretch of the River Ivel near Blunham before and after river works in 1978*

	1977	1979	1982
Little Grebe	2	0	0
Mallard	1	0	1
Moorhen	6	2	1
Kingfisher	1	0	0
Sedge Warbler	7	0	0
Reed Bunting	3	0	1
Total	20	2	3

TABLE 2.2 *A survey of nests on the River Great Ouse near Clapham before and after river works in 1981*

	1980	1982
Coot	7	0
Moorhen	5	1
Little Grebe	1	0
Total	13	1

15

Figure 2.12 *The River Great Ouse at Great Barford, a classic haunt of the Kingfisher*

In 1980 the Water Space Amenity Commission published its Conservation and Land Drainage Guidelines showing how improvements could be made without producing such a negative impact on wildlife. These guidelines have been adopted by the Anglian Water Authority

Figure 2.13 *Dunstable Sewage Works, important for wintering Gadwall and Shoveler*

and it is hoped that this will mark a turning-point in the management of Bedfordshire's rivers.

The use of boats on the river has increased considerably since 1975 and in 1978 it was made possible to cruise to the North Sea from Bedford. The impact of boating and the creation of moorings has not been assessed.

Despite human interference, the rivers still provide an important habitat for several species such as Little Grebe, Moorhen, Kingfisher, Reed Warbler, Sedge Warbler, and Reed Bunting.

The old type of sewage purification works may have effluent lagoons which are particularly attractive to birds. Their waters are rich in nutrients and have an abundant aquatic insect fauna. Many rare waders have been recorded at sewage works. These have included all five records of Pectoral Sandpiper as well as Temminck's Stint, Sharp-tailed Sandpiper, Wilson's Phalarope, and Avocet. Unfortunately for birdwatchers, most of these areas have disappeared with the introduction of modern sewage treatment.

A recent addition to the types of still water habitat in the county is the farm irrigation lagoon. They tend to lack marginal vegetation and as the water level fluctuates greatly they have as yet had little influence on the surrounding bird life.

2.4 Woodland

Until Neolithic man began clearing the forests of England some 3,000 years ago the Bedfordshire landscape would have been dominated by primeval woodland. Today the wild woods are gone forever with only relict secondary woodland and mixed plantation now in existence. Indeed Bedfordshire is one of the country's least wooded counties with only 5% of tree cover remaining, the majority of which is fragmented along the Greensand Ridge. There are fewer than 20 woods over 50 hectares in size, along with many small predominantly farmland copses and spinnies, most of which are of little importance to birdlife due to neglect and isolation. However, the diversity of woodlands across Bedfordshire is such that a typical cross-section of English lowland species can be found; albeit in lesser numbers and in woods of less splendour than in some of our neighbouring counties.

Of our three main woodland types the plantations on the Greensand Ridge are probably the most important, forming a scattered canopy across the centre of the county from Heath and Reach to Potton. Stockgrove Country Park contains a fine example of a dry sessile oak wood and supports good numbers of hole-nesting species such as woodpeckers, tits, and Nuthatch. The nearby complex to the west of Woburn is made up of predominantly alien conifers with some native Scots pine, birch, and sweet chestnut, often with an understorey of bracken, bilberry, and rhododendron. Here Nightjar, Redstart, and Wood Warbler still cling precariously to their status as breeding birds, while in winter a passing Hen Harrier or Buzzard may occur. Further east the even-aged plantation woodland near Maulden is much damper

Figure 2.14 (Top) *Maulden Wood, a typical Greensand woodland managed by the Forestry Commission, stronghold of the Lady Amherst's Pheasant*

Figure 2.15 (Lower) *Coopers Hill, one of the few relic Greensand heaths in the county, home of the Tree Pipit and Green Woodpecker and formerly the Red-backed Shrike*

Figure 2.16 *Marston Thrift, a deciduous wood with some coppiced areas, part managed by the Beds and Cambs Wildlife Trust*

as it is situated on a clay cap, and hosts an important naturalised population of the spectacular Lady Amherst's Pheasant. An abundance of leaf and scrub warblers can be found in the young thickets of oak, ash, and larch, and the numerous fire-break rides create precious edge habitat. Nearby Warden Wood is different again, containing many limes and hornbeams. Woods around Northill and at Potton harbour fluctuating populations of Nightingale and Grasshopper Warbler, while Woodcock and Tree Pipit can occur throughout the Greensand woodlands displaying across open glades. Heathland is now very scarce along this dry ridge with the only significant survivals at The Lodge, Sandy and Coopers Hill, Ampthill, where the Woodlark and Red-backed Shrike of yesteryear are no longer present. The woods of the Greensand Ridge continue to throw up surprises with occasional breeding Firecrest and Crossbill, the elusive Long-eared Owl, and perhaps the secretive Goshawk amongst the abundant Sparrowhawk sightings.

North and west of the Greensand Ridge in the boulder clay country around Sharnbrook and Odell occur our larger deciduous woods. Odell Great Wood is the finest, comprising typically oak and ash standards with an understorey of maple and hazel of which some evidence of

Figure 2.17 (Top) *Bramingham Wood, a clay-with-flint wood owned by the Woodland Trust, on the outskirts of Luton*

Figure 2.18 (Lower) *Flitwick Moor, a damp carr-type wood in the Flit valley, which supports the county's only regular breeding population of Water Rail*

former coppicing remains. Wide tracks dissect the wood with inden-
tations forming the species-rich woodland edge strip. West Wood,
Halsey, Great Hayes, Forty Acre, Dungee, and Park Wood are similar
in type and together form an important complex for familiar woodland
species together with increasing numbers of winter Buzzard records.

The third main woodland type is associated with the area to the
south of Luton and Dunstable on the clay-with-flints. The majority
are only small copses of oak, ash, sycamore, hornbeam, and birch,
with a scattering of holly and wild cherry. Some, such as Deadmansey
Wood, are now of little value for birdlife as alien conifers have matured
into tight dark blocks of timber, which is in stark contrast to Bush
Wood at Chaul End where the county's most ancient hornbeams exist.
The light airy birch woods at Luton Hoo are of particular interest as
here regularly occurs the Hawfinch, our most 'difficult' passerine.

An important woodland which falls outside the three main types is
found at Flitwick Moor. Situated in the Flit valley it is a very wet
carr-type wood of alder, birch, and willows with much herbaceous
growth during the summer months. Water Rail regularly breed
amongst the tangle of growth and often substantial flocks of Siskin
and Redpoll occur. Another river valley wood of interest is found
along the Ouse at Willington where straight rows of poplar have been
planted. The soft timber is particularly loved by woodpeckers, and
Whitethroats are commonly found nesting in the luxuriant nettle
cover. Other smaller carr-type pockets of woodland exist at Felmersham and Arlesey.

Looking to the future for the county's woodlands some encouraging
signs are emerging. Bramingham Wood on the edge of Luton is a
shining example of what can be done to improve an almost 'dead' wood
by rotational coppicing and creating glades and rides. Parts of Marston
Thrift have been likewise improved and sporadically attract Nightingale to breed in the blackthorn thickets and at The Lodge, Sandy,
active management by the RSPB has re-created a rich woodland/heath
habitat.

However, perhaps the most exciting project was the recent planting
of a new wood on existing farmland at Pulloxhill by the County Council, to be known as Centenary Wood. Comprising 13 hectares, the
woodland will provide a wide range of native trees and shrubs,
benefiting all forms of wildlife for generations to come. The County
Council is to be congratulated for its vision, and will one hopes show
the way forward to other landowners in an effort to restore our scant
woodland cover.

2.5 Farmland

The surface area of Bedfordshire is, today, predominantly farmland,
of which the majority is intensively worked arable land. The landscape
in the north of the county and between the Greensand Ridge to the
chalklands in the south is typically dominated by broad fields of cereals, mainly wheat and barley, and oil-seed rape. In places the local

Figure 2.19 (Top)   *Farmland at Steppingley*

Figure 2.20 (Lower)   *Typical flat open 'prairie' arable land at Potsgrove*

scenery has taken on a prairie-like appearance with only the widely scattered farmhouses and outbuildings breaking up the monotony. Field boundaries are normally defined by well-drained ditches, surviving hedgerows, usually low and stunted, and border roads or tracks. Consequently bird densities are lower in this habitat than anywhere else in the county. The Skylark, Yellowhammer, and Corn Bunting are familiar farmland birds as well as the two partridge species, and during the summer the Whitethroat is present. The ash is a common hedgerow tree, and important for hole-nesting species such as the Little Owl and Tree Sparrow as well as providing observation perches for Kestrel and Hobby.

In recent years increasing acreages of field bean and pea have been grown and are proving most attractive to early nesting Lapwing, while later on in the breeding season Quail have found a preference for pea fields. Reed Bunting and Yellow Wagtail have also adapted to these leguminous crops, with the former species in particular having also found a breeding niche in oil-seed rape.

Ley meadows and permanent pasture are now very scarce in Bedfordshire due to changing farming practices and the river valley flood meadow is almost a distant memory. Most hay fields consist of rye grass for silage making and, when cut, attract flocks of corvids and Starlings for a day or two. Pastureland, such as can be found in the Totternhoe/Eaton Bray district, continues to attract the gregarious Rook and is of particular importance during the winter months for passerines feeding on livestock foodstuffs. Across the county stock consists of a mixture of dairy and beef cattle, horses, and occasional flocks of sheep.

In the Ivel Valley market gardening still thrives with a particular emphasis on brassica and root crops. Golden Plover and Lapwing flocks favour this area in winter and from time to time the Merlin is reported hunting parties of Skylark, finches, and buntings which frequent the many 'weedy' fields.

Although much of the county's farmland is geared for maximum crop production and is consequently detrimental to wildlife, there are some encouraging signs ahead. A greater awareness by landowners and farmers, together with the 'set aside' scheme have brought about improvements such as reinstated hedgerows, tree planting, and unsprayed field boundaries. These all bode well for the future and with sympathy and vision there is no reason why good crop yields and conservation cannot go hand in hand into the next century.

2.6 Downland

The section of chalk downland straddling the southern tip of the county is but a small part of the Chiltern Hills range, an Area of Outstanding Natural Beauty, with the viewpoints at Dunstable Downs and Sharpenhoe Clappers two of the finest in Bedfordshire. The region is perhaps more important botanically, especially in areas where management programmes have been implemented such as at Warden Hills and Whipsnade Downs.

Until the nineteenth century the chalklands were extensively sheep-grazed, ensuring a close-cropped sward for a whole community of interdependent plants and insects. The Skylark would then have been an abundant species, both during the breeding season and in the autumn when many thousands were trapped annually for food. The eerie cry of the Stone Curlew was heard at nightfall and Whinchat and Red-backed Shrike bred commonly in the hawthorn and bramble patches. Today hawthorn scrub dominates the scene and the curlew, chat, and shrike are no more. The warbler tribe is now the main bird family with Willow Warbler, Garden Warbler, and Whitethroat

Figure 2.21 *Blows Downs, an important migration watchpoint, particularly in the spring when Ring Ouzel are regularly noted*

predominating. Turtle Dove, Linnet, and Yellowhammer have also exploited the thick cover along with the ever numerous Magpie, which form large winter roosts at Whipsnade Downs.

From Warden Hills across to Pegsdon the countryside is open crop downland, mainly cultivated, but interspersed with several areas of classic calcareous pasture. Probably most impressive of all is the Great Combe at Deacon Hill, which was one of the last strongholds of the Red-backed Shrike in Bedfordshire. Meadow Pipit and Skylark breed commonly on the nearby lynchets whilst 'eared' owls and raptors are often recorded hunting over the scrub.

Where a patchwork of scrub occurs migration can be more easily monitored filtering along the escarpment. Recent fieldwork at Blows Downs during the spring has proven a steady passage of Wheatear, Ring Ouzel, and Redstart. Further studies are required on the more protracted autumn passage in order to establish the pattern of returning thrushes and warblers.

Beech, common elsewhere along the Chilterns, never reaches the spectacular heights of a Buckinghamshire hangar and is restricted to Sundon Hills, Sharpenhoe Clappers, Barton Hills, and Totternhoe Knolls. Intermingled amongst the hawthorn scrub are elderberry, dogwood, wild rose, and bramble and at Skimpot Down a blackthorn thicket is of particular note. On Winsdon Hill several patches of spindle occur while further down the slope a small wood of hornbeam, ash, and sycamore has developed adding to the variety of cover.

2.7 Parks and Gardens

The parkland habitat on Bedfordshire's country estates is richer in species than almost anywhere else in the county. The lure of woodland, water, and scattered timber on permanent pasture, often in private environs, is nowhere more exemplified than at our two grandest stately homes at Woburn Abbey and Luton Hoo. Ancient parkland oaks are attractive to Nuthatch and woodpeckers as well as Jackdaw, Stock Dove, and Little Owl. At Woburn deer park large numbers of gulls and corvids congregate on open pastureland during the winter months and the peripheral deciduous belts support an abundance of woodland species. Wildfowl are well represented on the still waters with occasional passage waders attracted to the lakeside margins. Other prime examples of parkland habitat can be found at Wrest Park, Southill, Shuttleworth, and Ampthill.

Town parks in Bedford and Luton, complete with shallow boating lakes and a wide range of native and exotic tree species provide much-needed open space for the human population as well as our more familiar garden birds.

Gardens in both town and countryside vary considerably. Where

Figure 2.22   *Woburn Park: permanent deer pasture with ancient oaks attracts a wealth of parkland species such as Jackdaw, Nuthatch, and Stock Dove*

Figure 2.23 *Tim Sharrock's back garden at Blunham, headquarters of* British Birds

several large gardens merge together to form extensive shrubberies many species occur, particularly in winter when bird feeding stations are maintained to augment food supplies. Apart from the usual collection of tits and thrushes the majority of the county's Waxwing records have occurred in the garden environment. Buildings are often important for breeding species, none more so than the Swift and House Martin which nest almost exclusively in an urban setting.

3
Systematic List

This systematic list follows the sequence and scientific nomenclature of Voous (1977). It contains records up to and including 1987: further selected records for 1988 and 1989 are given in Appendices C and D. Map references are to the maps in Chapter 4, taken from the *Bedfordshire Bird Atlas* (Harding 1979). The fieldwork for this frequently mentioned volume took place in the 10-year period 1968–77. Square brackets denote doubtful records, either possible escapes or with insufficient information for a full county attribution. For the abbreviations see Appendix B.

Red-throated Diver

Gavia stellata

A very rare winter visitor.

Steele-Elliott (1904) listed six winter records between 1886 and 1898, all of which were killed. One at Felmersham in January 1897 was found to contain, in its gullet, nine roach, each from three to four inches long.

The period 1946–87 produced 12 occurrences predominantly from November to February but there were also two records in April and May which probably relate to passage birds. All except one were in non-breeding plumage and many showed signs of oil pollution. This species is prone to 'wrecking', as in 1958, also hard weather influxes, such as in 1979, described by Chandler (1981). Records for the post-war study period were as follows:

- 1947 One on the River Ouse near Kempston on 22 February.
- 1956 A single, oiled bird at Kempston Hardwick ClP 27–30 December moved to Stewartby ClP where it stayed until the end of April 1957 when it died: its remains were found on an island.
- 1958 One, found in a ditch at Henlow on 29 November was released at Tring Reservoirs, Hertfordshire the next day but died on 6 December. Singles at Shefford and Chicksands, also on 29 November, were released at Stewartby ClP the following day. All three records were part of a 'wreck' which took place across much of south-east England.
- 1963 One on the River Ouse near Bedford SF on 20 January.
- 1966 An oiled bird in partial summer plumage at Stewartby Lake on 6 April.

1967 One, also oiled, on the River Ouse near Bedford SF and Barkers Lane GP between 11 April and 21 May.

1970 One at Kensworth on 30 January was taken to Whipsnade Park Zoo where it died two days later.

1979 Singles at Blunham Lake 22–4 January and 16–24 February.

1986 One at Stewartby Lake on 11 January was found entangled in fishing net and released unharmed.

Black-throated Diver

Gavia arctica

A very rare winter visitor.

The corpse of a supposed Great Northern Diver shot at Cardington Mill on 4 February 1830 is in the Steele-Elliott collection at Bedford Museum, where it has recently been identified as a Black-throated Diver. A second-hand report of a Black-throated Diver on a fishmonger's stall at Northampton on 20 February 1897, said to have been shot at Wootton (*Journal of the Northants Natural History Society and Field Club*) was the only record known to Steele-Elliott (1904).

This species has occurred in only 10 years (including one corpse) between 1946 and 1987, all except one from January to March, as follows:

1946 An immature at Southill Lake on 24 February for two weeks followed north-east gales.

1947 A dead immature at Kempston Hardwick ClP on 28 March.

1954 One at Arlesey ChP between 23 and 30 January.

1957 An immature at Arlesey ChP from 23 January to 13 February.

1960 One at Stewartby ClP from 31 January to 21 February.

1963 The remains of a male (about three weeks dead) were found at Stewartby Lake on 31 March.

1966 One, slightly oiled, bird at Wyboston GP from 27 February to 6 March.

1978 One at Elstow ClP 25–6 February.

1985 One at Stewartby Lake on 19 January stayed until 2 February.

1986 One briefly at Harrold CP on 30 November.

Great Northern Diver

Gavia immer

A very rare winter visitor.

The first supposed record of this large diver in the county came from Cardington Mill on 4 February 1830 when one was shot on the frozen River Ouse (Steele-Elliott 1904). This record was also included by F. O. Morris (1860). However, recent studies of the corpse at Bedford Museum have revealed it to be a Black-throated Diver. One shot at Cox's Pit, Biddenham in December 1876 was therefore the only nineteenth-century occurrence.

Subsequently there have been only three recent records:

- 1977   One in partial summer plumage at the Blue Lagoon, Arlesey 26–30 November coincided with other records in southern England.
- 1978   One at Stewartby Lake on 15 January.
- 1983   One briefly at Priory CP on 3 February.

Little Grebe

Tachybaptus ruficollis

A widespread resident and winter visitor (**Map 1**).

The Little Grebe was formerly a scarce breeding bird in the county, nesting irregularly on the country park lakes at Woburn, Southill, and Luton Hoo, and along the quieter reaches of the Rivers Ouse and Ouzel (Steele-Elliott 1904). It was known locally as the Didchick, Diadobber, or Dabchick, the latter name being widely used today.

As a result of the expansion in quarrying activities during the post-war period the Little Grebe's breeding status has improved and it now breeds on the majority of the county's still waters. Harding (1979) recorded evidence of breeding in 53 (14%) of the county's tetrads with confirmed breeding at 10 sand and gravel pits, five clay pits, two chalk pits, seven parkland lakes, and at five riverside localities. A survey conducted by a team from Cambridge University in 1983 suggested that this species is under-recorded along the county's river systems as nine confirmed breeding territories were found along a two-mile section of the River Ouse.

29

The Little Grebe prefers to breed on waters with thick marginal and emergent vegetation, in which it can anchor its nest made from water weed and other aquatic plants. From March onwards its distinctive whinnying trill can best be heard at dawn or dusk as it becomes highly territorial. Two, sometimes three broods of four to six young are reared, making for a protracted breeding season.

During the autumn and winter months the smaller waters are largely deserted as birds move to the larger lakes or disperse further afield outside the county. Alternatively at this time of year incoming migrants flock together with resident birds forming loose groups of up to ten. The following larger counts have been noted:

1951 26 at Southill Lake on 26 December.
1953 23 at Brogborough CP on 30 August.
1954 17 at East Hyde and 39 at Bedford SF on 3 February.
1955 20 at East Hyde during January and February.
1956 20 at Stewartby ClP on 8 April.
1958 20 at Stewartby ClP on 10 August.
1960 26 at Stewartby ClP during August.
1961 30 at Stewartby ClP on 5 December.
1967 28 at Barkers Lane GP during February.
1972 30 at Blunham GP on 22 October.
1973 27 at Blunham GP on 18 February.
1978 34 at Blunham GP on 12 November.
1979 18 at Blunham GP on 18 October, 21 at Luton Hoo on 28 October.
1980 18 at Blunham GP on 25 September.
1986 15 at Luton Hoo on 15 October.

Great Crested Grebe

Podiceps cristatus

A widespread resident, passage migrant, and winter visitor (**Map 2**).

Elegant and distinctive in its nuptial plumage, the Great Crested Grebe is one of Bedfordshire's most beautiful birds. Unfortunately, in past years, these attributes, together with its confiding nature, rendered it a favourite target for the Victorian plume hunters who pursued it remorselessly.

The first confirmed breeding record in the county was at Southill Park where Steele-Elliott (1904) together with a Mr J. King recorded a pair with young during August 1894. Reports from the local gamekeepers at Southill suggested that this species may have bred one or two years previously, as birds were present throughout the breeding season. On the Woburn Estate it was first observed in 1894 when a pair nested and reared three young, and at nearby Battlesden Lake two pairs were present in 1899. A pair bred at Tingrith Manor in 1898, with Luton Hoo being colonised in 1922.

In 1931 the national Great Crested Grebe Inquiry (*British Birds* 26: 62–92) revealed a total of 18 pairs breeding in Bedfordshire for the following four localities; Battlesden Park, 3 pairs; Woburn Park, 5 pairs; Luton Hoo Park, 9 pairs; Southill Park, 1 pair.

As quarrying activities commenced around the middle of the twentieth century numbers began to rise as birds colonised the ever-increasing areas of still waters. W. E. K. Piercy (1952) provided the following details.

TABLE 3.1 *Adult Great Crested Grebes reported from various sites, 1946–51*

	1946	1947	1948	1949	1950	1951
Southill	6	2	6	10	12	16
Woburn	8	6	6	4	2	4
Battlesden	2				4	4
Tingrith				2		
Kempston Hardwick			2		2	2
Leighton Buzzard						2
Arlesey						2

The expansion in numbers continued, particularly in the Marston Vale with Coronation ClP being colonised in 1954, and in the south of the county breeding was also confirmed at Houghton Regis ChP. By 1956 nesting was reported at Stewartby ClP followed by 15 breeding pairs there in 1957, and 10 pairs in 1958 which all failed due to the raising of the water level. Millbrook, Vicarage Farm, and Brogborough clay pits were all subsequently colonised during this period and when a census was carried out in 1967 40 pairs were confirmed breeding across the county mainly in the Marston Vale, and the Ouse valley gravel pits at Harrold, Radwell, Felmersham, Barkers Lane, Chawston, and Wyboston. A BTO survey on 31 May and 1 June 1975 counted 105 adults at 24 waters but made no mention of numbers of breeding pairs.

Harding (1979) recorded evidence of breeding in 40 (11%) of the county's tetrads with a high instance of confirmed breeding in 33 tetrads, correlating strongly with the aforementioned mineral excavations and country estates.

This species breeds in shallow water where it can anchor its floating nest constructed from aquatic vegetation. The breeding season begins in March followed by egg-laying in April or May. There is generally only one clutch of three to four eggs. An early example of egg-laying was recorded at Luton Hoo on 10 March 1968 when a nest was found with a full clutch of four eggs. By the end of July the breeding cycle has usually finished and post-breeding assemblies can then be found at most of the county's larger waters. Up to 50 birds are sometimes present at Stewartby Lake during this period and in August 1968 a maximum of 118 was counted. Elsewhere counts of up to 50 have been recorded at Vicarage Farm ClP throughout the 1970s.

During the winter months numbers at many localities are augmented by the arrival of migrants from other parts of Britain. Since Stewartby Lake was flooded in 1958 it has regularly attracted a flock of up to 50 individuals during most winters. Counts in excess of 50 are listed below:

1971 70 on 12 December.
1975 58 in March.
1976 85 on 15 February and 98 on 12 December.
1977 123 on 9 January.
1978 c.200 on 12 February.
1980 70 on 13 January.
1981 79 on 24 December.
1982 90 on 10 January.
1983 66 on 22 February.
1984 50 in January.
1985 240 on 6 January.
1986 110 on 12 February.
1987 121 on 18 January.

During the 1980s, Radwell GP, Harrold CP, and Priory CP have begun to record small wintering flocks of up to 30 birds. There are two interesting recoveries relating to Great Crested Grebes ringed in the county. One ringed at Blunham on 31 March 1979 was recovered at Alton Water, Ipswich on 7 August 1980 and a bird, also ringed at Blunham on 25 February 1979 was recovered on 14 August 1985 at New Brighton, Merseyside having moved 234km north-west.

Red-necked Grebe

Podiceps grisegena

A rare winter visitor and very rare autumn migrant.

This species was described as a 'rare winter visitant' by Steele-Elliott (1904) who knew of only three records. The first was at Renhold in February 1863, followed by one at Wilden on 11 February 1870 and another at Bedford on 8 November 1885. On 22 October 1944 at Southill Lake I. J. Ferguson-Lees (1944–5) recorded two adult birds in transitional plumage.

Between 1946 and 1987 the Red-necked Grebe occurred in 10 years involving approximately 24 individuals. The majority of records have been since 1979 and it has been annual from 1984. This apparent trend can, perhaps, be linked to more suitable open water habitat becoming available, as more and more clay and gravel pits have since been flooded. Another reason could be the series of severe winters in the Baltic region during this period, forcing birds away from their regular winter quarters into eastern England. The winter period from November to March is when most sightings occur with only single records each in August, September, and October of passage migrants. Extreme dates were on 15 August 1987, Brogborough Lake and 21

March 1979, Blunham GP. Stewartby Lake, with eight records, is the most favoured locality followed by Blunham Lake and Wyboston Lake with three records each, and Harrold CP and Brogborough Lake with two apiece.

Prior to 1979, in the study period, this species was only present in four years: one at Arlesey ChP on 8–19 January 1955; two at Wyboston Lake on 25–8 December 1968; a single at Sandy GP on 9 November 1969; and one at Blunham GP on 31 December 1972. There were no further records until 1979 when severe weather in Fenno-Scandia caused an unprecedented influx, mainly into eastern Britain, as documented by Chandler (1981). This movement resulted in four Bedfordshire records, the first being at Wyboston Lake on 20–4 February, followed by another at Stewartby Lake on 25 February, a third on the boating lake at Bedford on 20 March, and finally a single at Blunham Lake on 21 March. One at Barkers Lane GP between 14 September and 2 October 1981 was in partial summer plumage. Since 1984 records are as follows:

1984 One at Stewartby Lake on 15 December stayed into 1985.
1985 The Stewartby bird remained until 10 February and was also noted at Millbrook ClP. It was joined by another at Stewartby on 19–20 January, with a different individual at Brogborough Lake on 22 January, and one at Stewartby Lake again on 22 February. At Harrold CP one stayed from 24 December into 1986.
1986 The Harrold bird stayed until 5 January when it probably moved to Stewartby Lake on 10 January with another there on 8 February, both leaving on 9th due to icing. A single was at Stewartby Lake 30 November to 1 December.
1987 One picked up alive in the frozen Grand Union Canal at Linslade on 11 January died at the recorder's home at Dunstable on 12 February.
Singles at Stewartby Lake 15–31 January; Harrold CP 8 February to 22 March; Brogborough Lake 15 August; Radwell GP 7 November to 6 December; Blunham Lake 14 December.

Totals of Red-necked Grebes by calendar month observed in Bedfordshire 1946–87:

Aug.	Sep.	Oct.	Nov.	Dec.	Jan.	Feb.	Mar.
1	1	1	3	8	7	6	3

Slavonian Grebe

Podiceps auritus

A scarce migrant primarily in spring, and a winter visitor.

This species is normally encountered wintering in the coastal waters of the British Isles particularly in the sheltered bays and estuaries of southern England. Its drab winter dress contrasts markedly with its showy nuptial plumage, a condition it is often seen in during its spring migration through Bedfordshire. There is a small, steadily increasing breeding population in Scotland but most of our birds probably originate from individuals of the northern European stock.

'As far as my memory serves me, about a dozen have been received by me in the flesh, nearly always in February or March during their return movements north and invariably they have been in winter plumage. Blunham, Willington, Pavenham, Milton, Harrold, Odell, and by the ash plantation along the river at Clapham are localities that just occur to me as I write, where they have been obtained. The most recent one was brought in that had been picked up off the edge of a pond along the Kimbolton Road, about 1890, apparently exhausted and frozen to death.' So wrote Mr A. Covington, a Bedford taxidermist, in correspondence with Steele-Elliott (1904), who also mentions winter records from the Luton area, Fenlake, Felmersham, and at Southill Lake on 27 March 1865.

Since 1946, this species has appeared in 19 years involving some 34 individuals. Prior to 1960 it occurred in only four years, 1947, 1950, 1954, 1957, with an increase in sightings through to the 1980s as the flooding of exhausted quarries made available more suitable open water habitat. Since 1983, it has been recorded annually. The majority of records have come from the passage months of April and to a lesser degree October, and in the winter months from December to February. The only months it has not been noted in are June and July. Extreme dates were three at Harrold GP on 21–2 August 1976 and one at Steppingley Reservoir 28 April to 3 May 1983. Many of the spring records are of birds in breeding plumage. Of the 34 records between 1946 and 1987 27 were of individuals. The only group sightings were the three at Harrold GP on 21–2 August 1976, two at Stewartby Lake on 12 April 1960, and two at Priory CP on 5 April 1987.

The latter year was an unprecedented one for the Slavonian Grebe in Bedfordshire with a total of eight birds as follows: one at Stewartby Lake on 18 January; one at Brogborough Lake 20–9 March; one at Chimney Corner ClP on 27 March; two at Priory CP on 5 April; one at Stewartby Lake on 6 April; one at Chimney Corner ClP 11–17 April; and a single at Brogborough Lake 17–19 April. It is apparent that this species rarely remains in one locality for long, one or two days being the normal stay; although one at Stewartby ClP on 21 October 1956 remained until early December, and in 1985 one at Harrold CP stayed from 17 November to 14 December.

A site by site analysis shows the majority of records to have occurred in the Marston Vale clay pits, particularly at Stewartby Lake with 11 records, and at the gravel pits along the Great Ouse and Ivel river valleys. There are no records from the Ouzel river valley sand pits or from the south of the county.

Totals of Slavonian Grebes by calendar month observed in Bedfordshire 1947–87:

Aug.	Sep.	Oct.	Nov.	Dec.	Jan.	Feb.	Mar.	Apr.	May
3	1	5	2	5	4	4	2	12	1

Black-necked Grebe

Podiceps nigricollis

A scarce, but now almost annual passage migrant and rare winter visitor.

In its plain non-breeding plumage the Black-necked Grebe can be confused with the previously described species from which it is separated at all times of the year by its characteristic tip-tilted bill and steep forehead. In spring it it unmistakable with black upperparts and golden 'ear fans', which are used for courtship display. The British breeding population is very small and therefore it is likely that most of the birds reaching Bedfordshire are migrants from central and western Europe. This species was unknown to Steele-Elliott and the first recorded occurrence in Bedfordshire was of one on the River Ouse near Bedford SF on 9 March 1947.

Subsequently it has occurred in a total of 20 years up to 1987, involving some 41 individuals. It has been noted annually since 1979, becoming the most regular of the three scarce grebes. It is usually seen singly, there being only five records of pairs as follows: Stewartby Lake 2 February 1960; Wyboston Lake 20 March to 24 April 1971; Barkers Lane GP 21 September 1980; Blunham Lake 19 September 1983; Blunham Lake 12 August 1986. At Blunham GP on 18 April 1974 a remarkable influx took place when eight individuals arrived, all in summer plumage; two pairs were noted displaying on 28 April but numbers gradually dwindled to a solitary bird by 1 May.

Although this species has been recorded in all months except June and July the peak passage months are April (16) and September (7) with first and last dates respectively on 6 August 1983 at Brogborough No. 2 pit and on 1 May 1974 at Blunham GP. The autumn peak correlates with the much larger concentration further south on the London reservoirs.

As a winter visitor to the county the Black-necked Grebe is quite a rarity. This is due to its winter quarters being more southerly than those of the Slavonian and Red-necked Grebes, thereby making it less susceptible to cold weather movements. Seventy-five per cent of the Bedfordshire records have come from only three localities: Blunham GP, in the Ivel valley with 16; Stewartby Lake, in the Marston Vale with 10; and Barkers Lane/Priory CP in the Ouse valley with six. As with most migrants the duration of stay is rather brief, typically for one or two days, although one remained at Barkers Lane GP from 24 September to 11 October 1980.

Totals of Black-necked Grebes by calendar month observed in Bedfordshire 1947–87:

Aug.	Sep.	Oct.	Nov.	Dec.	Jan.	Feb.	Mar.	Apr.	May
5	7	5	1	1	1	4	5	16	1

Fulmar

Fulmarus glacialis

A very rare vagrant.

There are only four records of this pelagic species in the county:

1888   An adult picked up at Goldington on 1 October was placed on a nearby pond where it died a few days later. It was taken to Mr A. Covington who skinned it and found it to be 'extremely emaciated' (Steele-Elliott 1904).

1890   One found dead at Woburn on 26 November is now a part of the Steele-Elliott collection in Bedford Museum.

1977   A single flew north-east over Houghton Hall, Houghton Regis on 31 May.

1981   One near Biggleswade on 26 April.

Manx Shearwater

Puffinus puffinus

A rare, usually storm-blown vagrant.

This species is a common summer visitor along the western seaboard of Britain, where it breeds colonially in large numbers on remote islands and peninsulas. It is, not surprisingly, mainly encountered inland following autumn gales. Some are moribund when found and never survive, while others, if returned to the coast quickly recover and fly strongly out to sea.

Steele-Elliott (1904) knew of only two records, one at Stopsley (date unknown) and one in his collection which was picked up alive at Cotton End, near Haines, in the autumn of 1885 and is now in Bedford Museum. In recent times the Manx Shearwater has occurred in only the following nine years:

1948   One shot at Bedford on 3 September died on 9 September.

1950   One found exhausted at Bedford on 31 August was fed by the bird recorder and released on 2 September at Gibraltar Point, Lincolnshire.

1952   A dead bird picked up at Eaton Socon on 27 July had been ringed the day before at Cambridge.

1953   A single picked up on Warden Hills on 7 September was released at Walton-on-the-Naze, Essex on 13 September. Another found dead on Warden Hills on 9 September, while one seen swimming on a farm pond at Renhold on 10 September died on 13 September. A corpse was recovered at East Hyde SW in early October.

1973   One picked up exhausted at Biggleswade Common on 4 September was released on the Norfolk coast the following day.

1980   A single found near Sharnbrook on 6 September and released later that day at Dungeness, Kent was part of a small 'wreck' across south-east England.

1983   One found alive at Willington on 16 September was taken to Stagsden Bird Gardens and was later released at Hunstanton, Norfolk.

1984   An exhausted bird picked up at Barton on 31 August was released the following day at Cley, Norfolk.

1987   On 24 June one found under a car at Shefford was brought to The Lodge, Sandy and successfully released that evening at Tollesbury, Essex. On 12 September a single was found on the A1 at Wyboston and on 14 September another at Bedford: both were released at Salthouse, Norfolk on 19 September.

Storm Petrel

Hydrobates pelagicus

A very rare vagrant.

The Storm Petrel is a summer visitor to the British Isles where it breeds colonially, often in large numbers, on rocky offshore islands along the Atlantic seaboard.

Steele-Elliott (1904) documented nine records as follows:

1878   One in November at Staplow.

1879   One picked up near Ashburnham Road, Bedford on 30 October.

1880   One shot at Ridgmont on 13 December was also reported by *The Field*. One also in October was caught in the old tanyard at Shefford.

1889   One found in Midland Road, Bedford on 7 October.

1890   One caught at Old Borough Police Station in Silver Street, Bedford on 20 October.

1893   One caught in a garden at Peel Street, Bedford on 5 December.

1894   One found dead near Colmworth Wood (date unknown).
A Major Brooks also reported that one had been taken at Toddington 'a few years previously'.

This century there has only been one record:

1983   Following gale force westerlies on 2 September one was seen at Brogborough Lake on 3 September.

Leach's Petrel

Oceanodroma leucorhoa

A very rare autumn vagrant.

This species occurred on three occasions last century, according to Steele-Elliott (1904) as follows:

1877   One picked up at Wilstead Park on 16 November.

1878   During the last week of December a male was found alive near the Grove, Bedford (*Zoologist*).

1880   'On 2 November a flock of seven of these birds was said to have been observed along the river at Goldington, and Mr Covington, from the description given at the time, thinks they were undoubtedly of this species: two days afterwards one was sent to him from Fenlake, the adjoining parish.'

Of the two commoner British petrels, Leach's Petrel is more susceptible to being blown inland. It has been recorded in four years between 1946 and 1987, involving nine individuals as follows:

1952   Following strong westerlies five specimens were found, some alive but all died shortly afterwards: one at Turvey on 29 October; one at Bromham on 30 October; singles at Stewartby and Thurleigh on 8 November; one at Leighton Buzzard about 8 November.

1970   One at Stewartby Lake on 4 October.

1978   A single on 1 October at Stewartby Lake coincided with large numbers along the west coast of Britain.

1983   Singles at Stewartby Lake on 4 September and at Kempston on 18 October.

Gannet

Sula bassana

A rare vagrant.

According to Steele-Elliott (1904) there were only two occurrences of the Gannet, or Solan Goose as it used to be known, in the county. The first came from Mr A. Covington, a Bedford taxidermist, who remembered one being caught locally, 'many years ago'. At Langford during the first week of February 1895 a Mr J. King saw two Gannets flying north-eastwards.

Subsequently between 1946 and 1987 this magnificent seabird has been recorded in the following six years:

1946   Found on Dunstable Downs after severe easterly gales in early January an immature was taken to Whipsnade Park Zoo (*Sunday Express*, 6 January 1946).

1948   A storm-blown immature was found injured at College Farm, Keysoe on 7 or 8 September.

1951   One picked up exhausted at Renhold on 20 September was taken in and fed, then released at Hunstanton, Norfolk by the bird recorder.

1955   An adult found at Cople on 20 April died later, and the corpse was preserved for a Mr D. W. Elliot.

1966   A dead immature was recovered near Elstow on 9 October.

1981   An adult flew west over Renhold on 27 April, followed by another at Brogborough Lake, 28–9 April. These two records were part of a large influx of seabirds into inland Britain during April as documented by Nightingale and Sharrock (1982).

Cormorant

Phalacrocorax carbo

A common passage migrant and winter visitor.

This large, dark primeval-looking species is a common breeding bird around the rocky coastline of western and northern Britain, where it nests in small loose colonies. It often comes into conflict with fishermen, particularly outside the breeding season when it haunts the fish-rich lakes and reservoirs of lowland England.

The Cormorant was known to Steele-Elliott (1904) as 'a rare straggler' and he could only quote three instances of it being received by Mr A. Covington, the Bedford taxidermist, and once by Mr T. Cane at Luton. A Mr J. King from Langford mentioned seeing one at Southill Lake about 1875 and again on 3 May 1901. This species was still considered rare enough to comment upon in 1910 when H. Lewis (1910–11) wrote to the monthly journal *British Birds* concerning a single sighting at Woburn Park on 31 December.

Subsequently the status of the Cormorant in Bedfordshire has changed considerably, to the extent that it is now a familiar part of the county avifauna. A study of data between 1946 and 1987 shows it to have occurred in all but seven of the 42 years with an annual presence from 1972 and a quite dramatic increase in numbers during the last seven years. This increase can be correlated to the flooding of several large clay pits in the Marston Vale, particularly at Brogborough and Stewartby, and also the gravel extraction sites at Harrold, Radwell, Bedford, Blunham, and Wyboston. The resulting large sheets of open still waters, some of which have retained islands and many of which are well stocked with fish, have proven to be an ideal winter habitat for this species, or when on migration a suitable stopping point.

Figure 3.1 reveals April as the peak month for sightings comprising mainly transient birds that have wintered further east, returning

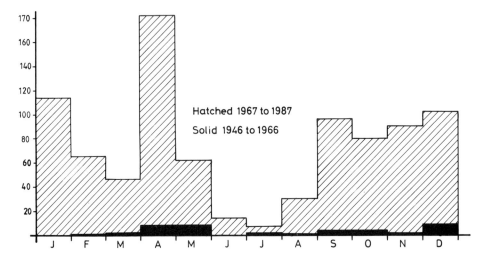

Figure 3.1 *Cormorant: total monthly counts, 1946–66 and 1967–87*

overland to their western breeding grounds (Coulson and Brazendale 1968). Away from wetland sites further evidence of this passage has been recorded during the 1980s along the chalk escarpment at Blows Downs and Whipsnade Park Zoo, where the direction of flight is nearly always westwards. A particularly large passage group of 21 was noted flying west over Priory CP on 18 April 1984. When on passage this species can occur almost anywhere in the county although the majority of records are from the Bedford clay pits.

As a winter visitor good numbers are regularly noted at Stewartby Lake, Chimney Corner ClP, and Brogborough Lake, with the latter being used as a roost site. Up to 15 can be present but in January 1987 as many as 21 were counted on a small tree-covered island. Harrold CP, Radwell GP, Priory CP, Blunham Lake, and Wyboston Lakes are also regularly utilised throughout the winter months and it is likely that many birds originate from the established wintering population at nearby Grafham Water and Little Paxton GPs, Cambridgeshire. The largest number recorded together in this part of the county and indeed anywhere in Bedfordshire, was a group of 24 over Twin Bridges GP on 23 February 1985.

To summarise, it appears that the Cormorant, once a rare bird in the county, is now an established winter visitor and passage migrant and may even establish a small breeding population as has happened in Little Paxton GP a few miles into Cambridgeshire.

Shag

Phalacrocorax aristotelis

A scarce and irruptive, mainly winter and autumn visitor.

The Shag is a far more sedentary species than the Cormorant, prefer-ring to stay mainly within its coastal breeding grounds for its entire lifespan. Periodically, however, for reasons which are not fully under-stood but are probably weather related, this species erupts inland, often in large numbers, resulting in birds appearing in atypical sur-roundings. Ringing data have shown that the majority of 'wrecked' individuals occurring in inland counties are immatures originating from colonies along the east coasts of Scotland and England (Coulson 1961). Steele-Elliott (1904) afforded this species a similar status to the Cormorant, that of 'another rare straggler'. He quoted four records that were received by two county taxidermists between *c*.1859 and 1887. Only two of these records were dated and both were in late summer; at Biggleswade on 29 August 1877 and at Renhold on 28 August 1887.

Since 1946, the Shag has been recorded in nine years up to 1987, involving approximately 110 individuals. About 90% of those records relate to the 'wreck' years of 1954, 1958, and 1984, with 1958 produc-ing about 70% of the overall total. January to March are the peak months with the majority of sightings occurring after northerly gales and associated low cloud cover.

A closer analysis of the three 'Shag years' reveals instances of unparalleled peculiarity regarding locations and circumstances:

1954   A party of 15 briefly settled in an elm tree at Steppingley on 3 February before flying off low across farmland. One struck a power line and died: another picked up injured at night was later released on Woburn Ponds. On 4 February a single flew over Bedford SF. About mid March an immature was found at Bromham Mill and became very confiding, cohabit-ing with domestic ducks and fishing along the River Ouse. On several occasions it was seen plunge-diving from trees into pools near Bromham Hall. Another single was recorded at Bedford on 21 and 23 September and six were noted at Arlesey ChP on 4 and 5 September.

1958   An unprecedented year with approximately 70 recorded indi-
        viduals. This particular 'wreck' was also recorded in adjacent
        counties and involved mainly first-winter birds from the
        north-east coast of Britain. Apart from being documented in
        British Birds, accounts also appeared in the *Luton News*
        and the *Bedfordshire Times* (*Beds Naturalist* 13: 37). On the
        evening of 24 January 20–30 Shags were found at Shillington
        Church perched on the building and on the graveyard tomb-
        stones in what must have been one of the most remarkable
        sightings in the annals of Bedfordshire ornithology. On 3
        February three were at Henlow ClP, followed by three more
        on 13 and 14 February at Goldington Power Station, which
        were rescued from the cooling towers and released on Ste-
        wartby Lake on 16th. On 17 February one was seen to 'fall
        out of the air' apparently from exhaustion and die at Apsley
        Guise. Other isolated records of this species were reported to
        the county recorder before a party of 24 were seen flying
        north over Southill on 22 February. One found dead at Arle-
        sey on 17 March had been ringed as a nestling on the Farne
        Islands, Northumberland, on 4 August 1957.
1984   Following severe north-westerly gales one was found at Brog-
        borough Lake on 22 January with another at Stewartby Lake
        on 25 January and two there on 28 January. On 13 February
        there were four at Stewartby Lake and singles at Priory CP
        and Harrold CP. Three remained at Stewartby Lake during
        March, the last one leaving on 14 April; a single was seen in
        Bedford in mid March and an adult was at the Blue Lagoon,
        Arlesey on 4 March.

The other six years (1955, 1960, 1962, 1968, 1981, and 1983) accounted
for a total of 12 individuals including one on the River Ouse at Bedford, which roosted on the town bridge, between 21 February and 4
August 1960. One found dead at Sharnbrook on 2 February 1981 had
been ringed as a juvenile on the Isle of May, Fife on 17 July 1978
having moved 460km south-south-east.

Bittern

Botaurus stellaris

A rare winter visitor.

In common with several other specialised British birds the Bittern
has recently again declined as a breeding species, mainly through the
disappearance of its reed-bed habitat, water pollution, and increasing
human leisure activities at a number of wetland complexes. Significantly over half of the surviving population are present on protected
nature reserve sites where access is strictly controlled. By 1986 there

were less that 25 'booming' males recorded in England from 12 localities (Spencer *et al.* 1988).

In former years when there was a thriving population in East Anglia this species would probably have been a regular winter visitor to the county's river systems and still waters. The earliest documented record was of one shot at Blunham *c.*1850 (Steele-Elliott 1904), followed by another, which was mentioned in the *Zoologist* in January 1856, obtained on the border with Hertfordshire at Lawrence End near Luton. In all, Steele-Elliott catalogued about 30 individuals between 1850 and 1900, the majority of which were killed and found their way to the county taxidermists. The winter of 1899–1900 witnessed a remarkable influx of Bitterns into Britain, 'and in Bedfordshire such a "Bittern year" is hardly likely to occur again': unfortunately there are no further details. Steele-Elliott (1928–9) later documented one at Biddenham in January 1903; one at Kempston in January 1907; a single at Goldington on 25 January 1909, with another at the end of November; two shot at Goldington at the end of January 1918; one killed at Barton on 15 December 1927 and one at Elstow on 28 December.

During the period 1946–87 the Bittern has occurred in 21 years involving some 23 individuals of which over 50% have been recorded in the winter months, particularly January. There is another peak in August and September which possibly relates to post-breeding dispersal; although, apart from one record at Luton Hoo in August 1986 all records for this period come from 1948–53 (when one individual was noted by Oakley on the River Ouse for six successive years), and at Felmersham GP in 1955. With the native British population so low, it seems likely that a substantial proportion of our winter visitors are from the continent, although Bittern movements are still poorly understood (Bibby 1981). There is no one site that is especially favoured: as long as there is some reed or sedge cover in which this species can conceal itself, it can occur at almost any riparian locality. The winter records all refer to single birds: at Bedford for the winter 1948–9; on the Ouse at Eaton Socon in January 1951; Felmersham GP on 31 January, 29 March, and in December 1954; Stanford Brook on 23 February 1956, found dead on 27 February; Southill Lake on 23 January 1960; Wyboston GP 27 January 1963; Southill Lake, early spring 1967; City Field Farm GP on 11 February 1968; Southill Lake 18 January 1970; Felmersham, dead female on the road on 15 February 1979 (NB record in *Beds Naturalist* 34: 15 incorrect); Ampthill Park and Stewartby Lake on 3 January 1982; Felmersham NR 26–7 December 1983; Luton Hoo 19 January 1985 and again on 19 January 1987. The only record that does not fall into the two patterns was a single which occurred at Langford GP in May 1970 and stayed until May the following year.

American Bittern

Botaurus lentiginosus

A very rare vagrant.

This Nearctic species breeds in North America wintering south to Mexico and the West Indies. Nationally it is an extreme rarity with only eight records in Britain and Ireland between 1958 and 1985 (Dymond *et al.* 1989).

There is one Bedfordshire record, a female that was shot near the old racecourse at Elstow on 13 November 1886 (Steele-Elliott 1904). This specimen is a part of the Steele-Elliott collection now at Bedford Museum.

Little Bittern

Ixobrychus minutus

A very rare vagrant.

This species is a summer visitor across much of central and southern Europe, appearing annually in Britain in small numbers and very occasionally breeding. Bedfordshire records relate to nineteenth-century occurrences.

Steele-Elliott (1904) referred to 'a female or immature specimen, which was obtained in September 1894 by some youths whilst boating down the river [Ouse]; it had been shot as it sat upon the head of a pollard willow near Castle Mills [Bedford].' There are two other second-hand references from that era: one shot *c.*1870; Mr A. Covington, Bedford taxidermist, mentioned that he had received a case for repair, containing two Little Bitterns which 'had been killed in the county many years previously'.

Night Heron

Nycticorax nycticorax

A very rare vagrant.

Edward Newman, the editor of *Montagu's Ornithological Dictionary*

44

recorded the following: 'We are informed by Lord Upper Ossory that this species was shot on the borders of the river Ouse in the year 1791, a few miles from Ampthill, and that it is now in His Lordship's museum. It is remarkable too, that the bird was killed in the summer.' There was also a probable sighting recorded by a Mr J. King at Langford, date unknown (both in Steele-Elliott 1904).

There is only one recent occurrence of this cosmopolitan species in Bedfordshire, an adult at Felmersham NR on 16 June 1970 (*British Birds* 64: 345).

Little Egret

Egretta garzetta

A very rare vagrant.

Found across much of the southern Palearctic region this species has occurred twice in Bedfordshire in recent years:

1965 One at Heath and Reach on 5 June (*British Birds* 59: 285).
1986 One at Priory CP on 15 May (*British Birds* 80: 522).

Grey Heron

Ardea cinerea

A resident but localised breeding species and a non-breeding visitor (**Map 3**).

Formerly known as the Heronshaw or Mollhern, the Grey Heron is a familiar sight across the county's wetlands. When hunting it can remain elusive, until flushed, when its large size and slow, ponderous flight enable instant recognition. This species is wary of man but is a great opportunist feeder, exploiting easy food sources such as ornamental fish ponds, often in the heart of our two large towns, Bedford and Luton.

The fortunes of the Grey Heron as a breeding bird in Bedfordshire have fluctuated considerably over the past 100 years, in relation to human persecution and the availability of nest sites. Whilst the main breeding sites are on private land, affording some protection, restricted access has often denied accurate and sustained documentation of nesting pairs and their success rate. The data available are therefore mainly unquantified from the Victorian age through to the inception of the national Heron Census in 1928 and on to the present day. During this period there have been four main localities utilised, all of them at parkland lakes on country estates at Bromham, Luton, Sandy, and Southill.

Bromham Hall was first mentioned in the census of Herons (*British Birds* 23: 325) when a pair nested in 1927, followed by two pairs in 1928 and three pairs in 1929. There is no further documented evidence

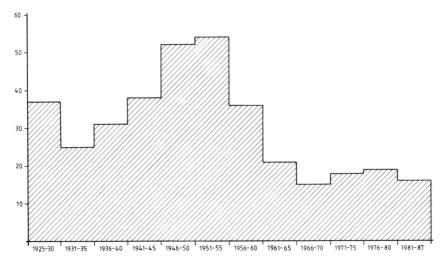

Figure 3.2 *Heron: total number of nests recorded in the Heron census periods of 1925–87. The last period is of seven years*

of occupancy at this site until W. E. K. Piercy's note (1952). It seems probable that numbers steadily increased until his report, when between 1943 and 1951 an average of 15 pairs bred annually, with a maximum of 21 pairs in 1944 and 1946. From 1951 a similar average of 15 occupied nests was maintained until a decline in 1954 which was considered due to a cold February. This was followed by a tree-felling incident at the beginning of the 1955 breeding season from which the colony does not seem to have recovered. From the mid 1950s until 1987 only between three and six pairs have bred, albeit almost annually.

The second major heronry still used regularly is at Southill Park and was initially referred to by Steele-Elliott (1904) when a pair 'nested on the small island in the lake previous to 1895'. In 1944 three pairs were present, rapidly building to a peak of 20 pairs by 1951 and 1952 from when there was a steady decline to an average of nine occupied nests during the 1960s and 1970s. Since 1980 this colony has been little studied but probably averages about five breeding pairs.

According to Davis (1874) there was a heronry at Luton Hoo until c.1869 when a gale damaged 'The Island', blowing down some of the nesting trees. The Heron Census of 1928 recorded 'several pairs', and then there is no further documentation of breeding until fieldwork for Harding (1979), when a juvenile was noted in 1975 followed by probable breeding in 1976, and three to four tenanted nests in 1977. Subsequently a small colony, not exceeding five pairs, has been established.

The only locality known to Steele-Elliott (1904) which regularly supported a heronry was at Sandy Warren (now the headquarters of the RSPB). This was due to the owner, Viscount Peel's interest, and when Steele-Elliott visited the site in August 1900 he found evidence that breeding had occurred that year, and at least one pair had bred in the preceding 13 years. The Heron Census of 1928 revealed two pairs in 1901 and 1902; three pairs in 1910 and 1911; none in 1916–17; three or four pairs from 1923, increasing to 10 pairs by 1928. In 1946 eight pairs were known to have bred with a peak of 14 pairs in 1950 dropping to seven pairs in the following year. In 1956 there were 12 nests, which produced no young, and in 1957 the last recorded breeding attempt was noted at this locality.

Elsewhere in the county the Grey Heron has bred sporadically at a number of isolated localities, predominantly along the Ouse valley as follows: Woburn, two pairs in Cowhill Rookery c.1885; Twin Woods Clapham, several pairs until c.1850; Cardington/Castle Mills, one pair in 1880; Pavenham Bury, two pairs 1920–3; Clapham Wood, eight pairs 1928–9; Howbury Park Renhold, one pair 1928; Ford House, Eaton Socon (then in Beds), ten nests in 1928, deserted by 1942; Harrold, one pair in 1940, 1941, and 1949; Goldington, one pair in 1945, two pairs in 1946, and one pair in 1947 and 1948; Tempsford, two pairs in 1948–9, four pairs in 1950–1, three pairs in 1952, two pairs 1953, one pair 1957–9; Little Barford, one pair in 1954; Leighton Buzzard, one pair in 1955, two pairs in 1956–7; Clapham, four to five pairs in 1961; Pavenham, one pair in 1962; Ickwell Bury, one or two nests in 1972–4. All the Bedfordshire heronries are in mature trees, varying from introduced conifers to native ash and the single clutch of four to five eggs is laid in February or March.

Post-breeding assemblies are often encountered at suitable wetland sites, the following being of note: 25 at Bedford SF during autumn 1967; 24 at Bedford SF on 22 July 1969; 24 at Luton Hoo on 26 August and 12 September 1976; 27 at Grovebury SP on 8 July and 21 on 20 August 1984; 25 at Priory CP on 8 August 1985 and 22 on 15 August 1986. The majority of these birds are from outside the county and from the available ringing data seem to come from random directions. The furthest recovery of a Bedfordshire ringed bird was a juvenile ringed as a nestling at Southill on 7 May 1970, found dead at Ireby, Cumbria on 18 October of that year, having moved 356km north-west. There is one foreign recovery of a juvenile ringed at Eaton Socon (then in Beds) on 19 April 1939, recovered at Treauville, France on about 15 September 1939 having moved 318km south-south-west.

Purple Heron

Ardea purpurea

A very rare vagrant.

This elegant south European heron has occurred in Bedfordshire on four, or possibly five occasions:

1955   An immature at Felmersham GP 10–16 September (*Beds Naturalist* 10: 29–30).

[1958]   A probable adult at Dunstable SF on 16 May and 18 May. (*Beds Naturalist* 13: 37).

1966   An immature at Wyboston GP from 10 August to 10 September (*British Birds* 60: 312).

1973   An adult was shot at Caddington in August (*British Birds* 67: 314).

1977   One at Luton Hoo on 4 September (*British Birds* 71: 490).

White Stork

Ciconia ciconia

A very rare vagrant.

A familiar summer visitor across much of central and southern Europe. There has only been one acceptable record.

[1974]   One in the Studham and Whipsnade area from the end of December 1974 to March 1975 (also noted at Linslade in February 1975) was considered to be an escape.

1983   One at Potton on 5 May (*Beds Naturalist* 38: 25).

Spoonbill

Platalea leucorodia

A very rare vagrant.

There has been only one occurrence of this species in the county, as documented by Steele-Elliott (1926–7):

'Spoonbill in Beds.

Three Spoonbills visited the Ouse Meadows at Renhold in 1916 and one of the trio was unfortunately shot on March 24 by a local farmer, through whom I obtained confirmation of their occurrence. This bird was subsequently purchased, in the flesh for 75 shillings by the local taxidermist Mr A. Covington, who also advised me of this species being in his possession.

For obvious reasons of the law I was requested by him to suppress the recording of the same at the time, but now owing to his death in 1925, I feel I am at liberty to publish this, the first known instance of the species visiting the county.'

Mute Swan

Cygnus olor

A fairly common resident (**Map 4**).

Originally a wild bird in this country, it was semi-domesticated during medieval times for culinary purposes but has been reverting gradually to its wild state during the last two or three centuries. The earliest record of this species occurs in the Great Charter of William de Beauchamp (1165) where the Baron of Bedford granted the right of keeping swans to Newnham Priory. In the sixteenth-century records of the Priory of Grove near Leighton Buzzard two swans were sold in the lady's household for 6 shillings. The beauty of this bird has perhaps always been recognised but unfortunately the early ornithologists, such as Davis (1874) and Steele-Elliott (1904), considered this species as domesticated and no details were recorded. The Bedford School Natural History Society Bird List for 1941–3 gives its status as being found 'All along river and large ponds' but the *Beds Naturalist* for 1946 is even less informative and just records its status as a resident.

Little interest seems to have been taken in the status of this species until 1951 when the flock along the River Ouse in Bedford (between Queens Park and Newnham), was estimated at more than 70 during the winter months with about half that number remaining during the summer as a non-breeding flock. By the following winter this was estimated as being nearly 100 and remained so until at least 1963 when a more accurate count of 105 birds was made during the first winter period. The non-breeding flock was estimated as at least 40 during the summer of 1955. Fortunately P. J. Wilkinson carried out a study of this flock from November 1963 to May 1969 the results of which are summarised in Table 3.2.

The Bedford flock reached a peak around 1964–5 but from the summer of 1965 a significant decline in numbers took place. This was thought to have been brought about by a succession of severe winters. From his more detailed results Wilkinson was able to demonstrate an annual pattern with a low point being reached in May followed by a

TABLE 3.2   *Maximum numbers of Mute Swan on the River Ouse at Bedford, 1963–9*

Year	1st Winter Period	Summer	2nd Winter Period
1963	–	–	110
1964	78	120	85
1965	115	72	74
1966	90	60	60
1967	55	50	53
1968	50	40	–
1969	44	–	–

build-up during June and July for the summer moult. Numbers decreased after the moult before increasing again with the onset of winter, peaking in December and January. A further annual pattern emerged when the age composition of the flock was considered. Birds under one year old started to arrive at the beginning of the winter and continued to increase in numbers right through the winter even though the number of older birds had started to decline.

Counts by J. C. Palmer (pers. comm.) along the same stretch of river during the first winter period of 1984 give an interesting comparison with those of Wilkinson and indicate a continued gradual decline.

1965		1984	
1 October	60		
6 October	60		
		14 October	10
		21 October	16
		28 October	28
		4 November	21
		11 November	21
		8 December	32
11 December	60		
		15 December	50
21 December	66		
		22 December	40
		23 December	34
28 December	74		
		29 December	20

During the winter of 1986–7 a small wintering flock of 50 established itself at Harrold and Radwell GPs, and this increased to a maximum of 57 the following winter.

The first breeding census was carried out in 1955 when at least 37 pairs were located in the county, but it was thought that some pairs may have been overlooked. In the following year at least 38 pairs nested and this included a pair at City Fields Farm GP at Henlow which produced two normal cygnets and two of the 'Polish' (white) variety. Unfortunately these died.

A Wildfowl Trust sample breeding survey in 1978 was disrupted by heavy rains prior to the census which caused flooding, washing away many nests and making access to probable sites impossible. A BTO

50

survey in 1983 revealed 20 territories along the River Ouse and confirmed the 1968–77 survey results which showed that, although some birds breed on parkland lakes and flooded sand, gravel, and clay pits, the vast majority breed along the river systems of the county.

The decline in the population on the River Ouse in Bedford during the mid 1960s did not result in such a dramatic reduction in the breeding population. However, by the end of the 1970s and particularly during the early 1980s it was noticed that some birds were suffering from lead poisoning. This caused infertility or death amongst some breeding birds and several cygnets died. A ban on lead fishing weights was imposed in 1987 which may help in returning this species to its former status but a recent increase in river pollution could counteract this positive step.

Bewick's Swan

Cygnus columbianus

A fairly regular winter visitor.

The Bewick's Swan visits us during the winter from western Siberia and is the more frequent of the two species of 'Wild Swan'. It is smaller than the Whooper with a shorter neck in proportion to its size. The number wintering on the Ouse Washes has increased dramatically in recent years from just a few in the 1940s to over 5,000 in 1985 and this has undoubtedly influenced the numbers being seen in, or passing over, Bedfordshire.

The only certain record known to Steele-Elliott (1904) was of three which were procured within a mile of Woburn during the third week of January 1864. Mr A. F. Crossman observed two Wild Swans on 29 November 1890 near Cardington Locks which, by their small size and call, he considered to be Bewick's.

The first record of recent times was of a party of 16 observed by the Duke of Bedford at Woburn Park ponds on 13 March 1951. This was followed in 1956 by two records; two at Eastwood's ClP on 12 February and a party of 15 flying north above Pope's Meadow, Luton, on 19 February. Since then this species has been observed in all years since 1960 except 1982. Many records have been of parties passing over but often small groups rest for a few days at gravel or clay pits, flooded fields, and other suitable sites. The birds may arrive as early as the last week of October (earliest 27 October) with a few more records (11%) during November. The peak months are December and January with just over half of the 125 records since 1946 occurring in this period. About 14% of records have been during February with the same number in March. All birds have usually departed by the end of this month but in 1963 two remained at Sandy GP until 7 April and one was observed there in June and again in July. In 1971 one remained at Girtford GP from 6 March to 9 May.

Large numbers recorded since 1970 are as follows:

1970   28 west over River Ouse Bedford on 22 December.
1971   c.40 east-north-east over The Lodge, Sandy on 10 March.
1974   32 West over The Lodge, Sandy on 30 October.
1985   21 over Carlton on 4 January.
1987   33 over The Lodge, Sandy on 12 January.
       42 at Brogborough Lake on 13 March. This included 4 colour-marked birds from Slimbridge.
       44 arrived at Brogborough Lake on 14 March to join the 42 mentioned above making a total of 86.
       46 flying north-east over Everton on the same day probably involved some of the same birds.
       19 at Radwell on 23 March.
       20 flew south-west over Radwell on 4 November.
       There were thirteen other occurrences during 1987 making it the best year for this species in the county and continuing the upward trend of this species.

Whooper Swan

Cygnus cygnus

A scarce winter visitor.

Similar in size to the Mute Swan with a more extensive area of yellow on the bill than a Bewick's Swan, the Whooper Swan is a scarce visitor. It was originally thought that the birds which winter on the Ouse Washes were from the Scandinavian/Siberian population, but of 46 birds marked with neck-collars in Iceland in 1981, four were re-sighted on the Ouse Washes showing that at least some, if not a majority, are of Icelandic origin (Brazil 1981).

Steele-Elliott (1904) mentions that Wild Swans were frequently observed passing over the county in the severest winters and was of the opinion that both Whooper and Bewick's were involved though he was inclined to think that the Whooper was the more frequent of the two. One was shot at Newmill End, near Luton, in the winter of 1890–1. Mr A. Covington, in writing to Steele-Elliot, mentions that the only one of local origin he knew of was of a bird killed at Milton many years previous to it first being seen by him in 1865. It was eventually purchased by him and remained in his possession for several years 'until in a fit of vandalism I cut off the head, which I retained for a time, and destroyed the other parts.'

Mr W. J. Chalk (Steele-Elliott 1904) mentions that flocks of Swan used to pass over Wilden occasionally in the winter which, from their great size, he considered to be Whoopers.

There is a confusing record mentioned to Steele-Elliott by Mr C. F. Woods of a party of seven Wild Swans, two adults and five immatures, which visited the Basin and Large Drakelow Pools at Woburn either in 1862–3 or 1863–4 and remained for several weeks. During the night they visited some corn stacks at Speedwell Farm where one was shot by Mr F. Freeman and, it is thought, cooked for the table. Another bird Mr Woods killed one night by skating rapidly up to them as they swam about in a hole cut in the ice for the tame swans. Mr G. B. Clarke, the local taxidermist, identified them as Whooper Swans. The three Bewick's Swans shot near Woburn in 1864, mentioned under that species, were taken during the same period and Steele-Elliott was of the opinion that they could have referred to the same birds.

The Whooper Swan is a much rarer bird in the county than the Bewick's but has shown a slight increase since 1980. The first record of recent times was of a party of four on the River Ouse at Bromham in February 1947 but it was not until 1961 that the second record, three at Wyboston on 8 September, occurred. This is also the earliest record for the county. Up to the end of 1987 there have been no October records and only three in November. December with six records and January with 14 are the months when the Whooper Swan has been seen most often but there have been four occurrences in February and two in March with the latest being a single bird at Blunham GP on 23 March 1982. All but three records have been of four birds or less, more usually one or two, but seven were seen in the Bedford SW area on 2 January 1963, 11 were flying near Leighton Buzzard on 17 December of the same year, and a party of 15 was observed flying over Sandy Lodge on 25 February 1965. There were two records in 1962, five in 1963, one in each of 1965, 1967, and 1970, two in 1974, and one in 1976. From 1981 records became more frequent, being seen in each year until 1987 when it was not recorded. There were four records in 1981 and five in 1982. It was during this year that four were introduced at Blunham and four of the five records were at the same locality, doubtless attracted by the introduced birds. Apart from these feral birds (which had decreased to two by the end of 1984), one was present at Brogborough Lake on 28 December 1983 and one at Millbrook ClP on 22 and 25 January 1984. Two wild individuals arrived at Blunham GP on 10 January 1985, remaining until 19th. They were relocated at South Mills GP on 25th and returned to Blunham GP on 26–7th. Two seen by the River Ouse near the A1 on 29th were presumably the same birds. One over Brogborough rubbish tip on 17 November was seen later the same day over Stewartby CP. Two adults at Radwell GP on 24–5 December were the only records of wild birds for 1986. It is interesting that there were no reports of wild birds of this species in 1987 although it was such an exceptional year for the Bewick's Swan.

Bean Goose

Anser fabalis

A very rare winter visitor.

The separation of the Bean Goose and Pink-footed Goose into distinct species was announced to British ornithologists in 1839. As with other species of grey geese, the observer of the nineteenth century, without the optical aids which we have today, had great difficulty in identifying this species. Earlier records indicate that grey geese passed overhead far more frequently than they do now. In severe winters small parties, usually of five or six, but sometimes of 15–20 would be seen feeding on agricultural land, particularly in the northern parts of the county. During the winter of 1896–7 100 or more grey geese were said to have been present on the Race Course Meadow at Elstow late one afternoon but as none of them were shot they remained unidentified. Steele-Elliott (1904) was of the opinion that many of these records would involve the Bean Goose. The Bean Goose was a very common winter visitor to East Anglia during the earlier nineteenth century. In many localities it was the commonest species of goose, but a decline took place in the 1860s and 1870s and by the turn of the century there were only a few places in East Anglia where it occurred.

Two from a flight of seven were shot along the River Ouse at Wyboston Corner in January, about 1870. Only one was retrieved as the second fell into the river, dived under the ice and was lost. One was shot from a small flight flying over Southill on 10 December 1871 and seven fed on the Biddenham and Kempston meadows on 28 December 1883. Two of these were shot.

Recent records are as follows:

1978   One at Harrold GP on 17 and 28 December might have been of captive origin, but numbers in Norfolk were high that winter with some reaching the Ouse Washes.

1979   One at Harrold GP on 9 September and then irregularly to 23 December was of suspect origin.

1980   One at Harrold GP on 1 January and 16 February was of suspect origin.

1985   A party of six flying over Brogborough Lake on 12 January were considered to be of wild origin.

There are obvious difficulties in ascertaining whether any of the recent records of this species in the county are of escapes or truly wild birds but the 1985 record seems to be almost certainly of wild birds as they occurred in very severe weather conditions which coincided with good numbers wintering in the Yare Valley.

Pink-footed Goose
Anser brachyrhynchus

A rare winter visitor and passage migrant.

None of the early writers make any mention of this species. As with the previous species, visual identification of birds passing over the county would have been impossible. However, the fact that none was shot, even after the Bean Goose and Pink-footed were separated into distinct species (1839 in this country), lends credence to Steele-Elliott's belief that the Grey Geese passing over were probably Bean Geese.

The first published record for the county was of a party of 30–40 which frequented the meadows between Biddenham and Kempston Church during late December of 1948. Six were still present at Box End on 7 January 1949 and up to 40 there on 10 January.

Thirty-eight were at Barkers Lane GP on 31 December 1953 and a party of 38, presumably the same birds, flew low over the River Ouse near Cardington on 2 January 1954. Two among a party of 14 which were feeding in the marshy fields near Bedford SF on 7 January bore blue identification rings but unfortunately their origin could not be traced. However, in 1955 some clue as to the origin of this species was given when one from a party of three was shot at the end of January near Shefford. It bore a ring which showed that it had been ringed at Arnafallsalda Thjorsarver, Iceland, on 29 July 1953. This is the main breeding area of the British wintering population but the much smaller population on E. Greenland also visit this country.

One at Harrold GP from 12 to 16 June 1977 was almost certainly an escape. After a long absence of wild birds from the county a party of 21 was present at Kempston Hardwick ClP on 4 January 1979. One which associated with feral Greylags at Radwell GP on 6 May 1979 must be of suspect origin as must one which again associated with feral Greylags seen sporadically at Blunham GP from 13 February to 14 April 1981 and one with Greylags at Blunham GP on 11 January 1982. Five at Radwell GP on 16 January 1983 were considered wild in origin. One at Harrold GP on 28 January 1984 remained in the Harrold/Radwell area until 5 March.

White-fronted Goose
Anser albifrons

A scarce winter visitor and passage migrant.

Steele-Elliott (1904) knew of only two confirmed records of this species although he considered that it was probably represented amongst the many 'Grey Geese' that flew over the county during severe winters. A flock of 14 remained for several days near Cople in about 1863 but were extremely shy. A male from this flock was killed. A second was shot from a party of four on the Cardington Meadows on 19 December 1901.

The first recent record of this uncommon winter visitor from the north-west USSR was in 1946 when two birds were seen at Bedford SW in January. Between 1946 and 1979 it was seen on 22 occasions. From 1980 to 1987 there have been a further 24 records. Birds may begin to arrive in this country in late November but in general the main arrival does not take place until late December and January. Return migration is a relatively rapid affair commencing in early March with very few birds remaining in the country by the middle of the same month. All but one of the records outside this period in Bedfordshire have involved single birds and although it could be argued that any birds seen outside this period may be unfit for the return flight most of them would almost certainly be escapes. The increase in experienced observers and observer coverage has undoubtedly contributed towards the increase in records since 1980.

Totals of White-fronted Goose by calendar month observed in Bedfordshire 1946–87:

Sep.	Oct.	Nov.	Dec.	Jan.	Feb.	Mar.	Apr.	May	Jun.	Jul.
1	0	10	104	164	17	185	5	2	2	1

Records of five or more:

1963   70 at Bedford SF area on 2 January with 12 present 3–19 January.

1967   c.175 flying north-east over Wyboston on 4 March.

1968   Five at Dunstable SF on 3 March had decreased to three by 9 March.
     61 flew over Houghton Regis on 29 December.

1969   14 flew north-east over Luton on 29 January.
     Seven flew north-east over Luton on 22 February.

1981   16 circled over Blunham GP on 16 January.
     c.10 were near Stanbridgeford on 15 December.

1982   17 flew NW over Dunstable on 22 January.
     10 arrived at Harrold on 4 December remaining in the area until 20th.
     10 flying over Langford GP on 13 December probably refers to the same birds.

1985   Nine flew west over Brogborough Lake on 16 November.

1986   Six immatures and two adults at Radwell GP on 1 January were joined by another immature on 2nd. The whole group remained until 11th.

1987   Seven at Radwell 16–17 January.
     Five at Dunstable SW on 17 January.
     12 at Brogborough Lake 24–6 January.
     Seven at Stewartby Lake on 27 January.
     14 flew west over Blunham on 14 December.

Greylag Goose

Anser anser

Resident breeding population of feral birds, but it is probable that it is also a rare winter visitor (**Map 5**).

The Greylag is the ancestor of our domestic goose and before the draining of the Fens in the early nineteenth century nested as far south as Cambridgeshire, but by the beginning of this century was restricted as a breeding bird to Scotland. Introductions were made in England, particularly between 1961 and 1970, during which time WAGBI (now the British Association for Shooting and Conservation) released 938 hand-reared Greylags at 33 sites in 13 English counties (Ellwood 1971) and further introductions have been made since. Thus the vast majority of Greylags seen in Bedfordshire since 1960 are almost certainly from introduced stock and ornamental wildfowl collections. It is possible that truly wild birds may occasionally occur during the winter but it is difficult to prove.

Mr T. Caine, in a letter to Steele-Elliott, writes: 'From the Bogs near Luton, which are now drained and under cultivation, I once saw three Grey Lag-Geese that had been killed at one shot.' A farmer took two specimens to Mr A. Covington which he had killed from a small flock at Ravensden in about 1868 and during the same winter another bird shot from a 'gaggle' at Biddenham was probably from the same flock. A year or so later a farmer, whom Mr Covington believed to be living near Westoning, winged a wild goose which he pinioned and kept alive for several years. This specimen he also thought to be a Greylag Goose.

This species remained an uncommon bird in the county until the late 1960s. There were only six records between 1946 and 1966. The first was thought to be a wild bird at Radwell on 4 April 1948. This was followed by three records in 1956; one frequented Longholme Lake in Bedford from 31 March to 1 April, seven flew south over Oakley on 3 November, and seven were observed feeding on stubble at Houghton Conquest on 24 December. Two were on the meadows at Harrold on 21 April 1957 and two were identified at Brogborough Lake on 30 April 1961. The first record of a large number was a flock of *c*.60 on the river meadows near Bedford SF on 5 January 1967. Two at Dunstable SF on April 1968 and two at Garsides SP in December 1969 were the only published records for those years and none were reported the following year. Feral flocks of six and 25 frequented the Blunham–Wyboston area during the early part of 1972 with numbers reaching 48. Restocking and controlled shooting resulted in fluctuating numbers at these sites. Reports were received from a further six sites. Numbers gradually increased in the north of the county during the 1970s with 74 at Blunham GP in January 1975 and 27 at Harrold GP in February 1976. Thirty-four at Harrold GP in June 1977 increased to 52 in July and 63 in November. Seventy-seven at Harrold GP and 82 at Roxton GP were the largest flocks during 1978 with the flock at Harrold GP increasing to more than 150 by 1980. The increase in the county's population continued in the following year with 100 at Harrold GP throughout the year, with peaks of 150 in January and 163 in June. The flock at Blunham attained 61 during the first half of the year and smaller parties were noted from 10 other sites. The sites at Harrold/Radwell and Blunham remained the main sites during the 1980s with peaks as follows:–

Year	Harrold/Radwell	Blunham
1981	163	61
1982	201	–
1983	250–300	63
1984	234	152
1985	404	247
1986	200	c.220
1987	300	163

A single with White-fronts at Dunstable SW on 17 January and three at Cardington Airfield on 18 January 1987, during a period of freezing weather, may have been genuine wild birds.

An active ringing programme at Harrold CP has shown that most of our birds do not move very far with no recovery over 100km.

The first breeding took place at Girtford GP in 1971 and, apart from 1972, it has bred in the county in every year since then. The number of young Greylag Geese reared in the county from 1971–87 was:

71	73	74	75	76	77	78	79	80	81	82	83	84	85	86	87
–	37	6	5	13	34	21	44+	124	34	118	72	–	21	90	14

[Snow Goose]

[Anser caerulescens]

Undoubtedly most, if not all, Snow Geese records in the county are of escaped birds, but as usual it is almost impossible to be sure. Nearly all records are of birds associating with Greylags and Canada Geese. Although there has been some speculation about some of the birds which have occurred during the winter, records have been fairly evenly distributed throughout the year and there is no evidence of any increase during the winter months (although this does not preclude the possibility of wild birds being involved). Snow Geese were introduced at Woburn and were present there in the 1940s.

Other records are as follows:

1971 Two flying south over Brickhill on 14 April.
1977 One at Eversholt Lake 11 December.
1978 One at Harrold GP from 9 June to 31 December.
1979 One at Radwell GP 19 January.
       One at Dunstable SW on 27 February.

One at Harrold GP from March to December with four on 31 May.

A pair at Roxton 25–8 June.

1980 Present frequently at Harrold GP and Radwell GP with four on 11 October.

1981 Up to four associating with Canada Geese at various sites in the county throughout the year.

1982 Singles at Harrold GP in January, Radwell GP in April, and Brogborough Lake in September. Six, including a blue-phase bird, frequented Harrold GP during October.

1983 Singles at Radwell GP in January, Woburn in February, Radwell GP in August, and Brogborough ClP in October. Four at Harrold GP on 16 October.

1984 Singles at Woburn and Millbrook ClP in January and at Brogborough Lake in September.

1985 One at Millbrook/Brogborough ClPs all year.

An adult blue-phase at Brogborough Lake 12–14 January.

An adult white-phase at Kempston Hardwick ClP on 12 January.

Four immature blue-phase birds at Millbrook ClP on 15 February were joined by another on 16 February, remaining in the area until 4 April.

1986 One recorded at Millbrook in January with two in the Marston Moretaine area from early March until 29 March.

Singles at Kempston Hardwick and Radwell GP in May.

Canada Goose

Branta canadensis

A well-established resident breeding species (**Map 6**).

The first record of this species is a specimen in Bedford Museum which is labelled as being shot in front of Oakley House on 13 April 1831. Davis (1874) confines his comment to 'Visits occasionally Luton Park'. The records of Bedford School Natural History Society for 1941–4 record it as breeding at Southill Lake but this pair departed when the estate was under military occupation later in the war. The same records report it being at Bedford SF during the winter of 1942 and six at Southill Lake on 22 September 1944.

Since these records and one of a small party on the River Ouse at Box End, Kempston in February 1947 this species failed to become well established until after the first recent breeding record of a pair at Luton Hoo Park in 1971. Records during this period include 10 flying north over Elstow on 20 July 1949, eight flying between Wilstead and Elstow in July 1952, and 18 at Wyboston GP on 22 April 1967. Apart from these records it occurred in 1950, 1957, 1959, 1963,

1966, 1968, 1969, and 1970, but all of these records involved three birds or less, usually one or two.

The pair which bred at Luton Hoo in 1971 produced three young and two pairs bred there in the following year raising seven young. Pairs also bred in 1972 at Battlesden Lake and Eversholt Lake. The introduction of this species at parkland lakes has undoubtedly had the greatest influence on what has now become a common species in the county. Three at Southill Lake in 1970 were thought to have been

TABLE 3.3   *Maximum counts of Canada Goose at selected sites 1976–87*

	76	77	78	79	80	81	82	83	84	85	86	87
Eversholt	72			29								
Wrest Park	95											
Southill	45				180			241	73	50		
Clay Pit Lakes		110	195	75	160	430	357	220	243	400	450	430
Harrold/Radwell		103	65	150	151		200+	225	187	170	400	310
Luton Hoo			35	56	75		365	130	327	320	415	107
Barkers Lane					58		234					
Woburn								271	305	340	100	
Grovebury Farm SP									141	138	110	400

introduced as were birds at Woburn Park which numbered *c.*30 in 1972 and 'some' in Wrest Park in the same year. In 1973 the flock at Woburn had increased to 55 and that at Wrest Park to 30, the latter including two Greylag × Canada hybrids. By 1975 the *Beds Naturalist* recorded it as being 'well established' in the county. Harding (1979) wrote that by 1977 'it was obvious that Canada Geese were becoming a pest in the north-east of the county causing concern to farmers and it may be necessary to impose some control on the rising population before the situation becomes out of hand.' The rise in the population continued and during the winter of 1982 a cull of about 200 birds took place. However, as is often the case in such situations, the population soon recovered and continued to grow with more sites being used regularly.

TABLE 3.4   *Canada Goose breeding records 1971–87*

	71	72	73	74	75	76	77	78	79	80	81	82	83	84	85	86	87
Pairs	1	4	4	3	5	3				15+		19					13
Young	3	11+	11	9	23	15	58	48	50		67	60+	70	18+	90+	117	
Sites	1	3	3	2	5	3	6	8	7	6	6	6	7	7	6	6	11

The majority of ringing recoveries have been of local birds but there is a suggestion that some birds visit the county from further north in winter, with two birds ringed during the summer in Nottinghamshire and one from North Yorkshire being recovered in the county during the autumn and winter.

Barnacle Goose

Branta leucopsis

An uncommon feral resident and visitor from neighbouring counties which is slowly establishing itself in Bedfordshire. Also a very rare winter visitor.

There are only two early records. An adult male was purchased by Mr A. Covington in 1885. It had been shot near Renhold and was in very poor condition. Mr A. F. Crossman observed a flight of eight over the River Ouse near the Britannia Iron Works in Bedford on 24 December 1890.

Six were recorded at Luton Hoo Lake on 23–4 December 1952 and it is thought that these could have been wild birds. Two at Woburn Lake in January 1953 were considered to be escapes as were four flying south-west over Bedford SF in 1962 (no date given). There were no other records until 1977 but since that date this species has been recorded in every year, mainly at the clay-pit lakes, with an increase in records from 1985 onwards. This correlates well with the fact that free-flying young have been raised by captive birds in Hampshire since the late 1970s. Although this species is more frequently recorded during the autumn and winter this increase in recent years has tended to occur from September onwards which again suggests that feral birds are involved. Although most of the pre-1985 records have been of single birds some of the larger parties occurring before and since then have been during the early autumn. These have involved five at Harrold GP in October 79, up to five at Harrold/Radwell GPs from 29 August 1982 to the year end, three at Harrold GP on 16 September 1985 to the year end, four at Millbrook ClP on 7 August 1986, and seven at Brogborough on 7 September 1986 with a peak of nine on 3 November. These early dates suggest that feral birds are involved.

The Stewartby/Brogborough complex held a maximum of five birds in January and February 1986 where they were last recorded on 29 March. The behaviour of four of these, which arrived on 2 January, suggested that they could have been wild in origin. Although the wild birds which winter in Britain are from the Greenland and Spitzbergen populations, in severe winters birds from the Siberian population which winter in the Netherlands are sometimes forced to cross the North Sea and arrive in East Anglia. Even so, the earliest arrivals on the Norfolk coast are usually recorded during early November and they are unlikely to occur in Bedfordshire before this. An exception might have been in 1985 when the earliest arrival on the East Coast took place in mid October. However, when a large influx into Norfolk took place in 1984 there was little evidence of it in Bedfordshire with only single birds being recorded during the summer and autumn.

Brent Goose

Branta bernicla

A rare winter visitor.

There are several early records of this species. C. F. Woods in Steele-Elliott (1904) reports them as being occasional winter visitors to Woburn with four staying for some time in 1863. Four Brent Geese were killed from a party of 13 at Great Barford by Dr C. Sprigge on 11 February 1871. An adult male was obtained on 3 December 1877 from the Osier-bed Island along the Embankment close to Longholme, Bedford. Mr Covington received this bird and mentioned to Steele-Elliott that others had been seen the day before at Cardington. On 11 October 1881 'whilst watching a Merlin near to Clapham Wood' Mr A. Covington observed a party of 47 Brent Geese flying over towards Oakley and heard a few days later that a 'Black-headed Goose' was shot in the neighbourhood of Pavenham. A single Brent Goose was observed by A. F. Crossman passing over the Clapham Road near Bedford Waterworks on 10 March 1892 and he reported that several were seen on Bedford Sewage Farm on 5 November of the following winter. Mr W. J. Chalk in writing to Steele-Elliott mentions that he occasionally observed the Brent Goose passing over Wilden. In particular he mentions a flock of them passing north-east over the hedge at the back of Wilden Rectory so low as to come within ten yards of him . . . 'and I remember vainly striking at them with a stick.'

The next records were in 1979 when one was seen at Radwell GP on 6 February and one was observed in flight over Harrold/Radwell GPs on 25 February. Other records are as follows:

1981   A single bird was present near Silsoe on 22 December.
1982   18 flew south-west from Girtford GP on 23 October.
1983   One at Brogborough Lake 3–4 March.
        One at Brogborough Lake 1 May.
        One at Brogborough Lake 13 November.
        Three over Harlington on 13 November.
1985   One at Elstow on 31 March.
        One at Kempston Hardwick ClP on 4 April.
        An immature was at Radwell GP from 22 December to the year end.
1986   The immature of 1985 remained in the Radwell/Harrold area until 9 March.
        One briefly at Blunham GP on 4 January.
1987   One at Grovebury Farm Pit on 25 January.
        One at Stewartby ClP on 31 March.

All of the recent records were of the nominate race (*B. b. bernicla*), which breeds in the northern coastal areas of western Siberia.

This recent increase in records of birds in the county reflects the great increase which has taken place in the wintering populations in

Britain, particularly around the Wash and in North Norfolk. Here a wintering population of 13,000 in the winter of 1976–7 increased to over 36,000 by the 1982–3 winter and has fluctuated around 30,000 since then (Owen, Atkinson-Willes, and Salmon 1986).

The number of Bedfordshire records in late March, April, and even early May might at first seem unusual but the population around the Wash stays much later into the spring than elsewhere in Britain (Salmon *et al.* 1988), and those occurring in the county at this time are probably stragglers.

Egyptian Goose

Alopochen aegyptiacus

A rare visitor.

The Egyptian Goose was admitted to the British and Irish list in 1971 as a category C species (an established introduced species which is self-maintaining). Before this time little interest was shown in it by birdwatchers. During the nineteenth century several full-winged freely-breeding colonies were established on private estates including Woburn. It is not known how long this colony remained viable but there are no recent records. The population in Norfolk has gradually increased and present estimates indicate that this population is about 400. Most, if not all, of the recent county records are probably due to the dispersion of these birds.

1978   Three at Harrold GP on 23 January, then two to 19 February.
1979   One at Blunham GP on 27 June.
         One at Blunham GP on 1 September.
1985   Three over Dunstable SW on 11 August.
1986   Two in the Radwell/Felmersham area from 14 April to 18 May with one remaining until the year end.
         One at Stewartby ClP on 21 December and Brogborough ClP on 23 December.
1987   The Radwell bird of 1986 remained until at least 3 January. One flew north-east over Stewartby ClP on 11 January and was seen later the same day at Rookery ClP.

[Ruddy Shelduck]

[*Tadorna ferruginea*]

One at Bedford SF on 23 May 1943 was thought to have been an escape. Two at Dunstable SF on 7 April 1971 were very tame and presumed to have been escapes.

A male was present on the River Ouse outside County Hall, Bedford, on 3 June 1985 and moved to Priory CP on the evening of 5 June. It readily came to be fed and was doubtless an escape.

Shelduck

Tadorna tadorna

A regular winter visitor and passage migrant. Scarce breeder (**Map 7**).

Mostly associated with tidal mudflats and estuaries, this large white, black, and chestnut duck is becoming a more frequent visitor to our county and, in recent years, has been added to our list of breeding birds. This has been due to increased numbers nesting inland, particularly in the Fens. It is perhaps most noted for its unusual moult migration which takes place after the breeding season, when thousands of birds gather in the German section of the Wadden Sea where they moult with other birds from western Europe before returning for the winter. Recently much smaller gatherings have appeared on the Forth, Humber, Wash, and Bridgewater Bay but the origin of birds passing through the county in August has not yet been determined.

Steele-Elliott (1904) gives the status of this species at that time as occurring 'with us at rare intervals wandering inland from its sea-loving haunts.' The earliest records are of two preserved by Mr A. Covington, the taxidermist, one having been shot at Cardington in 1864 and the second at Great Barford 'several years later.' Mr Covington, in writing to Steele-Elliott, says that he purchased a case containing two immature Shelducks 'many years ago' which were simply labelled 'Goldington'. During the severe winter of 1894–5 about 20 were observed near Wyboston Corner. Two were recorded in February 1900 in the same area and a further two were seen together at Great Barford. The Duchess of Bedford recorded one at Woburn Ponds on 22 February 1925.

Up to the mid 1960s the status of this species was that of a scarce winter visitor and passage migrant, rarely occurring on more than three occasions during any one year. During the period 1946–65 the Shelduck was recorded in 17 years on 34 occasions with about 80% of the records involving one or two individuals, but up to six were recorded. Most occurred between December and April with the occasional record during early May followed by a complete absence in June and July. Dispersal movements were noted during August at about the same level as in the winter and were much reduced from September to November before increasing again in December.

A change in status began after the mid 1960s and was associated with the increase in lakes made available after the extraction of clay and gravel. The pattern followed much the same as in previous years, both in the time of occurrence and the size of parties involved; however, the frequency increased greatly. By 1986 the number of annual sightings, not including breeding birds, was about 38, more than ten times that of the 1965 figure. Although numbers seen at any one time usually remained at three or less a party of 20 at Stewartby ClP on 7 September 1966, nearly all juveniles, was quite exceptional.

The first breeding record for the county occurred at Millbrook ClP in 1972. Young were found at Grovebury Farm SP in the west of the county in 1981 and again in 1982 but an attempt in 1983 at the same site proved to be unsuccessful. Two pairs bred in 1984, and in 1985 two ducks hatched 17 eggs (only two surviving): at Radwell GP where a pair had one young which did not survive and at Vicarage Farm ClP where a pair raised two young. In 1986 pairs were recorded in the breeding season at four sites, one holding two pairs, but breeding was confirmed from only one site where two juveniles were seen in August.

[Wood Duck]

[*Aix sponsa*]

A tame female was present on the River Ouse in Bedford from 21 January 1973 to spring 1974. Two were reported from Shuttleworth College Lakes in November 1980 and up to three males and two females frequented the same locality in 1981. A male was present on the River Ouse at Fenlake on 1 March 1984.

Mandarin

Aix galericulata

An uncommon resident (**Map 8**).

This species was added to the British and Irish list in 1971 due to the establishment of self-supporting feral populations and it was only at this time that observers began to make accurate notes of its occurrence. As a result little is known of its previous history within the county. We know that there was once a thriving population at Woburn. Lever (1977) states that 300 were introduced at Woburn at the beginning of the century but numbers had declined to about half this by the end of the First World War and again had declined by half by the end of the Second World War. The first published county record in recent years was of a drake on Battlesden Lake on 30 September 1967 but this species was not recorded again until 1972 when a pair was seen by the Grand Union Canal at Old Linslade on 21 March with a male there on the following day. Two males and four females were observed at Bison Pond, Woburn Park, on 19 November in the same year.

Although breeding must have taken place in previous years, particularly at Woburn, the first published record was in 1973, continuing as follows:

1973   A pair at Old Linslade raised at least five young from a clutch of 10 eggs.
1975   One pair bred on the River Ivel near Blunham.
1976   One pair bred on the River Ivel near Blunham.
1977   Two pairs bred on the River Ivel near Blunham.
1978   One pair bred at Woburn and produced seven young.
       One pair at Eversholt Lake produced two young.
1981   Three broods totalling 18 young were observed at Eversholt Lake.
1983   Bred at a site on the River Ouzel where three males and four females were present. Broods of six and seven were raised.
1984   One pair bred in Luton Hoo.
1985   One pair raised six young at Luton Hoo.
       A pair hatched five young at Eversholt Lake.
1986   Two or three pairs raised at least 13 young at Woburn Park. Three juveniles were seen at East Hyde on 1 June.
1987   Two pairs nested at Eversholt Lake with at least one being successful, producing three young. A pair reared five young at Luton Hoo.

It is very difficult to make an accurate assessment of the changes in the county population as until 1971 little notice was taken of this species. Between 1967 and 1987 the Mandarin has been recorded at 32 sites throughout the county. The largest totals (not including young) have all been recorded during the winter at Woburn where they collect at this time. Maxima since 1971 are as follows:

1973   Seven at Woburn.
1974   19 at Woburn.
1981   22+ (including 18 young) at Woburn.
1982   14 at Woburn.
1983   10 at Woburn.
       Seven at Harrold GP.
       Five at Turvey.
1984   20 at Woburn.
1985   35 at Woburn (also 20 males on 16 February).
1987   45 at Woburn.

Wigeon

Anas penelope

A regular fairly common winter visitor.

During the late nineteenth century this species occurred frequently in small numbers in winter along the Ouse and Ivel and on the main lakes but only rarely did parties exceed 20. The earliest records in Steele-Elliott (1904) were given by Mr J. King whose records refer to the Ivel around Great Langford. Seventeen were flushed in that locality on 21 March 1855, singles shot on 10 March 1857, 5 January 1858, and 21 November 1874. A male and a female were shot near Langford Mill on 28 November 1879 and a female was killed on 28 February 1895. Mr T. Pearse (in Steele-Elliott) mentions 'A flock of Wigeons, upwards of twenty in number, and mostly males, at Fenlake, on 22nd February 1894' and 'another flight of fifteen . . . on 2 January 1895.' It was occasionally recorded at Flitwick Marsh and Davis (1855) mentions it as being a common winter visitor around Luton.

The first birds usually arrive during late October or November (occasionally as early as August), and most have departed by the end of March. A few birds have remained into April but occurrences outside this period are most unusual. There have been four May records, two in June and one in July as follows:

1981   One at Barkers Lane GP on 11 May.
1984   Two at Stewartby Lake on 18 May.
1985   One at Vicarage Farm ClP on 12 May.
1986   One at Harrold CP on 17 May.

1973   Two at Brogborough ClP on 24 June.
1986   One at Vicarage Farm ClP on 28 June.

1973   Two at Dunstable SF on 26 July.

The flooded fields around Bedford SF proved to be ideal for this species during the 1940s with over 150 present during the floods on 2 February 1946. Kempston Hardwick CIP also attracted good numbers during this period with c.200 there on 13 February 1949. Parties of 60 or less were recorded in the Coronation ClP, Eastwood's ClP, Felmersham GP, Goldington, Stewartby ClP, and Woburn, but Bedford SF provided the most consistent numbers. By the mid 1950s the area around Bedford SF became less suitable and Stewartby ClP increased in importance with winter maxima of over 100 during 1961 and 1962. Flooding again occurred at the rear of Goldington Power Station in 1963 and near Bedford SF in 1964 and peaks of c.100 were recorded in both years. The winter of 1968–9 proved to be a good year nationally and this was reflected at Stewartby ClP with a party of 230 on 5 January. Although the clay pits at Brogborough, Kempston Hardwick, and Vicarage Farm were additional sites visited by small parties during the 1970s, the gravel pits, many of them newly created during the 1960s, began to dominate as sites for this species from the mid 1970s with Radwell, Harrold, Blunham, and Priory CP (Barkers Lane GP) providing some of the highest totals ever recorded. The gravel pit sites were often surrounded by suitable feeding habitat which encouraged these grazing birds to remain with us for longer periods.

Counts of 100+ in Bedfordshire 1946–87 were as follows:

1946   150 at Bedford SF on 2 January.
1949   c.200 at Kempston Hardwick ClP on 13 February.
1956   c.120 at Eastwood's ClP on 12 February.
1961   162 at Stewartby ClP on 3 January.
       190 at Stewartby ClP on 11 January.
1962   c.100 at Barkers Lane GP/Bedford SF on 1 January.
       150 at Stewartby ClP on 17 January.
1969   230 at Stewartby ClP on 5 January.
1975   133 at Harrold GP on 2 February.
1977   114 at Harrold GP on 9 January.
       142 at Harrold GP on 6 February.
1978   120 at Radwell GP on 17 December.
       128 at Harrold GP on 28 December.
1979   130 near Harrold GP on 28 January.
       200+ at Radwell GP on 25 February.
       150+ nr. Harrold GP on 24 February.
       113 at Blunham GP on 24 December.
1980   115 at Blunham GP on 6 January.
       242 at Blunham GP on 16 January.
       241 at Blunham GP on 25 January.
1981   120 at Harrold GP on 17 January.
       100 at Harrold GP on 8 February.
       221 at Barkers Lane GP on 13 December.
1982   178 at Priory CP (Barkers Lane GP) on 10 January.
       170+ at Radwell GP on 23 January.
       217 at Priory CP (Barkers Lane GP) on 16 February.
1984   200+ at Radwell GP on 19 February.
       213 at Radwell GP on 16 December.
1985   139 at Harrold CP on 2 January.
       250 at Radwell GP 6–27 January.
       200 at Priory CP (Barkers Lane) on 6 January.
       175 at Priory CP on 13 January.
       267 at Stewartby/Millbrook ClPs on 13 January.
       300 at Stewartby/Millbrook ClPs on 20 January.
       145 at Radwell GP on 29 December.
1986   250 at Harrold CP/Radwell GP on 11 January.
       130 at Priory CP on 18 January.
1987   357 at Harrold CP/Radwell GP area on 3 January.

Gadwall

Anas strepera

A scarce and irregular breeding species in recent years and a fairly common winter visitor, sometimes in quite large numbers at particular sites.

Although numbers in Norfolk were increasing at a rapid pace during the second half of the nineteenth century their dispersal to other counties was quite slow and Steele-Elliott (1904) could cite only two instances within the county. The first was of an immature male shot by Mr J. King on the River Ivel in the meadows at Langford on 5 April 1861 and the second was of a female shot at Blunham during the winter of 1889–90.

The Gadwall arrives in the county as a winter visitor from September onwards, usually reaching a peak in late December before gradually declining in numbers until the end of April when most have departed. There have been occasional May and August records away from breeding sites. Up to 1978 there had been only three June sightings. The origin of our wintering birds is uncertain; birds wintering in Bedfordshire may contain some which have dispersed from breeding haunts in Britain but those which arrive during December originate in Scandinavia and the Low Countries. Of the four foreign recoveries of birds ringed at Blunham, three have been recovered in northern France and one in the Netherlands. Of the three birds ringed abroad and recovered in the county, two were ringed in northern France and one in East Germany.

It appears that during the first half of this century it still remained a rare bird. This is not surprising as the Gadwall feeds on floating and submerged plants by immersing the head or by upending. It thus requires well-vegetated shallow lakes, a habitat in very short supply in Bedfordshire at that time. One could not expect this species to appear in the county to any extent until the gravel pits created during the Second World War and the 1960s had matured.

J. A. Miller (1944–5) recorded a male at Bedford SF on 30 April and 2 May 1944 and thought this to be the only occurrence this century. Of the three records in the period 1946–57 a drake at Woburn in November and December 1947 and a pair on Drakelow Pond, Woburn in February 1949 were thought at the time to have been 'escapes'. The third record was of a male at Battlesden Lake in November 1953 and could also have been of suspect origin but there is no other evidence, apart from the area involved, to support this idea. A change in status did occur from 1958 onwards. In that year alone there were six records involving 10 birds during six of the seven months from October to April, with January being the only month during this period when this species was not recorded. Although there was some fluctuation in numbers during the following years, the status remained about the same with an average of five records each year during 14 of the 17 years 1959–75. Apart from the two years of 1965 and 1966, when there were no records, the lowest number of records was two (1964), both singles, and the highest was 11 involving 23 birds in 1960.

A further change in status took place from 1976 when 16 occurrences involving 34 birds were recorded. The gravel pits at Blunham saw a dramatic increase during the following years with a maximum of 20 in 1977, increasing each winter until 1981, after which a decline began at this site. However, Priory CP (Barkers Lane GP) was used during the winter of 1981/2 with Dunstable SW and Luton Hoo in following years. This fairly recent change coincides with a large increase in the breeding population of continental Europe as well as in Britain.

Interestingly, although the number of birds estimated to be in the county during November and December of 1986 was about 200, the number of sites at which it was recorded was 14, compared with 58 birds at 15 sites 10 years earlier. The Gadwall prefers shallow freshwater lakes and this suggests that the number of suitable sites has not changed significantly during this period.

TABLE 3.5   *Maximum winter counts of Gadwall at Blunham GP, Priory CP, Dunstable SW, and Luton Hoo, 1977–86*

	77/8	78/9	79/80	80/1	81/2	82/3	83/4	84/5	85/6	86/7
Blunham GP	20		55	23	133	121		30	41	32
Priory CP					81				14	
Dunstable SW							40	54	55	96
Luton Hoo									15	56

It was not surprising that, after the rapid increase which took place from 1977, this species bred in the county. The first suspicions were aroused when a pair was seen prospecting for a nest site at Girtford in May 1978 and in the following year the first breeding took place at Luton Hoo Lake when a pair raised three young. It was not until 1982 that the second pair bred, with 10 young being seen at Girtford GP. During 1985 although there were no breeding records, a pair was observed mating at Luton Hoo Lake in June and there were three other June records.

Teal

Anas crecca

Two sub-species, the nominate European race, *Anas c. crecca* and the American Green-winged Teal, *Anas c. carolinensis* have occurred in Bedfordshire and are referred to separately.

Teal *Anas crecca crecca*

Fairly common winter visitor and scarce breeding bird (**Map 9**).

The status given by Steele-Elliott (1904) was that of a winter visitor, arriving during October, sometimes earlier, and met with frequently along waterways and occasionally flushed from small streams, ponds, and ditches. He knew of it having bred in former years. At Southill Lake Mr J. King recalled at least three nests and eggs being found there before 1880 and a nest with eggs was found there in 1893. At Luton Hoo nesting occurred in 1895 and at Newnham Farm eggs were taken in 1896 and again in 1898 when conditions were particularly suitable. Although an immature was shot near Stagsden on 4 August 1891 its origin could not be confirmed and it could have been reared over the nearby county border of Buckinghamshire.

Birds arrive to spend the winter with us from September onwards and most have departed by the end of April. These birds have their origins in North Russia, the Baltic States, Fenno-Scandia, and the Low Countries of Europe. There have been two ringing recoveries from Finland and one from northern France. The number arriving in this country is very much dependent on weather conditions: cold weather in particular will cause them to move further west, as also will drought or heavy rainfall (Ogilvie in Lack 1986). In Bedfordshire their distribution also depends upon temperature and food availability, with the first birds to arrive occupying flood waters and boggy fields, if they exist at that time. During the autumn months the large quantities of seeds which occur at these sites are particularly attractive and suitable to their feeding strategy. Being a small dabbling duck a water depth of much over 25cm is unsuitable. The gravel-pit lakes, being shallow, and the shallow areas of clay-pit lakes such as at Brogborough ClP are also utilised, particularly after any flood waters have subsided. Being shallow-water feeders, any gravel-pit lake adjacent to a stretch of river which is liable to flood is very attractive. When the temperature is low enough to cause the freezing of these shallow lakes they will move to the clay-pit lakes which, being much deeper, are the last to freeze.

A recent problem, that of sailing and sailboarding, is also having an effect on the Teal populations of small-lakes and those without a disturbance-free zone for wildfowl. Kramer (1986) found that at Priory CP Teal was the most sensitive species and would depart as soon as a single sailboard was launched, but the introduction of a disturbance-free zone greatly improved the situation.

During the middle of this century the most important site was Bedford SF which regularly provided numbers in excess of 200 until 1963. Flooding of the River Ouse near to the Sewage Farm greatly increased the area of suitable habitat and it was in such conditions in early January 1946 that more than 500 were present. Southill Lake and Stewartby ClP were also used during this period by smaller numbers and Wyboston GP provided a site between 1960 and 1970.

Numbers remained low between 1971 and 1977, when an influx took place in November and included the first large numbers (150+)

to appear at Harrold GP as well as *c.*200 at Bedford SF and *c.*100 at Barkers Lane GP, both in November. During this period, when this species was low in numbers at most sites, 50–100 were present at Southill Lake in most years, the oldest traditional site other than Bedford SF.

In 1980 Radwell GP held good numbers (*c.*150) for the first time and this site was used again in 1982 when 220 were present in January.

Large Numbers (200+) of Teal recorded since 1946 are:

1946   500+ at Bedford SF on 2 January.
1948   200+ at Bedford SF on 16 March.
1950   250–300 at Bedford SF in mid February.
1951   *c.*200 at Bedford SF on 25 March.
1952   *c.*250 at Bedford SF in January and February.
1955   *c.*250 at Bedford SF in January.
1956   *c.*300 at Bedford SF on 12 January.
1957   *c.*200 at Stewartby ClP on 23 January.
1958   *c.*200 at Bedford SF in February.
1961   *c.*450 at Bedford SF/Barkers Lane GP 19 November to 3 December.
1963   *c.*250 at Bedford SF on 3 March.
1968   *c.*350 at Wyboston GP in December.
1969   259 at Wyboston GP in January.
       *c.*300 at Wyboston GP in February.
       *c.*200 at Stewartby ClP in December.
1970   *c.*200 at Wyboston GP in January.
1977   *c.*200 at Bedford SW on 11 December.
1978   *c.*200 at Barkers Lane GP on 26 October.
1982   *c.*200 at Bedford SW on 3 January.
       220 at Radwell on 23 January.
       227 at Priory CP on 30 January.
       200 at Fenlake on 14 March.

Although breeding was known during the nineteenth century there were no further published records until a pair was suspected of breeding at Eversholt in 1958. The first confirmed breeding in recent times occurred in 1977 when a female was disturbed from a nest of nine eggs in Chicksands Wood. A pair nested at Harrold GP in 1978, on the River Ouzel at Old Linslade in 1983 and South Mills NR in 1984, 1985, and 1987.

American Green-winged Teal   *Anas crecca carolinensis*

A very rare vagrant.

A male at Radwell GP on 12 April 1987 was the first county record (*British Birds* 81: 547).

Mallard

Anas platyrhynchos

Common resident breeder and winter visitor (**Map 10**).

At the end of the nineteenth century the Mallard was both common as an immigrant during the winter months and also as a breeding bird. Steele-Elliott (1904) makes the comment that the numbers of this species were considerably increased in certain localities by rearing and 'are reared more or less in a state of domestication, as at Woburn, Battlesden, Oakley, Luton Hoo, Tingrith and Southill.' He also noted that in very mild winters even small flights were rarely seen, but numbers increased when the weather was severe, especially after a north-east wind when, he says, 'duck shooting along the waterways and at various lakes may be carried on for a time with fair success.' Flooding, particularly along the River Ouse and other streams, resulted in large flights being observed.

Towards the end of August and during early September numbers reach a peak which coincides with the end of the harvest, and many are to be seen at this time feeding in the early morning in nearby stubble fields. These move to the lakes to feed again and then roost during the day. Numbers then fall and a second peak occurs during the main winter period but this can be very much related to weather conditions, particularly temperature. When this falls below freezing for a few days the shallow gravel-pit lakes are the first to freeze and birds move to the deeper clay-pit lakes. Birds from continental Europe may be involved: the only foreign ringing recovery of this species ringed in Bedfordshire was recovered in Sweden.

During the first half of this century the most important wintering areas for this species were the man-made lakes of Southill, Battlesden, Woburn, and Luton Hoo, with Bedford SF and Kempston Hardwick ClP providing other suitable habitats. From 1960 onwards the clay and gravel pits increased in importance. The largest parties recorded during the 1940s and early 1950s were of 300 or less, but Stewartby lake proved to be an attractive site in later years with numbers up to 500 in 1958, over 1,000 during November and December 1960, and 1,500 in early January 1961. During the severe winter weather of 1963 the total at Stewartby increased to 2,000 by 28 December. In October 1967 the clay-pit lakes were estimated to contain about 2,500. The maxima at the county's seven principal waters remained at about this level until 1980 when it fell to about 1,800 and then further to about 1,400 by the mid 1980s.

As a breeding bird the Mallard is the most common and widespread of our breeding ducks. Harding (1979) showed that breeding was proved in 131 of the 371 tetrads in the county and was probable in another 14. The nest is usually on the ground amongst thick vegetation often near a lake, pond, or river, but one was recorded nesting about 30ft above the ground in a rick at Stagsden in 1951 whilst in the same year at nearby Burdelys Manor Farm two nests were recorded almost next to each other in the crown of a pollarded willow. In 1983 a breeding survey along the River Ouse revealed 232 territories with at least 80 broods. During the same year over 150 young were reared at Priory CP but the vast increase in dog walkers and visitors and the consequent disturbance at this site resulted in an 80% decrease by 1987.

Pintail

Anas acuta

An uncommon but regular winter visitor.

The status given by Steele-Elliott (1904) was that of a winter visitor, 'resorting to our rivers and pools most years but in very limited numbers.' He suggests that it had been recorded more frequently towards the end of the nineteenth century with females and immature males predominating. The earliest record is of one shot at Southill Lake about 1860. A male was shot near Harrold Hall on 11 January 1892 and an adult female was shot at Newnham Farm on 18 September 1894. During the winter of 1899–1900 a female was shot at Roxton, two females at Renhold, and an adult drake on the Ouse at Goldington. Steele-Elliott mentions two other records, one of four together on flooded meadows at Great Barford, but no date is given, and one 'locally' in the winter of 1899–1900. Davis (1874) includes this species in his list of birds of the Luton district. A male was recorded at Bedford SF on 9 January 1943 (Alexander 1943–4).

Since 1946 this species has continued to occur in the county as a scarce, but regular, winter visitor, being recorded almost every year in parties of five or less, but more usually singly or in pairs. Most occurrences have been at the larger water areas formed by the extraction of clay and gravel as well as the man-made lakes, but sewage works, chalk pits, and flood-meadows have also been utilised to a lesser degree. Birds may be seen from October onwards with larger numbers during late December, January, and early February. Large parties have also been recorded during March, suggesting that a return passage takes place at this time. There have been only a few records outside this period, the earliest being four at Harrold GP on 25 August 1984 and the latest two males at Bedford SF on 17 May 1960. An unusual record was of 'what was probably a female' at Bedford SF on 29–30 July 1973. The Pintail occurs in quite high numbers on the Ouse Washes and in good numbers along the Nene Valley and it is perhaps surprising that it is not encountered more frequently in Bedfordshire.

Counts above six in the period 1946–86 are:

1950 Eight at Stewartby ClP on 15 December.
1958 12 at Stewartby ClP February–March.
1960 14 at Stewartby ClP on 29 December.

1961　c.14 at Stewartby ClP on 9 January.
　　　22–4 at Stewartby ClP on 5 February.
1962　Seven at Stewartby ClP on 28 January.
1963　17 at Wyboston GP on 10 March.
　　　29 at Bedford SF on 10 March.
　　　12 at Stewartby ClP on 17 March.
1969　10 at Wyboston GP on 2 March.
1979　100 over Melchbourne 28 January.
1981　25 south over Blunham on 6 March.
1982　14 at Fenlake on 14 March.
1985　10 at Stewartby ClP on 9 January.
1986　19 at over Priory CP mid December.

Garganey

Anas querquedula

A scarce but regular passage migrant. Has bred.

The earliest record is of a male shot on Fenlake about 1872. A very late bird, again a male, was shot at Ravensden in November 1890, a female was obtained at Clapham in the spring of 1891, and one was killed at Milton in about 1892. Other instances of its occurrence, including one at Luton Hoo before 1895, were mentioned to Steele-Elliott but without further details. W. B. Alexander (1943–4) mentions one at Bedford SF on August 13 1938 and 'a considerable number' on August 13 1939, when six were seen on the wing together with others certainly present. A male was recorded at Bedford SF on 30 May 1943 (1943–4).

Since 1946 this species has been recorded in every year except 1949, 1960, 1977, 1979, 1980, and 1985. In years with sightings there have been five years in which no spring passage has been recorded and no autumn passage in 14 of the 42 years covered here (1946, 48, 50, 51, 52, 54, 57, 63, 64, 65, 73, 74, 78, 84). About 60% of records have been on spring passage and about 38% on autumn. Most records involve singles or pairs (70%) but the majority of larger parties have been recorded during the autumn. Nearly all records have been at gravel pits, sewage works, and parkland lakes with very few at the deeper clay-pit lakes.

Birds may begin to arrive from North Africa from mid March (earliest 11 March 1964), with most recorded in April. There has been a scattering of May records but only three June occurrences, apart from breeding birds, since 1946. Return passage may begin towards the end of July but the main passage occurs in August and declines during September. There have been two October records (latest 11 October 1981). The only winter record is of a pair at Kempston Hardwick on 9 December 1946.

75

The first recorded attempt at breeding was in 1948 when a nest with eight eggs was found at Bedford SF on 29 May. The nest was photographed but a few days later it was destroyed, apparently by cattle. The only additional breeding record is of a pair swimming along the river near Bedford SF with eight ducklings on 28 May 1953.

Significant counts 1946–87 are as follows:

1955 12 at Luton Hoo Lake on 3 August.
1961 8–10 at Stanford GP on 8 September.
1964 5 at Felmersham GP on 11 March.
1966 7 at Wyboston GP on 4 September.
1971 5 at Stagsden in late August and September.
1982 5 at Dunstable SW on 8 August.

Blue-winged Teal

Anas discors

A very rare vagrant.

One was observed at Dunstable SW on 11 October 1987, age and sex uncertain (*British Birds* 81: 547).

Shoveler

Anas clypeata

A scarce breeding bird but a fairly common passage migrant and winter visitor (**Map 11**).

The Shoveler is mentioned by Steele-Elliott (1904) both as a winter visitor and breeding bird. He refers to a pair which were reported to him as having nested at Luton Hoo in 1893 but he visited this site in subsequent years and was unable to find the species again. One, possibly two, pairs nested at Newnham Sewage Farm in 1898 but their eggs were taken. There are several instances of their being shot in winter during the late nineteenth century from such places as Chawston, Goldington, Great Barford, Kempston, Newnham Farm, and Wyboston. A note in *British Birds* 2: 53 (1908–9), says that this species was 'now known to breed regularly in several places'.

During the first half of this century the Shoveler was a fairly uncommon visitor from autumn through to spring with often less than a dozen records in any year. Numbers involved were usually less than five, although parties of nine were recorded on two occasions during the 1950s. In 1947 Henry Key stated: 'There has been no record of the breeding of this species in the county for many years.' The first signs that any significant increase was taking place occurred in 1960 when 26–8 were present at Bedford SF in March and up to 24 were recorded at Stewartby ClP in April. Sixteen were present at the latter locality in December. A further slight increase took place at the end of the 1960s but from 1973 onwards the increase in our wintering population became more firmly established with Dunstable SW being a particularly favoured site.

Maxima recorded at selected sites are as follows:

1969   22 at Wyboston GP in February.
        30 at Wyboston GP in March.
1975   33 at Dunstable SW on 19 August.
1976   33 at Southill Lake on 30 October.
        35 at Southill Lake on 13 November.
        35 at Dunstable SW on 13 November.
        67 at Dunstable SW on 21 November.
        30 at Dunstable SW on 28 December.
1977   29 at Dunstable SW on 23 January.
        40 at Blunham GP on 11 December.
1978   70 at Dunstable SW on 10 September.
1979   70 at Dunstable SW on 11 November.
1980   63 at Dunstable SW during August and September.
1981   92 at Dunstable SW on 15 September.
        52 at Brogborough ClP on 2 November.
        50 at Priory CP (Barkers Lane GP) on 7 December.
1982   100 at Dunstable SW on 7 September.
1983   60 at Dunstable SW on 14 October.
        31 at Southill Lake on 26 November.
1984   32 at Priory CP on 24 August.
        79 at Dunstable SW in December.
1985   67 at Dunstable SW on 21 October.
1986   52 at Dunstable SW on 10 November.

Family parties of British breeding birds pass through the county during August and September. This movement is completed in October and from this month onwards birds begin to arrive from Fenno-Scandia and the USSR. The only foreign recovery of a bird ringed in Bedfordshire was recovered in Izmail, USSR, 2,261km east-south-east. Numbers reach a peak during November declining gradually unless hard weather causes a sudden departure. Spring passage takes place in March and April on a much smaller scale than that of the autumn and by the end of May most birds have departed. Apart from breeding birds July records are most unusual. The Shoveler prefers water areas with shallow margins with a plentiful and available supply of aquatic plants and is thus notably absent in anything over single figures from the deep clay-pit lakes whose steep sides result in little marginal vegetation.

The first breeding record of recent times is of a pair with six young at Southill Lake in 1964. A record of a female accompanying a juvenile at Bedford SF on 14 August 1948 and claimed as being an 'almost certain' breeding record for the county is doubtfully so as family parties often pass through the county at this time of the year.

Other breeding records (all of a single pair at each site) are as follows:

1965 Southill Lake.
1971 Harrold GP.
1973 Sandy SF.
      Luton Hoo Lake.
1974 Girtford GP.
1976 Dunstable SW.
1978 Luton Hoo.
1982 Girtford GP.
      Dunstable SW.
1983 Girtford GP.
      (Houghton Regis ChP failed)
1984 Houghton Regis ChP.
      South Mills GP.
1985 Dunstable SW.
      (Houghton Regis ChP failed)
1986 Chimney Corner C1P.

Red-crested Pochard

Netta rufina

It is difficult to assess the status of this species as although some may have escaped from captivity or have been deliberately released, it is thought that some wild birds may be involved. Records are as follows:

1943 Male at Bedford SF on 14 January (Miller 1943–4).
1972 Female at Wyboston GP on 18 and 26 March.
1974 Female at Wyboston GP on 19 January.
1976 Pair at Blunham GP on 11 December to 13 February 1977.
1977 Female at Blunham GP on 25 December.
      (Also see 1976.)
1978 Female arrived at Blunham on 21 January, was joined by a male on 15 February and showed sporadically until 6 April. Pair at Blunham on 9 November.
1979 Adult male at Blunham on 3 April.
1980 Pair at Blunham on 21 September.
      Female present on 8 October.
1983 Female at Harrold CP 29 January to 6 February.
      Immature male at Brogborough Lake 1–15 October.
1984 Male at Brogborough Lake on 22 January.
1985 Male at Blunham GP on 12 January.
      Female at Brogborough Lake 25–31 January.
      Female at Blunham GP on 27 January.

Male at Blunham GP on 2 February.
Female at South Mills GP 12–24 May.
Male and two females at Harrold CP on 21 August.
Male at Brogborough Lake from 1 December to 27 March 1986 was joined by a female 9–21 December.

1986 Male at Brogborough Lake 6–16 October.
Immature male at Battlesden Lake from 24 December into 1987.

1987 The male at Battlesden Lake moved to Brogborough ClP on 13 January, returned to its former site 22–31 January and reappeared at Brogborough Lake on 8 February.
A male flew west over Priory CP on 24 September, appearing at Harrold CP the following day.
A second, but different, male was present at Harrold CP on 25 October.

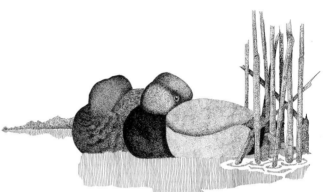

Pochard

Aythya ferina

A common winter visitor and scarce breeder (**Map 12**).

The earliest published comment about this species was made by Davis (1855) when he noted it as a winter visitor. Steele-Elliott (1904) knew of this bird as a fairly abundant visitor in winter and spring, occurring in small parties from November to March. Most of the records of that time refer to birds being shot, with records from Goldington (1870), Fenlake, Felmersham, Harrold, Stanford Mill, Wyboston, and along the Ivel between Shefford and Langford. It seems that until 1896 Steele-Elliott was unaware that this species occurred regularly at Luton Hoo Park. On 16 April 1896 he counted 30 on the two pools at this site and says '[I] was more interested to learn from the water-keeper that considerable numbers had been breeding there for many years past.' On a second visit on 26 May of that year he counted upwards of 40, 'most of the females being then with young.' However, when he again visited these pools in 1899 he found the number of Pochard considerably reduced. On a subsequent visit on 7 May 1901 he found only three. In the same year a pair was recorded during the breeding season on Battlesden Lake. Steele-Elliott found a pair breeding at Southill Lake in May 1920. The nest contained six eggs of which one was taken.

The numbers during the first half of this century were limited by the relatively few suitable water areas available and rarely numbered

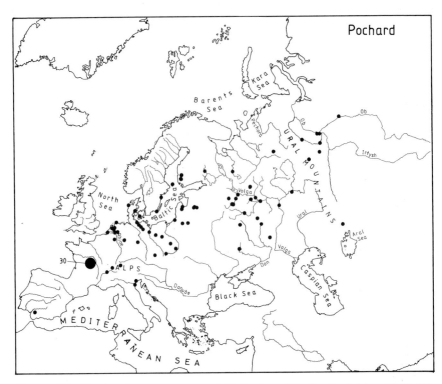

Figure 3.3 *Pochard: recovery map of birds ringed in Bedfordshire, 1946–87*

Figure 3.4 *Pochard: maximum annual counts 1968–87*

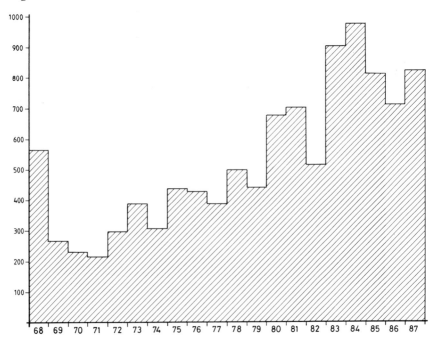

over 40. A flock of 89 at Southill Lake 25–30 December 1950 and c.200 at the same locality 13–30 January 1951 were the first published records of more than 50. The increase in flooded gravel and clay pits in subsequent years provided additional habitat with Wyboston GP and Stewartby ClP together with Southill Lake proving the most favoured areas during the 1960s. Brogborough ClP and Blunham GP were added to this list from the early 1970s, with Priory CP (Barkers Lane GP) also providing good numbers during the following decade.

The autumn increase is very variable, with the main arrival from the Baltic countries and the USSR usually taking place during October but sometimes as early as mid July or as late as November. This occasional early arrival was well illustrated in 1983 when 167 were present at Brogborough ClP on 25 July, whilst in 1946 the first arrivals were not recorded until three arrived at Southill Lake on 10 November. Severe winters resulting in the icing up of main waters can cause an almost total desertion of all sites, presumably as they move further south to France. There have been some very interesting movements of birds ringed at Blunham (Figure 3.3), with 34 recoveries in the Soviet Union, eight of which were over 4,000km away. Most of these were almost due east of Bedfordshire but the furthest was of one recovered 4,791km east-north-east in Khanty-Mansi. Other recoveries are as follows:

France	30
Baltic States	9
Germany	7
Netherlands	7
Poland	6
Finland	4
Denmark	3
Sweden	2
Spain	1

Although the winter population has fluctuated there has been a gradual upward trend since 1971 peaking in 1984. The largest party was one of 842 at Brogborough ClP on 3 October 1983, with the second largest of 630 at the same site in October of the following year. As Steele-Elliott noted, the males far outnumber the females, often in a ratio of 2:1 but sometimes as high as 3:1.

Although a very scarce breeding bird in the county it has bred in 22 out of the 42 years 1946–87 with 20 of these years in the period 1956–83. In most years only one or two pairs have been found breeding, but at least 10 pairs bred in 1959, six at Luton Hoo Lake (raising 35 young), three to four pairs at Millbrook ClP and one or two pairs at Stewartby ClP. Five pairs bred in 1967.

Ring-necked Duck

Aythya collaris

A very rare vagrant.

The first county record was of a drake at Luton Hoo Lake on 16 April 1972 (*British Birds* 65: 314). A drake was at Wyboston GP on 19–24 February 1979 and a drake was seen at Blunham GP on 27 March (*British Birds* 73: 499). A hybrid drake at Blunham on 26 February 1983 showed elements of this species.

Ferruginous Duck

Aythya nyroca

A very rare winter visitor.

One which was in Steele-Elliott's collection was purchased by him from Mr J. Cole the taxidermist. It was bought by him 'in the flesh' in the winter of 1890–1, having been shot on the River Lea, at Newmill End, close to Luton Hoo Park.

A specimen in Luton Museum which was bought by them for £2 10s is labelled as being shot, probably in Bedfordshire, on 28 August 1933.

Since 1946 sightings are as follows:

1948 An immature male at Kempston Hardwick Pool on 4–5 December.
1979 One at Wyboston GP on 20 February.
1980 Two males at Blunham GP on 21 December, one remaining until 7 March 1981.
1981 See 1980.
1983 A female at Blunham GP from 25 January to 26 February. A male at Brogborough Lake 3–6 September.
1986 A female at Blunham GP on 12 and 19 January.

Tufted Duck

Aythya fuligula

A common winter visitor and uncommon breeding species in increasing numbers (**Map 13**).

Davis (1855) first mentioned this species as a rare winter visitor, but in the 1874 edition this was changed to 'an occasional winter visitant', suggesting that a slight increase may have taken place between these two dates. Steele-Elliott (1904) mentions that although it was one of the less common species, it was constantly met with in small numbers from October onwards on any suitable lake or waterway. A possible breeding record was reported to Steele-Elliott by Mr W. C. Thompson who said that a pair bred at Luton Hoo Park in 1894, but the water-keeper was unable to confirm this. Mr Fred Sharman (1911–12) wrote saying that he found three nests containing eggs at a private water (presumably Southill Lake) in 1911 and was of the opinion that six pairs were breeding. His assumption that this was the first proven breeding record elicited a response from the Duchess of Bedford the following month (1911–12a) in which she expressed her surprise, suggesting that the lack of previously published records was 'because it is such an ordinary occurrence that it had not been thought worth reporting.' She supported this by reporting that this species had bred in the neighbourhood of Woburn for the last nine years and they were not imported birds. Steele-Elliott was obviously well aware that it bred at Southill Lake as his egg collection contains clutches taken in 1911, 1914, and 1917, all in June. A comment in the BNHS report for 1946 states that this species has 'not bred at Southill Lake for many years'.

The first immigrants may arrive from the Soviet Union and Scandinavia at the end of September and the build-up is often quite gradual, attaining a peak during late December or early January. Numbers are often sustained around this level until the end of February, after which a decline takes place at a more rapid rate than the autumn build-up.

Of 55 foreign ringing recoveries eight have been in the USSR, all 3,000–4,000km east-north-east. There have been 17 recoveries from the Netherlands, 14 from France, nine from Finland, three from Germany, two from Denmark, one from Poland, and one from Italy (Figure 3.5).

Wintering numbers have fluctuated greatly over the years but the general trend has been upwards. Until 1955 the highest numbers recorded were usually of less than 50 birds but in December 1956 *c.*100 were recorded from Southill Lake. After this, parties of more than 100 were recorded more frequently. The largest parties have been one of *c.*450 at Stewartby ClP in December 1967 and 458 at Brogborough in December 1987.

The increase in the county's breeding population of Tufted Ducks corresponds well with a similar increase in the national population. An increase was first noticed in the late 1950s and about 16 pairs

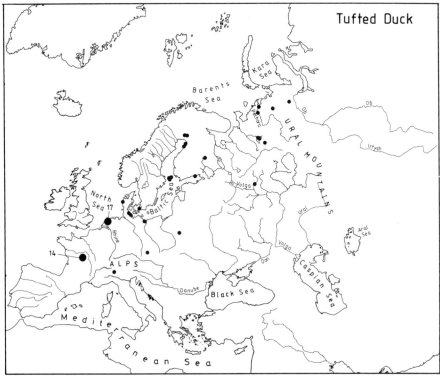

Figure 3.5 *Tufted Duck: recovery map of birds ringed in Bedfordshire, 1946–87*

were breeding successfully by 1967. The trend continued with 19 pairs in 1978, 23 in 1983, and 21 in 1987. The full list of breeding pairs recorded is as follows:

1948	2	1958	6	1967	c.16	1974	0	1981	6
1949	2	1959	–	1968	c.16	1975	0	1982	4
1951	1	1960	4	1969	c.16	1976	0	1983	23
1953	1	1961	4	1970	c.20	1977	0	1984	5+
1954	2	1962	9	1971	13	1978	19	1985	8+
1955	1	1963	14	1972	4	1979	12	1986	15
1956	4	1964	3	1973	17	1980	9+	1987	21
1957	9								

Scaup

Aythya marila

An occasional winter visitor and passage migrant.

Steele-Elliott (1904) states that by the end of the nineteenth century the occurrence of the Scaup was the exception in any winter rather

84

than the rule of previous years. He says that it used to be met with along the River Ouse almost as frequently as the Pochard, Tufted Duck, or Goldeneye and that Mr Josiah King considered it even commoner than any of them on the River Ivel in the neighbourhood of Langford. Although there was some retraction in range during the mid nineteenth century, other authorities at that time do not suggest that it was anywhere near as common before this period as is suggested by Steele-Elliott and the above statements should be treated with caution, particularly as identification is not always easy, especially without any optical aids as was the situation at that time.

Very few adult male Scaup were shot locally in his time, with not more than a dozen passing through the hands of Mr A. Covington, the local taxidermist, during a 30-year period. A drake was killed on the Ouse at Wyboston Corner and another on the river at Eaton Socon but no dates are given. Two other recorded instances (*Field* 1896 and *Zoologist* 1898) were thought to be wanders from the Woburn aviaries. On 30 December 1938, during very severe weather, a party of nine (five males, four females) were recorded at Arlesey Pit. Six were still present on 2 January 1939, two on 6 January, and one female stayed until 5 February (Miller 1939–40). An adult female was present on the River Ouse near Bedford SF on 31 December 1942 (Miller 1943–4).

Records since 1946 are:

1954   Three at Arlesey ClP on 27 January.
1957   Four at Southill Lake 3 February.
1958   One male at Arlesey ClP 25 January.
       One female at Wyboston GP on 13 April.
1959   A pair at Stewartby ClP on 1 October.
1961   One male at Wyboston GP 2–14 April.
1962   One male at Wyboston GP on 1 December.
       One male at Stewartby ClP on 23 December.
1971   One male on River Lea at East Hyde 18–23 January.
1976   One male at Harrold GP on 18 August.
1985   One female at Brogborough Lake on 12 January.
       One female at Priory CP 26 January to 10 February.
       One male on River Ouse at Priory CP 27 January to 10 February.
       Two females and one immature male at South Mills GP 2–3 February.
       Three males and a female at Stewartby ClP on 26 April.
       One male at Radwell GP 31 August to 29 September.
       One female at Brogborough Lake 27 November to 29 December.
1986   The above female remained at Brogborough Lake until 4 January.
       A female at Lidlington ClP 6–9 January may have been a different bird from Brogborough a few days earlier.
       A female at Stewartby Lake 17–18 January.
       One female at Harrold GP and Radwell GP 2–26 January.
       An immature/female at Blunham 2–4 February.
       A female at Elstow ClP 15 February to 31 March.
       One female at Chimney Corner ClP 15–19 April.
       One male at Brogborough Lake on 27 November.

1987 A female at Brogborough Lake 14–19 January. One at Millbrook on 25 February and at Brogborough on 8 March was thought to be the same as the January bird.
One female at Stewartby Lake on 30 September.
One female at Priory CP 18–22 November.
One female at Brogborough Lake from 19 December to year end. It was joined by an unusually marked bird, possibly an immature male or very old female, from 29 December, remaining into 1988.

Eider

Somateria mollissima

A very rare vagrant.

1982 An immature male was present at Brogborough Lake on 8–11 December. This is the only county record (*Beds Naturalist* 37: 27).

Long-tailed Duck

Clangula hyemalis

A very rare winter visitor.

Steele-Elliott (1904) knew of only two records. A female was shot at Goldington during a heavy snowfall in the winter of 1870–1. When shot it was flying up the New Cut. An immature bird, which was in the collection of Mr G. Pestell, was picked up 'some years ago' by Mr J. Bennett, also from out of the New Cut at Newnham.

1957 One at Stewartby ClP from 14 November 1957 to 13 April 1958.
1958 See 1957.
1964 One at Stewartby ClP on 12 January.
1970 One immature at Stewartby ClP on 8 November.
1980 One at Stewartby ClP on 27 January.
1981 One female at Brogborough ClP from 2 November to 4 December.
1982 One found shot at Radwell GP on 23 October.
One at Priory CP from 7 November to 8 February 1983.

One at Stewartby ClP on 7 November was joined by a second on 11 November with both birds remaining until 29 April.
1983   See 1982.

Common Scoter

Melanitta nigra

An uncommon but regular visitor and migrant particularly on spring passage.

Steele-Elliott (1904) considered this species to be a scarce but fairly regular visitor with nearly all the records occurring in the autumn. It usually occurred singly but there is one interesting record of a flight of 10.

The earliest record is of a male shot on the Ivel by Mr J. King on 21 October 1858. On a rough day in November 1865 a boy from Ravensden noticed a duck swimming along a brook and 'by creeping up very cautiously he got within a few yards of the bird, which, when it rose, he managed to knock it down with a stick'. It turned out to be a fine old male Common Scoter in beautiful plumage. Another bird was reported some years afterwards at Harrold and another at Great Barford, both during October. A male was killed on 19 August 1879 by Mr Hare at Campton and one was killed on 27 October 1890 on the Ouse at Cardington.

The destiny of any unusual wildfowl in the county during that time is well illustrated by Steele-Elliott's account of a flight of 10 of these birds observed on the 11 July 1870 by Mr P. Addington when out shooting along the Ouse by the Hillfields at Tempsford. 'As they flew past he pulled, but only to find his triggers not cocked; quickly setting these to rights he was able to bring down four with his first barrel and one with his second; the others soon after returned and two more were killed. Again the remaining three returned and a right and a left was made; the last cartridge had been expended or all would have been obtained, as even after these severe lessons the solitary bird came again within shot.' The nine shot specimens were composed of seven males and two females, all adults, and were forwarded to Messrs D. and W. Chamberlain, taxidermists, of St Neots.

Since 1946 there have been about 49 records of the Common Scoter involving 101 birds. During the 1940s and 1950s most were observed at parkland lakes and on the River Ouse but with the establishment of mineral extraction pits during the 1960s the clay and gravel-pit lakes became favoured sites. Although this species has been seen in every month, the vast majority have occurred on spring passage with 30 records (61%) during April involving 64 birds. Just over half have been of single birds; 10 at Stewartby ClP on 28 March 1984 and 10 at the same locality on 27 October 1985 are the only records of more than five.

Velvet Scoter

Melanitta fusca

A very rare winter visitor and passage migrant.

Steele-Elliott (1904) cites just one record of this species but as it lacks many details he was not very happy about its inclusion in his county avifauna. The bird in question was an adult male in the possession of Mr J. Cole, taxidermist at Leagrave. It was cased in company with a Common Scoter and Steele-Elliott was assured that they were killed together in the same locality in the winter of 1890–1. (A Ferruginous Duck and a Whooper Swan were obtained by the same person during that winter.)

Records from 1946 are as follows:

- 1983   A female at Chimney Corner ClP 19–20 November. One at Brogborough Lake on 6 December was thought to be the same bird.
- 1985   An immature male seen at Stewartby Lake on 19, 20, and 24 December was relocated at Millbrook ClP on 25 December and at Lidlington ClP on 27 December where it remained until 13 January 1986.
- 1986   Two at Stewartby Lake on 9 January.
  Two males at Brogborough Lake on 30 January.
  One at Stewartby Lake on 14 April.
  Three males at Stewartby Lake on 26 December.

Goldeneye

Bucephala clangula

A regular winter visitor in small numbers.

This species seems to have occurred more during the nineteenth century than today as Steele-Elliott (1904) says that it occurred frequently on the rivers and at times in numbers equal to Pochard and Tufted Ducks. Most were seen in small parties of usually five or less. Mr J. King recorded them on several occasions along the Ivel at Great Barford with his earliest record being of one on 8 February 1855. He shot others on 19 October 1857 and as late as 1 May 1862. During the late nineteenth century they were observed at Great Barford, along the river between Bedford and Willington, Wyboston, Cople, Cardington, Eaton Socon, and Woburn Park. Mr C. F. Woods (*op.*

cit.) stated that except for Mallard and Wigeon they were one of the commonest of waterfowl at Woburn and during some winters 'they were there in hundreds'. This however must be treated with caution. A pair was noted at Bedford SF on 27 February 1943 (Miller 1943–4).

The first birds of the winter can arrive from mid October but mid November is a more usual date. A record of one at Stewartby Lake on 2 August 1968 is quite exceptional. Numbers increase and reach a peak between January and February. After a gradual decrease during March there is sometimes a further small increase in late March or early April, reflecting passage, before numbers decline, all birds having departed by late April or early May. Since 1946 the Goldeneye has occurred in small numbers on the county's lakes and rivers in every year except 1950. Up to 1965 all observations had been of parties of less than 10, more usually less than five, but from this time onwards, although numbers fluctuated, the general trend was upward with Stewartby Lake being the most favoured site. A party of 18 there on 9 April 1968 was the highest number recorded up to that time. From 1984 Brogborough Lake became the main site and in 1987 attracted the highest numbers ever recorded in the county with 20–30 seen regularly during the first three months of the year and a peak of 39 on 15 February. Recent maximum sightings are as follows:

1983   18 at Radwell GP on 23 January.
1984   18 at Brogborough Lake on 19 February.
         23 at Brogborough Lake on 16 March.
1985   20 at Brogborough Lake on 1 January.
1986   24 at Brogborough Lake on 2 February.
         20 at Stewartby Lake on 3 February.
1987   39 at Brogborough Lake on 15 February.

Feral birds were introduced at Blunham GP in 1982 and five were still present in 1986.

Smew

Mergus albellus

A scarce winter visitor.

Mr Covington informed Steele-Elliott that three adult males were shot at Pavenham about 1870 and that others were shot at Milton (adult male) and Goldington (a female) a year or so later. In the winter of 1874–5 a female was killed at Clapham. Others were shot about 1870, one near Tempsford Bridge and another between Great Barford and Tempsford, but not in the same winter. Steele-Elliott (1904) was aware of other instances but details were unobtainable.

The Smew has been recorded in 25 of the years 1946–87 with about 62 records involving approximately 129 birds. A national decline was noted after 1950 but there was no apparent reason. This pattern was followed in Bedfordshire as during the 20-year period 1947–66 there were about 35 records in 15 years involving about 78 birds whilst in the following 20-year period it occurred on only 27 occasions in 10 years involving 51 birds with 10 of these records in 1985. The deep clay-pit lakes of Stewartby, Brogborough, and Millbrook have proved to be the most attractive sites but birds have also been seen at Felmersham GP, Wyboston GP, Harrold GP, Radwell GP, Priory CP, Houghton Regis ChP, and Coronation ClP. Most involve 'red-heads' (females or first winter birds) nearly all being in January or February. Most records have involved three birds or less but 12 (three males and nine 'red-heads') were present on the River Ouse near Bedford SF on 2–5 February 1954 and seven were in the same locality on 26–7 January 1963.

This species responds to adverse weather on the continent and these conditions were prevalent during the winter of 1984–5 when very cold air from continental Europe moved into Britain bringing three weeks of severe winter weather to Bedfordshire. From 12 January birds arrived at Stewartby Lake, Brogborough Lake, Millbrook ClP, and Dunstable SW. Numbers involved were the largest of recent times with up to seven at Stewartby and Brogborough Lakes and five at Dunstable SW. A second influx occurred during mid February with up to six at Stewartby by 16 February which moved to Millbrook and remained until 3 March when they were joined by a seventh. The last was seen at this locality on 7 March. All birds involved were 'red-heads'.

Red-breasted Merganser

Mergus serrator

A scarce winter visitor and passage migrant.

Mr A. Covington, the taxidermist, received about six specimens of this species, all either females or immatures; the first one being obtained with a female Goosander with the same shot during the 1870–1 winter. One was shot during a hard winter about 1875 when the greater part of the River Ouse was frozen over with the exception of Wyboston Corner, which was invariably open and a favourite haunt of wildfowl during such times. A flight of eight females which Mr A. F. Crossman concluded were mergansers was observed by him at Southill Lake on 23 April 1884.

This, the rarest of the 'sawbills' in Bedfordshire, normally winters around our coast and is only forced inland during hard weather. It has been recorded in 18 years and on only 36 occasions between 1946 and 1987, involving 62 birds. The earliest arrival was of one at Chimney Corner ClP on 29 October 1983 providing the only record in this month. There have been only three records in November and none in December. Most records have occurred from January to April, with six records in January, seven in February, six in March and 11 in April, indicating that return passage takes place in this month. There have been only two records in May, the latest being on 6 May 1954. Stewartby Lake has provided 15 of the 36 records with the other 21 being fairly evenly distributed at 13 other sites, (seven at gravel pits, two clay pits, two sewage works, one at Luton Hoo Lake, and one on the River Ivel).

More have occurred in recent years, with only 15 records in 1946–78 followed by 21 in 1979–87. The hard first winter period of 1979 was exceptional, providing eight records involving 19 individuals and including three pairs at Radwell on 23 February.

Goosander

Mergus merganser

A regular winter visitor and passage migrant.

Mr A. Covington, the taxidermist, recollected handling several 'red-heads' from different, but unspecified, localities and an adult male was obtained from Cox's Pits but unfortunately no dates were recorded. A female was killed near Turvey in 1862 and one about 1892 from Sharnbrook. A female was shot at Campton Mills by Mr G. Hare on 2 December 1879 and J. S. Wright killed one in about 1861 near Stanford Mill. One was shot on 24 October 1881 at Langford. An adult male was killed by Mr P. Addington, he believed in February about 1870 from Friar's Pits, Tempsford; a female which accompanied it got away. Three together were seen by him at Great Barford but no date is given. A female was obtained at Newnham on 28 November 1874. The Duchess of Bedford noted a female present at Woburn on 27 February 1909 (1908–9), two females were present at the same locality from 26 December 1910 to 27 January 1911 (Lewis 1910–11). An adult male was present on 1 January 1912 with two males at a later unspecified date (Bedford 1911–12) and the Duchess considered that the birds which had been recorded there during the previous three years had been attracted there by a single pinioned male. A male was observed at Woburn Pond on 7 January 1919, again by the Duchess.

The Goosander has increased as a breeding species in Scotland and the North of England but it has been shown that these birds do not move far from their breeding areas in winter unless the winter is very severe. It is in these conditions when their own lakes are frozen over that some move further south, but ringing recoveries have shown that many of the birds wintering in southern England have originated in Scandinavia, north-west USSR, the Netherlands, and east Germany. The shallow gravel-pit lakes in Bedfordshire provide the most suitable feeding conditions for this species but these are the first to freeze over and, when this occurs, the deeper ice-free clay-pit lakes provide an invaluable habitat.

In the decade following 1945 the Goosander was a scarce but regular winter visitor occurring in six years on a total of 11 occasions and involving 14 individuals. In the following decade records increased, with 16 records involving 55 birds; and from 1966 to 1975 there was a further increase with 35 records involving 62 individuals. During this 30-year period most records involved single birds. Numbers of more than five involved a party of 26 which were thought to be 'almost certainly' Goosander at Stewartby Lake in December 1959; nine at Wyboston GP on 14 January 1963 and nine at Bedford SF on 24 February of the same year; eight at Sandy Lodge on 6 January and nine at Stewartby Lake on 15 February 1970. The gradual increase continued during the latter part of the 1970s but from 1979 onwards the increase became more dramatic. The first four months of 1985 were the most spectacular when a minimum of 26 records during this period involved at least 170 birds.

Although numbers in Bedfordshire have increased it is worth noting that in neighbouring Northamptonshire, Thrapston GP has often held over 70 during the last decade with 174 there in March 1987.

Numbers of nine or more in Bedfordshire during the exceptional period January–April 1985 were:

16 January	16 at Luton Hoo Lake.
17 January	17 at Luton Hoo (different birds to the 16th).
19 January	24 at Stewartby Lake.
20 January	38 at Stewartby Lake.
	9 at Priory CP.
22 January	24 at Stewartby Lake.
26 January	10 at Stewartby Lake.
28 January	9 at Radwell GP.
10 February	9 at Radwell GP.

During 1987 this species was recorded from 13 localities with maxima of 11 on 24 January and 13 on 6 February at Radwell GP.

Ruddy Duck

Oxyura jamaicensis

The Wildfowl Trust imported three pairs of Ruddy Ducks to Slimbridge in 1948 and they began to breed there. It was found that greater breeding success was achieved by allowing the birds to rear their own young and because of this some young avoided being pinioned.

Between 1952 and 1973 about 70 escaped and it is from these and their offspring that our present population has become established.

The first mention of this species was in the *Bedfordshire Birds Newsletter* and is of a male and two females at Stewartby Lake on 15–17 January 1962. This record was never officially published because the birds would have been considered to be escapes. The first authenticated record was of a female at Barkers Lane GP, Bedford on 12 December 1980 which remained into January of 1981. Apart from Blunham, where eight were released, singles were seen at Barkers Lane GP in August, September and December, Tiddenfoot GP in April, Radwell GP in August and September, and Brogborough Lake in December. Since then records are as follows:

1982   One at Barkers Lane GP (Priory CP) on 10 and 12 January.
        One at Dunstable SW 17–23 January.
        One at Southill Lake on 4 April.
        One at Radwell GP on 12 December.
1983   One at Priory CP (Barkers Lane GP) on 1 January.
        Two at Priory CP 26 February to 6 March.
        Two at Woburn Lake on 11 March.
        One at Priory CP on 25 March.
        One at Priory CP on 28 March.
        Two at Stewartby Lake on 30 April.
        Three at Brogborough Lake on 21 August.
        Two at Brogborough Lake on 18 September.
        One at Priory CP 11–20 November.
        One at Radwell GP on 13 November.
        One at Harrold GP on 26 December.
1984   One male at Brogborough Lake on 8 January.
        Two immatures at Stewartby Lake on 12 February.
        Two males at Priory CP on 15 May.
        One male at Brogborough Lake on 26 October.
        One immature at Brogborough Lake on 25 November.
        One female at Priory CP on 29 November.
1985   (Maxima)
        Five at Stewartby Lake on 10 January.
        Eight at Stewartby Lake on 12 January.
        Nine at Stewartby Lake on 18 January.
        10 at Stewartby Lake on 27 January.
        Six at Harrold GP on 3 February.
1986   Three drakes summered at suitable breeding location but no females or young were seen. Outside the breeding season one or two birds were occasionally observed at Blunham GP, Dunstable SW, Stewartby Lake, Brogborough Lake, and Priory CP.
1987   There were records from three localities during the breeding season: Battlesden Lake, Dunstable SW, and Vicarage Farm ClP. Apart from these sites there were scattered records from Stewartby Lake, Luton Hoo Lake, Brogborough Lake, Elstow ClP, Priory CP and Radwell GP.

The first possible breeding activity was reported in 1983 from a site in mid Bedfordshire where two pairs remained throughout the summer with display taking place, but breeding was not proved. The first confirmed breeding took place at Battlesden Lake in 1985 with one young produced (*Beds Naturalist* 41: 52–3). A pair hatched four young at Battlesden Lake in 1986 and were seen when about 21 days old. Unfortunately they were not seen after this date and possibly did not attain maturity.

The Ruddy Duck is taking a long time to establish itself as a breeding species in Bedfordshire. This is not very surprising as its nest is usually a floating structure made of plant material and thus sites with well-established marginal and emergent growth are preferred. Many of the water areas in the county are of relatively recent origin and such peripheral vegetation is lacking or not well established. The sides of the clay-pit lakes are often too steep for vegetation to develop and the water is too deep to supply its food of insect larvae and aquatic seeds. The more mature ornamental man-made lakes are more likely to provide suitable habitat and it might be a few more years before it becomes better established as a breeding bird. Whether this will come to pass will depend very much on the management plans for the shallower gravel-pit lakes which are increasingly being used for recreational activities and where marginal growth is sometimes kept under control. Wintering numbers have also not increased as they have in other counties. This might be due to the proximity of Rutland Water, which in recent years has attracted a wintering population of over 300.

Honey Buzzard

Pernis apivorus

A very rare passage migrant and summer visitor.

Steele-Elliott (1904) considered the Honey Buzzard to be a rare summer visitor that had formerly nested in limited numbers. He knew of only five records all of which were 'taken', the earliest being *c*.1852 when a bird was caught in a vermin trap in woodland at Haynes Park. He noted an interesting account from the pages of the *Zoologist* in 1871 as follows: 'Mr. Covington, a bird-stuffer at Bedford received in June last a fine female specimen of the Honey Buzzard which was taken at Silsoe and sent to him for preservation. When he first had it, it was alive and would readily take and eat pieces of raw meat which he offered it. He took from it some eggs as large as sloes. Its crops contained a few grasshoppers and other insects. The scale-like feathers on the cheeks of the bird, which are numerous and well defined, conclusively indicate the species. The breast is spotted and blotched with white. Its dimensions were unfortunately not taken. W. J. Chalk. Wilden Rectory. 15 September 1871.'

The remaining three records were of a dark female shot at Warden Warren on 27 May 1874, one shot at Harrold on 2 October 1883, and a female killed at Potton Wood on 8 June 1901. Although there were no further records until 1946 it seems probable that this species could have summered during the intervening period, particularly during the war years when the persecution of raptors generally was less prevalent. However, in 1970 a Honey Buzzard was caught in a Jay trap at Grafham, Cambridgeshire on 10 June and was later released at The Lodge, Sandy where it was last seen on 23rd.

The first documented record of a natural occurrence in the county since 1901 was at Old Warden when a single bird was noted on 19 May 1976. In July of the following year a bird was again present at the same locality and breeding was suspected, although never proven despite a number of unspecified reports of buzzards in the area during the summer which probably related to this species (Harding 1979).

The only other records are one at The Lodge, Sandy on 14–25 June 1979, one seen in Odell Great Wood on 3 and 9 August 1980, and a single migrant over Bidwell Hill, Houghton Regis on 24 May 1982, which was probably the same individual seen flying over Shillington later the same day. Despite the paucity of records in recent years, coupled with the fact that nationally the Honey Buzzard is one of our rarest breeding birds, suitable breeding habitat does exist in Bedfordshire, and with it the possibility, however remote, that a pair of this most secretive of raptors could one summer breed again in the county.

Red Kite

Milvus milvus

Formerly a regular breeder, now a rare vagrant.

In the Middle Ages the Red Kite was a common scavenger across much of England, and even during the early 1800s it still bred locally in the more wooded parts of central and north Bedfordshire. Lord Lilford (1895) wrote: 'It seems that in Northamptonshire, till about 1844 or 1845, the Kite was common, both in that county and in Huntingdonshire', and it is on the borders of the latter county (now a part of Cambridgeshire) in the woods around Keysoe and Bushmead that Steele-Elliott (1904) refers to a gamekeeper recalling both kite and buzzard nestings 'as far back as 1813', and that he had often taken their eggs. Other known breeding localities were the woods around Haynes; a row of elms between Langford and Holme; Bolnhurst and Keysoe, where young birds were successfully reared; and at Silsoe Wood, where a pair nested but both birds were destroyed. A bird was shot 'some time in the late 1830s' at Bromham Park and another met a similar fate near Clapham Wood a few years later.

In recent years there have been six records which probably relate to individuals of the migratory continental stock, rather than from the sedentary relic population in the hill country of mid Wales. They are as follows:

1970   One watched for 10 minutes gliding over Whipsnade Zoo on 17 May eventually drifted south-west.
1976   An adult at Manor Farm, Harrold on 12 and 20 August.
1979   A single over Sundown Park, Luton on 26 March.
1982   One between Clapham and Milton Ernest on 9 January. One which flew over Greenfield and Flitwick Moor on 29 May was probably the bird noted in the Old Warden/Biggleswade area on 4 June.
1984   One south over Reddings Wood, Ampthill on 17 December.
[1986]   The unconfirmed report mentioned in *Beds Naturalist* 41: 34 was not substantiated.

White-tailed Eagle

Haliaeetus albicilla

A very rare vagrant.

Steele Elliott (1904) knew of only one record, which was extracted from the *Field* of 11 April 1863, concerning the capture of an Erne, or Sea Eagle, in the parish of Cardington on 15 March 1863. The bird was shot and wounded by a farmer and died four days later, whereupon it was added to a collection of British birds owned by a Mr Barlow of Cambridgeshire.

The Duchess of Bedford (1927–8b) contributed the following note: 'White-tailed Eagle in Bedfordshire – on 20 February 1928 a very large hawk was reported as having been seen in our park at Woburn for the first time. On 22nd I had a very good view of it myself and it has been seen daily by other observers and myself up to 11 March. It is undoubtedly an immature sea-eagle. The legs are bright yellow at the base shading to bluish-horn colour. The tail is almost triangular in shape and not squared. The general body colour is ashy-brown with darker markings and the primaries, secondaries and tail feathers are a very dark brown. The nape is darker. It is fond of sitting at the back of our ponds and swoops down over the waterfowl but has not been seen to kill any. It has a slow heavy flight, only getting high in the air if it becomes aware of the presence of human beings. It has lost some feathers in the left wing.'

On 1 May 1951 one was recorded attacking poultry at Bromham Road, Biddenham, Bedford, although the bird recorder of the day considered that the likelihood of an escaped bird could not be completely ruled out. The only other record of this species in the county was unearthed by the Manshead Archaeological Society in 1980 when they found the bones of a White-tailed Eagle at a dig near Friars Walk (now Friary Fields), Dunstable. It was discovered in a second-century Roman cess pit and the bones were identified by G. S. Cowles of the British Museum, Tring (*Beds Arch. J.* 15: 67).

Marsh Harrier

Circus aeruginosus

A very rare, mainly spring, passage migrant.

Two to three hundred years ago the Marsh Harrier was widely distributed across the East Anglian wetlands and would then have been a regular passage migrant in Bedfordshire; it may even have nested on occasions along the more suitable reaches of the Ouse valley. By the nineteenth century it had declined dramatically due to habitat destruction in the form of land drainage and direct persecution, to such an extent that Steele-Elliott (1904) knew of only three occurrences; one about 1865 seen at 'The Bogs', Luton (which was then a marshy swamp extending for about a mile along the Lea Valley and is today no more, except for an area now known as Cowslip Meadow); one killed at the latter site about 1870 in the collection of Luton taxidermist Mr T. Cane; and one that Mr A. Covington of Bedford had heard of being shot along the Ouse on an unknown date.

In recent times there have been 10 records, all but two in May, with the 1980s sightings reflecting this species' breeding resurgence in eastern England. They are as follows:

1966   An immature female at The Lodge, Sandy on 16 May.
1971   A female at Dunstable SF on 1 May drifted south-west after being mobbed by corvids.
1974   An adult female at Brogborough ClP on 12 May.
1981   A female or immature at Chicksands Wood on 11 August.
1982   A female or immature flew north over The Lodge, Sandy on 7 May.
1983   An immature male near Girtford GPs on 21 May.
1984   An adult male at Girtford on 4 May; one at The Lodge, Sandy on 9 May.
1987   An immature/female flew north between Priory CP and Bedford SW on 14 June.

Hen Harrier

Circus cyaneus

A scarce, mainly winter visitor.

During the early part of the nineteenth century, according to a second-hand account in Steele-Elliott (1904), the Hen Harrier was known to have nested in the parish of Colmworth, and in the Keysoe area as referred to by the Bedford taxidermist Mr A. Covington. Of three other records later in the century one at Potsgrove about August 1892 was particularly early. Davis (1855) refers to it as 'seldom seen in the Luton area'.

Analysis of data for the 42-year period 1946–87 reveals a minimum of 32 records from 13 years, although this figure could include some duplication of observations due to the nomadic nature of this species in winter. A monthly breakdown of the 32 occurrences gives the following results:

Oct.	Nov.	Dec.	Jan.	Feb.	Mar.	Apr.
2	9	5	10	2	2	2

The majority of sightings occur from November to January when birds may frequent suitable localities for several weeks at a time. Of the two October records the earliest was at Sandy on 12 October 1972 and of the two April dates one at Old Warden on 6 April 1975 was the latest. Prior to 1978 only single birds were noted in four years, 1953, 1966, 1972, 1975, until the severe winter of 1978–9 displaced birds from the Low Countries into south-eastern England (Davenport 1982). Bedfordshire received a then unprecedented five records: a 'ring tail' near Roxton between 4 and 7 December; one in the Pegsdon area on 1 and 8 January; one at Tempsford Airfield on 6 January; a single at Charle Wood on 16 January; and one at Blunham on 18 February. Another influx took place, also following adverse weather, in the 1982–3 winter, which coincided with fieldwork for the BTO's *Atlas of Wintering Birds*. Once again five birds were involved: a 'ring tail' near Shillington on 3 November, followed by a male between 13 and 15 November; another adult male at The Lodge, Sandy on 5 November and a 'ring tail' on 25th; and an immature male near Biggleswade on 31 December. Three of these birds stayed into 1983 with the final sighting at Home Wood, Sandy on 20 March. Subsequent winters have produced three records in 1983–4, four in 1984–5, and three in 1986–7. Interestingly there have been only four records of adult males.

A locality breakdown of the 32 records shows that 15 have occurred along the Greensand Ridge, mainly at Sandy and Old Warden, and eight on the Pegsdon Hills. Both these contrasting geological districts have one similar habitat requirement for the Hen Harrier, that is areas of rank vegetation which afford cover for its preferred prey of small mammals.

Montagu's Harrier

Circus pygargus

A very rare summer visitor, which has bred on one occasion.

The first documented record of this species in Bedfordshire came in 1945 when a pair nested on the Pegsdon Hills, close to the border with

Plate 1 (*Top*)   Red-throated Diver (Stewartby Lake, 10 May 1988). The only record of a summer plumage bird in Bedfordshire.   © *Paul Trodd*

(*Bottom*)   Red-throated Diver (Stewartby Lake, 11 Janaury 1986). A rare winter visitor.   © *Andy Tomczynski*

Plate 2 (*Top*)   Mute Swan (River Ivel, Henlow, May 1988). A pair with 15
cygnets.   © *Paul Trodd*
(*Bottom*)   Ringed Plover (Dunstable SW).   © *Bill Drayton*

Hertfordshire (Jenkins 1958). The eggs were stolen by schoolboys but were recovered at a later date and eventually sent to B. W. Tucker at Oxford for examination, who confirmed that they were eggs of a Montagu's Harrier, albeit large ones. The pair remained in the area until late September. This delightful raptor has occurred in only six subsequent years as follows:

1948   A male at Bedford SF on 18 August.
1960   A male at Galley Hill on 22 May. One recovered near Sandy on 14 June had been ringed as a nestling at Foulden, Stoke Ferry in Norfolk on 12 July 1958.
1968   A melanistic female at Chicksands Wood between 16 and 22 May and a male on 10, 28, and 29 June were noted in suitable breeding habitat although no indication of breeding took place.
1971   A male on 26 September at Upper Stondon.
1974   An adult female near Warden Hill on 9 June.
1975   A female over Bramingham Road, Luton on 9 June.

In parts of its breeding range within the Western Palearctic, the Montagu's Harrier has adapted to nesting in open 'prairie-like' cereal belts, a habitat which is increasingly available in north and south Bedfordshire. Perhaps it is not inconceivable that a pair could one year summer again in the county.

Goshawk

Accipiter gentilis

Status uncertain, the majority probably feral birds.

The majority of the small, yet increasing, British Goshawk population are considered to have originated from birds which have either escaped or been released from captivity by falconers.

It seems likely that Bedfordshire records have almost all come from feral stock, although the odd record of a true continental vagrant cannot be completely discounted. Not surprisingly the first mention of this species in the county was of an escape in the summer of 1950 but the exact whereabouts was not disclosed. One on 5 December 1960 was just over the county border at Eaton Socon, Cambridgeshire.

The following summary dates from the first acceptable 'wild' record:

1978   An immature/female at The Lodge, Sandy on 9 February.
1979   A female near Streatley on 25 February.
1984   One over Whipsnade Zoo on 26 June.
1986   One at The Lodge, Sandy in mid November.
1987   A female was observed killing a Moorhen at Whipsnade Zoo on 14 March, with a single at Whipsnade Common on 28

July and 18 August. At a locality on the Greensand Ridge a pair was seen in suitable breeding habitat on 22 April with just the male noted on 23rd.

It seems with the current increase in sightings that this powerful hawk could become an established part of the county avifauna, if given the chance to remain undisturbed during the breeding season.

Sparrowhawk

Accipiter nisus

A widespread resident (**Map 14**).

Steele-Elliott (1904) considered this species to be fairly abundant, yet gradually decreasing due to relentless human persecution in pursuit of game preservation. He recorded breeding in woodlands at Clapham, Bromham, Stagsden, and Thurleigh, and even in small spinnies adjoining towns, quoting a pair that nested in Deep Spinney close to Bedford as an example.

It seems quite likely that the Sparrowhawk was present in reasonable numbers throughout the first half of the twentieth century and may well even have increased slightly during the war years as, in common with other birds of prey, its destruction temporarily abated. However what was to follow was far more sinister and destructive than anything that had been meted out in the past. With the onset of the post-war intensification of agriculture, and with it the corresponding widespread use of organochlorine pesticides which entered the food chain, numbers plummeted dramatically, bringing the Sparrowhawk to the verge of extinction, not only in Bedfordshire but across much of lowland England. By the early 1960s the population reached an all-time low as less than five sightings in the county were recorded annually, although confirmed breeding was reported from Thorn Spinney near Houghton Regis in 1962.

Harding (1979) confirmed breeding in only three tetrads with probable breeding in a further three and presence in another 17. In 1979

a pair raised three young near Stockgrove Park, constituting the first known successful breeding for seven years; indeed signs of recovery were well under way by the late 1970s as many more sightings were reported to the county bird recorder. The resurgence continued into the 1980s with increasing numbers breeding successfully each year, so much so that by 1987 most of the county's wooded localities once again harboured breeding Sparrowhawks.

Several of the more suitable sites reported quite high densities, the Luton Hoo estate for example holding three to four pairs. Typically the majority of sightings are from the Greensand Ridge woodlands around Woburn, Ampthill, and Old Warden and also on the southern chalk downlands and the associated clay-with-flint copses. Oak and ash woodland on boulder clay in the north of the county around Odell is also a favoured habitat.

A typical Bedfordshire nest site would be in the top half of an oak or conifer, close to the trunk. The bulky nest is constructed of sticks, twigs, and pieces of bark, and sometimes an abandoned nest of a species such as Carrion Crow is utilised as a base. The single clutch of four to five eggs (Steele-Elliott noted a nest near Turvey Park which contained six eggs) is generally laid in early May and the young are on the wing by late July. There is only one brood. Studies by Newton (1975) have shown that most immatures disperse a maximum of 50km from their natal area and in a random direction, which would account for an increase in sightings between August and November. Ringing recovery data for the county supports this hypothesis with the furthest recovered bird found near Dunstable having moved 67km south from a nest in Brigstock, Northamptonshire.

Outside the breeding season the Sparrowhawk can be encountered hunting over a wide variety of habitats from farmland hedgerows to peripheral windbreaks around the Bedford clay pits, at winter roost sites, and in the town centres of Luton and Bedford, where it is often recorded taking garden birds. There is also an autumn passage of continental birds noted along the English east coast, with some probably penetrating into the inland counties.

Buzzard

Buteo buteo

A regular, mainly autumn visitor and potential occasional breeder.

This familiar species to the western uplands of Britain once ranged commonly over much of central southern England prior to large-scale changes in land use and subsequent persecution by man. It was classed by Steele-Elliott (1904) as a regular visitor and occasional breeder, a status similarly afforded to it today. He commented on its remorseless destruction at the hands of gamekeepers and collectors, a situation that was still true in the 1950s as the following three records from the bird reports of the day show:

1952   One caught in a hawk trap at Colesden.
1953   One caught in a vermin trap, locality unknown.
1955   One shot at Turvey.

In the second half of the nineteenth century Steele-Elliott referred to Buzzard sightings and killings at Southill Park, Luton Hoo, Odell Woods, Colmworth, Hinwick, and Melchbourne with confirmed breeding records from Putnoe Wood, where a female was shot on the nest, and at Oakley where a similar fate befell a female sitting on three eggs. Davis (1874) mentions one or two Buzzards being shot in the Luton area 'many years ago', and Hine (1934) refers to sightings during the early twentieth century at Pegsdon Hills, Southill, Luton Hoo, Warden Warren, and Langford.

A detailed analysis of the post-war years between 1946–87 shows the Buzzard to have occurred every year except 1949 with records from all areas of the county, but mainly along the Greensand Ridge, particularly the Old Warden area, along the Pegsdon Hills, and at Luton Hoo. It can be encountered at any time of the year with September and October the peak months (Figure 3.6), perhaps suggesting an autumn passage through the county of birds from north and east Europe which winter in the Mediterranean Basin and south into Africa. However, it is more likely that individuals dispersing from our own resident population in western Europe are involved. During the 1980s the number of Buzzard records has increased slightly, which could be linked with the post-myxomatosis recovery in the rabbit population and a more enlightened attitude from gamekeepers; and also due to more observers positively identifying the species, as the

Figure 3.6   *Buzzard: total observed in each month, 1946–87*

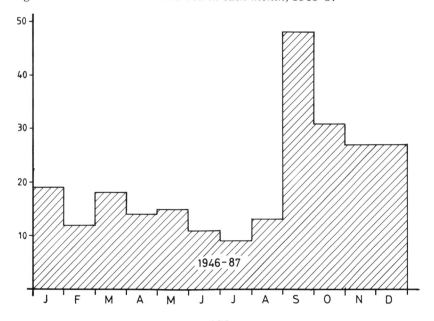

corresponding number of non-specific buzzard sightings has decreased.

Proof of breeding has been notoriously difficult to ascertain as the following summary from 1946 indicates:

1950   A pair summered on the Greensand Ridge.
1952   A pair noted in the Woburn area.
1953   One on the Woburn estate all year.
1956   A single summered at Woburn.
1968   One noted at Luton Hoo between March and October.
1974–6   One or two which summered in the Pirton area of Hertford-shire were also seen in Bedfordshire. Noted at Luton Hoo, May to December.
1977   A pair engaged in courtship display over Breakheart Hill on 12 March with three on 13 May at Palmers Scrub. Birds again present at Luton Hoo between March and June.
1981   A pair summered in the Sandy area.
1983   Two seen at Battlesden in June.
1986   An immature seen at Battlesden on 19 July, noted again on 2 and 3 August, and with two adults on 31st, was considered probably to have been bred locally.
1987   A pair frequented the Kensworth/Studham area all summer. Regular breeding season sightings occurred at Chicksands Wood and in the Sandy/Biggleswade area.

Rough-legged Buzzard

Buteo lagopus

A very rare autumn and winter visitor.

Steele-Elliott (1904) knew of only three occurrences of this species in the county, the earliest of which was one shot at Luton in 1839 (*Bedfordshire Mercury*). The second 'Woolly-legged Buzzard', as it was also known, was shot near Colmworth Wood in November 1892. The third record from a Mr Henry Gates of Sundon was described in a letter to Steele-Elliott: 'The Buzzard was caught early in December, 1894, I had seen it about two months previously; it seemed to keep to this range of hills [Sundon Hills] and I heard of its being five or six miles away. It was caught by pegging a rabbit down to the ground, traps covered over being set around. One of my workmen whilst going round to look at the rabbit traps saw the Buzzard and waited; eventually the bird sighted the pegged down rabbit and soared above for a few minutes finally pouncing down upon it, and was secured merely being caught by the claw. On these chalk hills rabbits abound and undoubtedly it had lived on them while in our neighbourhood.'

Hine (1934) mentioned two Rough-legged Buzzards at Hexton in 1910, which although in Hertfordshire, would have probably meant them straying over the county boundary to hunt, more than likely on the Pegsdon Hills where a single was noted in 1927.

Between 1946 and 1987 there have been seven documented records as follows:

1967   An immature on Pegsdon Hills between 12 and 23 March.

1973   A single at Pegsdon Hills on 26 October.

1974   One wintered on Pegsdon Hills from October to February 1975.

1983   One at Exeter Wood on 8 January was present in the area until 23 April. It, or possibly another, was seen at Ickwell Bury on 11 January, Sheerhatch Wood on 12th, Palmers Wood on 15th, College Wood on 16th, Warden Great Wood on 20th, The Lodge, Sandy on 7 February, and finally at Warden Tunnel on 9 and 23 April.

1986   One over Sandy Warren on 2 March.

[Golden Eagle]

[Aquila chrysaetos]

Steele-Elliott (1904) quoted three records from the Revd F. O. Morris concerning two birds of this species at Woburn Abbey in the winter of 1820, one of which was shot by Thomas Judge, the Duke of Bedford's gamekeeper. Another occurred at the same locality in the autumn of 1844. After failing to trace details of either of these records Steele-Elliott decided to 'square bracket' them as he was not completely convinced of their authenticity.

Osprey

Pandion haliaetus

A rare spring and autumn passage migrant.

The earliest documented record of this spectacular bird of prey in Bedfordshire was of one shot at Luton in 1839 (*Bedfordshire Mercury*) followed by another killed in Luton Park *c*.1844 (Davis 1855). Steele-Elliott (1904) described it as 'an occasional spring and autumn migrant', referring to nine occurrences mainly at Southill Park and along the Ivel valley. There was one record at Turvey in 1863.

Analysis of the 24 records in 1946–87 reveals an increase in sightings during the 1970s and 1980s correlating with increasing breeding success in Scotland; however, it is still a rare passage migrant through the county. There have been 13 spring and 11 autumn records, the earliest and latest at Blunham and Priory CP on 14 April 1983 and 5 November 1987 respectively. Prior to 1980 no significant distribution pattern had emerged, with scattered records from the parkland lakes at Southill, Woburn, Eversholt, Shuttleworth, and Luton Hoo, and Stewartby and Blunham Lakes. Sightings away from wetland areas are rare but migrating individuals have been noted over Bedford, Heath and Reach, Sandy Lodge, Cranfield, Warden Warren, and Barton Springs. Two over Studham on 5 September 1978 constitute the only multiple occurrence of Ospreys in Bedfordshire.

Since 1981 there have been six records, all except one from localities along the Ivel valley, as follows:

1981 One flew north over Biggleswade on 30 April.
1983 A single over Blunham on 14 April.
1984 One over Biggleswade on 13 May. An immature along the River Ivel at Henlow on 30 September was relocated at Langford Lakes on 7 October where it remained until 14th.
1986 A single at Stanford Pit on 18 April was observed catching a Carp, estimated to be approximately three pounds in weight, before flying off towards Arlesey.
1987 One at Priory CP on 22 October.

As the breeding population continues to consolidate in northern Britain, it seems likely that Osprey sightings will increasingly be reported from the county's still waters and river valleys for the foreseeable future.

Monthly breakdown of Osprey records 1946–87:

Apr.	May	Jun.	Jul.	Aug.	Sep.	Oct.	Nov.
6	5	2	–	2	5	9	1

Kestrel

Falco tinnunculus

Common resident and winter visitor (**Map 15**).

The status of this species appears to be about the same now as it was in Steele-Elliott's day when he described it as 'common, nesting plentifully though somewhat locally, even in unpreserved districts'.

Numbers declined in the 1960s when residual organochlorines entered the food chain causing widespread breeding failure; the population has since recovered and appears to be stable. Indeed the Kestrel is a familiar sight in Bedfordshire in a variety of habitats but it is most often encountered hovering over roadside verges, particularly along the M1 motorway, main trunk roads, railway embankments, and pastureland, in fact any area of rough grassland which is capable of supporting small mammals, its main prey. The Kestrel is common around the Bedford clay pits and river valley mineral excavations, particularly at sites such as Willington GP where exhausted workings have been infilled and planted with poplars. The more open plantation woodlands along the Greensand Ridge are suitable (e.g. Aspley Heath and Maulden Woods) but it avoids close canopy stands. Sightings in the town centres of Bedford and Luton are not uncommon and it has even been recorded at bird tables in the winter when meat has been supplied.

Entries in the *Beds Naturalist* Bird Reports 1946–87 are, in common with other familiar species, intermittent and not representative of the true status of the species in the county. Harding (1979) recorded it in 242 (65%) of the county's 371 tetrads, with confirmed breeding in 59 tetrads, probable breeding in 31 tetrads, and possible breeding in a further 152 tetrads. Intensive fieldwork in the 10km square TL02 in 1970 discovered six to seven pairs and by the end of the Atlas study period breeding was proven in 12 of the 25 tetrads, the highest density in Bedfordshire. The paucity of records in predominantly agricultural 10km squares such as TL06 and TL24 were attributed not only to pesticide poisoning, but also the effects of Dutch elm disease which robbed the Kestrel of important nesting sites. Hedgerow removal with subsequent tree loss has also been a problem, but the introduction of artificial nest boxes, successfully used elsewhere in lowland England and the Netherlands, could redress the balance.

The Bedfordshire nest site varies from hedgerow tree holes (now mainly in oak and ash) and farm buildings to cliff ledges in the deeper quarries. In woodland an abandoned corvid nest may be utilised and Steele-Elliott (1904) recorded an instance of an old Sparrowhawk nest being used. Breeding has been noted on man-made structures such as electricity pylons and, in Luton, on an old gas holder. The single clutch of three to six eggs is laid in mid April and hatches after a 27–9 day incubation period, the young fledging after about 30 days. There are two instances of broods of six being successfully raised in the county, at Stagsden and Kempston in 1972. At Toddington in 1950 a pair were noted feeding young on the exceptionally early date of 28 April, and at Willington Dovecote Kestrels have for many years bred in close proximity to a pair of Barn Owls.

Studies by Snow (1968) have shown that immature Kestrels tend to disperse mainly southwards during the autumn and one ringed at Clapham in July 1947 was recovered in Liège, Belgium in May 1948. Similarly there is movement from northern Britain into the county. As described by Mead (1973) winter visitors from Fenno-Scandia migrate into eastern England and on one occasion an individual was recovered at Dunton, near Biggleswade on December 1946, having been ringed at Jaeren, Norway during September of the same year.

Merlin

Falco columbarius

A rare winter visitor and passage migrant.

The Merlin was categorised by Steele-Elliott (1904) as a 'scarce winter visitant and of far more frequent occurrence years ago', referring to the first part of the nineteenth century. He mentioned 11 passage and winter records from September to April between 1889 and 1904 but by the turn of the century it was becoming much scarcer and in some years was absent. Many individuals were 'obtained', particularly in the parish of Elstow from where Mr A. Covington, a Bedford taxidermist, stated he had once received three Merlins in a week. A Luton taxidermist, Mr Cane, spoke of it as 'being taken in the Luton district nearly every winter'.

The period 1946–87 reveals approximately 21 records from 13 years (a 1954 possible record is omitted but a formerly unpublished record of a dead male at Bedford School on 14 November 1958 is included in the totals).

The records from the first nine of these years – 1946, 1952, 1955, 1958, 1966, 1976, 1977, 1981, 1982 – relate to single bird sightings randomly scattered across the county. From 1984 multiple records occurred at Priory CP on 4 February and Dunstable SW/Sewell on 4 November, followed by two birds in 1985 at Stewartby Lake on 8 February and The Lodge, Sandy on 2–3 November and 23 December. In 1986 a male frequented the Stewartby Lake/Millbrook area from 5 January to 8 February with another at Ampthill on 28 April, followed by one at Cardington Airfield on 7 December. 1987 proved to be the best year for Merlins in Bedfordshire, commencing on 2 January at the latter site with the sighting of what was probably the December 1986 individual, plus another at Brogborough Tip on 21 February. In the Ivel valley at Blunham one was noted on 16 October, along with two further sightings at nearby South Mills NR on 29 November and 25 December. Singles were also recorded at Rookery CIP and Flitwick on 1 and 15 November respectively. The earliest date for this species was at Stewartby Lake on 16 October 1955 and Blunham on the same date in 1987, and the latest date was one at Luton Hoo on 22–4 April 1977 which was reported to have stayed until early June.

Merlins occur in a wide range of habitats in the county, although there is a preference for more open country which supports its main prey of small ground-feeding passerines. Most Bedfordshire records relate to brown, immature/female types which probably originate from the more migratory and numerous Fenno-Scandia stock (Lack 1986), rather than from the declining British population which tend to have a more local post-natal dispersal (Mead 1973).

Total number of Merlin sightings by calendar month 1946–87:

Oct.	Nov.	Dec.	Jan.	Feb.	Mar.	Apr.	May	Jun.
3	7	4	3	5	3	1	1	1

Hobby

Falco subbuteo

A regular summer migrant and rare breeder (**Map 16**).

The Hobby was known to Steele-Elliott (1904) as a summer visitor and former regular breeding bird to the more wooded parts of the county around Warden, Colmworth, Thurleigh, Odell, Stagsden, and Woburn. He questioned whether or not it would survive into the twentieth century because of remorseless persecution and quoted approximately 20 instances of its demise, mainly from shooting but also by nest-trapping and egg collecting. Davis (1855) and Foster (1914) both refer to this species being shot in south Bedfordshire and it seems likely that the destruction continued as evidenced by singles that were shot at Priestly Wood in 1946 and Roxton in 1947. Thankfully the situation has improved somewhat since then, allowing this dashing little falcon to become established at a small number of widely scattered localities. By 1950 the first documented breeding record was published in *Beds Naturalist* when a pair successfully raised three juveniles in a wood on the Greensand Ridge. The same site was occupied for the following two seasons, although not until 1961 was breeding activity recorded again when a pair summered in the Whipsnade area. In 1963, on the northern border with the old county of Huntingdonshire, a pair produced three young and a similar number was raised by a pair in central Bedfordshire in 1967.

Harding (1979) recorded the Hobby in 32 tetrads from 13 10km squares. Only in five squares was breeding confirmed: one pair mid-county in 1968; in 1976 a pair raised three young near Yielden; a pair bred at Harrold; and a pair fledged young from Hardwick Spinney. In 1978 a pair was successful in the Charle Wood area. It is perhaps significant that during the study period the exceptionally long hot summer of 1976 was the peak year for fledging success. Milsom (1987) in studies at a New Forest nest site in 1984 and 1985 correlated temperature with the profitability of aerial insect-hunting, suggesting that Hobbies will not attempt to hunt below 13 °C. During 1976 the mean daytime temperature rarely fell below this, affording the Hobby optimum hunting conditions.

Although this species is on the margin of its British breeding range in Bedfordshire the period 1978–87 has seen it consolidate its status with confirmed breeding in seven years and suspected breeding in a further three. The best year was 1986 when four pairs bred and four others held territory. Of the 10 occupied breeding sites, habitats varied from riverine valleys of the Great Ouse and Ivel, open farmland (where a number of pairs probably go unrecorded), woodlands on the Greensand Ridge, and the southern chalklands around Pegsdon and Dunstable. The nest is usually sited in an isolated tree in a hedgerow, a small stand or spinney, or on woodland edge overlooking open country. An abandoned corvid's nest or squirrel's drey is often used as the nest in which a single clutch of two to four eggs are laid in mid June. Incubation is for about 28 days and the young are normally on the wing by mid August.

Spring migration begins at the end of April and becomes quite widespread by mid May when birds are particularly noticeable at riparian sites such as Priory CP, South Mills NR, and Harrold CP. An exceptionally early arrival was one at Felmersham NR on 27 March 1964. Return passage commences in late August, reaching a peak in early September; of four October dates the latest was at Everton on 15 October 1985.

Autumn hirundine roosts and breeding colonies are a good source of prey and a pair of Hobbies at Radwell GP in 1981 regularly hunted at a Sand Martin colony. Two or three Hobbies preyed on Swallows at an evening reed-bed roost at Harrold CP in September 1985 and Brogborough Lake in 1987. In 1983 bat-chasing was recorded at dusk from Priory CP where a bird was also seen to rob a Kestrel of prey on 16 May 1983.

In summary the future looks good for this dynamic bird of prey as a breeding species in Bedfordshire.

Peregrine

Falco peregrinus

A very rare winter visitor and passage migrant.

The status of this magnificent raptor has changed considerably since Steele-Elliott (1904) wrote of it as 'a regular winter visitor', and 'seldom a year passes but we hear of one or more being killed'. Many of his records came from taxidermists and gunners who relentlessly pursued this species whenever it visited the county. The battlements around Elstow Church were often used as a roosting site and a female shot near Bedford in 1880 was found, upon dissection, 'to contain eggs in its ovaries about the size of hempseed.'

Further documentation by Steele-Elliott (1927–8) revealed more Peregrine records in Bedfordshire and the statement: 'the species is possibly recorded every year; now being less frequent than usual, mainly from November–February but also from August–April.' The majority of sightings were of immatures and the Bedford taxidermist, Mr A. Covington, mentioned only three adults out of 25 birds killed in the county. The following table lists, in chronological order, the 38 documented Peregrine occurrences in the county between 1851 and 1927.

Biddenham	Nov 1851	Elstow	Nov 1897
Ickwell Bury	Feb 1879	Elstow	Jan 1898
Great Barford	Nov 1879	Elstow	Dec 1899
Colmworth	Apr 1880	Stevington	Nov 1899
Warden Great Wood	Nov 1881	Southill	Jan 1900
Felmersham	Mar 1882	Elstow	Nov 1900
Elstow	Aug 1885	Ravensden	Dec 1900
Great Barford	Nov 1885	Cardington	Jan 1905
Wilhamstead	Feb 1887	Renhold	Dec 1907
Cardington	Oct 1888	Flitwick	Sep 1913
Elstow	Dec 1891	Melchbourne	Jan 1921
Holme	Jan 1892	Harrold (2)	Feb 1921
Colesden	Jan 1892	Tempsford	Apr 1921
Elstow	Nov 1892	Elstow	Nov 1921
Wootton	Nov 1893	Cranfield	Nov 1923
Tingrith	Dec 1894	Marston	Sept 1925
Broom	Feb 1895	Tempsford	Feb 1926
Melchbourne	Nov 1895	Shefford	Mar 1927
Goldington	Dec 1895		

In the period 1946–87 the Peregrine was recorded in 11 years with the majority of sightings up to 1962, since when the only county record was at Yielden on 14 June 1976. Most occurred in the passage months of September and March with two June dates and one in July and August. The possibility of escaped falconers' birds cannot be ruled out completely, particularly for the summer records.

This species' continued absence since the 1960s, at a time when the British population is increasing slightly, is attributable to the declining status of the migratory Fenno-Scandia stock from which many of the former Bedfordshire records probably originated. With native Peregrines rarely straying more than 100km from their natal areas (Mead 1973) it seems as though this superb falcon will sadly remain a very rare visitor to the county.

Red-legged Partridge

Alectoris rufa

A widespread resident (**Map 17**).

This species of game bird was first introduced into south-east England from France in the late seventeenth century for sporting purposes.

It became naturalised following further introductions in 1790 and expanded its range across the region. The earliest documented Bedfordshire record was of one shot at Wilden in 1845 (Steele-Elliott 1904), while Davis (1855) regarded it as common in the Luton area. By the turn of the century it was classified as abundant throughout the county, although it was by no means as numerous as the indigenous Grey Partridge.

Modern reports since 1946 do not reflect the true status of the Red-legged Partridge as it was not until 1964 that a large covey of 25+ was reported at Wyboston on 15 November. In 1976, 40–50 were recorded in the Dunstable SW area on 5 December and 20 were at Vicarage Farm ClP on 1 August. Approximately 150 were counted in the western half of TL13 and the eastern half of TL03 during December 1977, and 40 were noted at Houghton Regis ChP on 23 January. Counts carried out in 1985 in the Totternhoe district showed presence on 32 occasions compared with only 13 occasions for the Grey Partridge. This ratio appears to be a typical reflection of elsewhere in Bedfordshire.

Harding (1979) recorded the Red-legged Partridge in 285 (77%) of the county's 371 tetrads, with confirmed breeding in 133 tetrads, probable breeding in 63, and possible breeding in a further 89 tetrads. Notable concentrations were apparent along the chalk downlands and the market garden fields around Biggleswade, Southill, and Keysoe. The nest is in a scrape in the ground amongst the shelter of a bank or hedgerow, on woodland edge, or close to farm buildings where straw stacks may be utilised.

The single clutch (sometimes two different clutches are laid in the same nest) of eight to eleven eggs is laid at the end of April/early May and is incubated for 22–5 days. Wet weather at the time of fledging in June may account for a high fledgling mortality rate.

The recent introduction of the Chukar (*Alectoris chukar*) for game shooting has resulted in hybridisation with the Red-legged Partridge (known as an Ogridge) and a subsequent bewildering array of progeny. Pure Chukar and hybrids have been noted from 1986 onwards mainly from observations by P. J. Wilkinson in the south of the county around the Luton Hoo estate. Elsewhere Chukars have been noted at Brogborough, Willington, Blunham, and Woburn, necessitating close scrutiny of all *Alectoris* partridges to arrive at a positive identification.

Grey Partridge

Perdix perdix

A widespread but declining resident (**Map 18**).

Steele-Elliott (1904) referred to this species as simply 'the partridge', and considered it to be very abundant, especially in the areas where the destruction of its natural enemies occurred. He noted many colour variations, particularly from the Pertenshall and Bolnhurst districts, involving albinistic and leucistic specimens. At the latter site on 18 September 1882 a 'white plumaged female was shot with eyes of pale grey'. Steele-Elliott suggested that these colour variants may have correlated with birds reared on heavy clay soils but goes on to say, 'it seems strange with so much similar land in the county that the records should be confined to this one locality.'

As with the Red-legged Partridge, data is sadly lacking from the county bird reports since 1946, although monitoring did improve slightly in the mid 1980s following an appeal from the county bird recorder for information, as a result of an apparent decline in numbers. In 1950 it was described as 'widely distributed', and on 21 January 1973 a covey of 50 was reported in a field near Bedford SF, the highest number ever recorded together in Bedfordshire. Other large gatherings have been as follows: 27 at Pegsdon Hills on 8 January 1967; c.20 at Streatley on 9 January 1977; 19 at Old Warden on 25 January 1984; 20 at Whipsnade Downs on 30 August 1985; and 20 at Barton Hill Farm on 13 February 1986. The majority of sightings in the 1980s were from farmland areas associated with well-drained calcareous soils around Totternhoe, Dunstable, Luton, and Pegsdon and on agricultural land across the centre of the county from Battlesden, Flitwick, Old Warden, and Biggleswade. Other records relate to a wide scattering of localities but involve only small numbers, generally between one and ten.

Harding (1979) recorded the Grey Partridge in 226 tetrads (61% of the county total) with confirmed breeding in 100 tetrads, probable breeding in 49 tetrads, and presence in another 77 tetrads. The distribution is widespread, with many proven records from the eastern and southern halves of the county.

Being a highly sedentary species, pairs establish a breeding territory early in the year and the single clutch of 10–20 eggs is laid in late April/early May in a nest concealed amongst ground cover usually in a bank or the base of a hedgerow. Wet weather at hatching in late May/early June exacts a high juvenile mortality rate and a run of poor summers from 1977 probably added to its decline, although the main reason seems to be attributed to changing agricultural practices resulting in an insufficient supply of insects and weed seeds caused by persistent pesticide and herbicide spraying (Potts 1980). As a result of work carried out by the Game Conservancy and studies by Shrubb in Sussex it has been proven that unsprayed field peripheries significantly help the breeding success of the Grey Partridge.

Quail

Coturnix coturnix

An irregular summer visitor and rare breeder (**Map 19**).

The status of this species has changed little since Steele-Elliott (1904) knew of it as an irregular summer migrant in limited numbers, although formerly it was far more plentiful. The majority of references relate to birds shot in the autumn period around Bedford, but one entry taken from the *Field* of 1886 concerning four to six brace obtained at 'Streetly' is of particular interest, as, 100 years on, the open aspect of this locality still attracts the Quail today. Miller (1943–4) refers to 'a bevy of about ten flushed from some long grass near the sewage works [Bedford] on August 9th 1942'. (The date 5 July given in *Beds Naturalist* 1: 70 is erroneous.) Henry Key (1946) mentions this species in the northern portion of the county, and 'in the Bedford district' in *British Birds* 38: 250 (1944–5).

A study of the data since 1946 highlights the Quail's preference for open, treeless habitats such as can be seen along the southern chalk downlands and the adjacent cereal belt. Favoured areas are Totternhoe and Stanbridgeford, Dunstable and Whipsnade Downs, Warden and Galley Hills, Streatley and Pegsdon Hills, where fields of wheat, oats, rye grass, potatoes, clover, and especially barley have all been utilised. To a lesser degree records have also come from the market garden region along the Ivel valley at Biggleswade and Clifton, and from the Greensand Ridge at Woburn, Maulden, Heath and Reach, Steppingley, Husborne Crawley, and on the clay at Stagsden. In 1947, which was considered 'a good Quail year', several were recorded at Stagsden and Steppingley from 25 May; a male was at Wick End, Stagsden all summer; one was shot at Heath and Reach in the autumn; and a nest containing 10 eggs was destroyed by pea-pickers at Roxton on 5 August, although several eggs were rescued and incubated with two juveniles surviving until December after being reared on a diet of ants' eggs. In 1967 10+ were recorded along the chalk downs in June and July and in 1970, another 'Quail year', eight males were at six traditional localities.

During the modern study period Quails were recorded in 24 out of 42 years, although since 1978 only 1981 and 1985 have been blank years. The earliest recorded migrant was at Galley Hill, near Luton on 5 May 1983 and the latest was at Kempston Hardwick on 18 October 1952. The only winter record was from outside the study period and came from Mr A. Covington, a Bedford taxidermist, when in correspondence with Steele-Elliott, who wrote of one 'that was killed at Renhold during heavy snow in January, circa 1877'.

As a breeding species the Quail remains something of an enigma as it is rarely sighted; when it is, a brief view of a small game bird crossing a track or 'tramline' in the crop is usually all that is observed; indeed if it was not for the male's diagnostic 'wet-my-lips' song this species would go almost unnoticed. Harding (1979) recorded the Quail in 21 tetrads (6% of the county total) with probable breeding in 19 tetrads and possible in two tetrads, 80% of the records coming from the 1970 'Quail year'. Late May to early August is when calling is most frequently heard with a peak in June and July, after which a territory is established and breeding occurs. There is some evidence to suggest that birds arriving in midsummer have already bred once in the Mediterranean Basin and moved northwards to raise second broods in southern England (Perrins 1987).

Pheasant

Phasianus colchicus

A common resident (**Map 20**).

The nominate race of the Pheasant, *P. c. colchicus*, a native of southern USSR, was introduced into Britain by the Normans in the eleventh century, and, supplemented by further releases, had spread to most areas of England by the sixteenth century. The Ring-necked Pheasant, *P. c. torquatus*, was not introduced until the late eighteenth century (Gladstone 1924–5) but soon established itself and interbred with the 'native' stock causing Steele-Elliott (1904) to comment upon the varieties of colour morphs to be found around the county.

It is most abundant in the vicinity of the main country estates at Woburn, Luton Hoo, Southill, and Silsoe where many thousands of birds are reared for sporting purposes and some very large bags are taken annually. Away from these districts it is less numerous and more retiring, but still frequents a wide range of habitats from farmland, woodland, disused mineral quarries, and even damp overgrown riparian settings along the county's river systems. In fact the only areas it shuns are close to the conurbations at Luton and Bedford.

Harding (1979) revealed its presence in 311 tetrads (84%) with confirmed breeding in 168 tetrads and probable breeding in 68 tetrads. The breeding season is from the end of March to early June when a single clutch of 8–15 eggs is laid in a shallow, unlined depression amongst ground cover. Incubation is between 23–8 days and is carried out entirely by the female. An exceptionally late breeding record came from Tempsford on 1 November 1954 when a female was flushed from eight eggs.

A small number of Mongolian Pheasants, *P. c. mongolicus*, were released at Woburn Park early this century by the Duke of Bedford and they were also noted at a wood near Whipsnade in 1947 (Lever 1977).

An unusual note (Kitchener 1963b) referred to a Pheasant landing on the water 30 yards from the bank at Stewartby Lake on 24 March where it quickly drowned. One possible cause for this strange behaviour was that it was used to landing on ice.

Plate 3 (*Top*)   Lapwing's nest (Houghton Regis ChP, May 1984).

© *Paul Trodd*

(*Bottom*)   Knot, juvenile (Brogborough Lake, 9 September 1983). A rare winter visitor and passage migrant.   © *Andy Tomczynski*

Plate 4 (*Top*) Sanderling (River Ouse, Bedford Town Centre, January 1987).
© *Andy Tomczynski*
(*Bottom*) Pectoral Sandpiper (Dunstable SW, September 1981). This classic Nearctic wader has only occurred at the county's two main sewage treatment plants at Dunstable and Bedford. © *Bill Drayton*

Golden Pheasant

Chrysolophus pictus

Formerly a small feral population now extinct (**Map 21**).

A native of the uplands of central China, the first known introduction of this pheasant into the wild in Britain was in Norfolk in 1845 (Lever 1977). In Bedfordshire it was probably kept at Woburn Park as an ornamental bird from where it colonised nearby coniferous woodland along the Greensand Ridge. Little is known of its distribution in the county until it was accepted onto category C of the British and Irish Bird List in 1971, as a species which, although introduced by man, had established a regular feral breeding population.

Harding (1979) recorded it in only 11 (3%) of the county's 371 tetrads with confirmed breeding in one tetrad and possible breeding in ten more tetrads. The confirmed record came from Maulden Wood in 1974. Presence was noted at Palmers Wood, Sandy Lodge, Moneypot Hill, Charle Wood, Pedley Wood, and at Luton Hoo in the south of the county, with the final record of a dead male by the A6 road at Maulden Wood on 20 March 1977. There have been no subsequent records other than single sightings at Woburn on 12 April and 24 October 1987 which relate to escaped captive birds from the estate.

In summary it seems that the Bedfordshire population was small and not self-supporting. Considering the competition for habitat with the closely related Lady Amherst's Pheasant, and the risk of hybridising with that more established species, further releases should be discouraged.

Lady Amherst's Pheasant

Chrysolophus amherstiae

A locally introduced resident (**Map 22**).

The Lady Amherst's Pheasant is a native of the uplands of south-west China, Tibet, and Burma, where it inhabits isolated mountain ridges covered in thickets of rhododendron and bamboo (Lever 1977). According to Mearnes (1988) the Flower Pheasant, as it is know in Asia, was

first brought to England in July 1828 by Lady Sarah Amherst, but did not breed in captivity until 1871.

This species was initially introduced into Bedfordshire, for ornamental purposes, at Woburn Park about 1890 from where it has gradually colonised woodland along the Greensand Ridge. Unfortunately several introductions of the closely related Golden Pheasant during the mid twentieth century have probably resulted in some hybridisation, although this has not been proved. The county's small, self-sustaining population has taken on special importance in recent years as the species status in Asia is uncertain. Most of the British population of Lady Amherst's Pheasant is resident in Bedfordshire, yet numbers are difficult to ascertain due to erratic recording and its secretive nature (although its call is distinctive). When it was admitted onto the British Bird List in 1971 birdwatchers began to record it more regularly.

Harding (1979) recorded it in 32 (9%) of the county's tetrads with confirmed breeding in eight tetrads, probable breeding in six, and possible breeding in a further 18. He noted 'large concentrations' in Charle Wood (40), Washers and Daintry Woods (25), and Chicksands Wood (10), and considered the county population to be at least 250 birds. Subsequent studies of the annual county bird reports suggest that the species remains widespread but is not as numerous as in Harding's study period. During the 1980s the majority of records have come from the Woburn and Millbrook complexes and from Maulden Woods. Rotational mixed forestry at these three localities ensures diversity of woodland habitat to support a viable population. Apart from the obvious need for thick cover, afforded by young coniferous trees and native shrubs, the importance of native deciduous plantations should not be underestimated as groups are often noted foraging amongst rich leaf litter.

From records in *Beds Naturalist* 1971–87, and conversations with local gamekeepers and landowners, the Lady Amherst's Pheasant has been recorded at the following Greensand Ridge localities:

Heath and Reach	One at Shire Oak in 1977 and three males at Fox Corner in 1985 are the only records in the Stockgrove CP/Kings Wood complex.
Battlesden	Two males at Home Wood near Battlesden Lake in September 1983.
West Woburn	At Charle and Lowes Woods on the border with Buckinghamshire presence has been noted throughout the study period. Numbers have fluctuated from a high of *c.*40 during the Atlas period to currently less than 10 pairs (P. Smith pers. comm.).
Aspley Heath	Confirmed breeding during the Atlas study period at Old and New Wavendon Heaths but with no subsequent records.
Woburn Park	Present within the park wall boundaries from the 1890s and recorded at The Evergreens, Sandylare Plantation, Hay Wood, Speedwell, and Milton Wood. Numbers

	are difficult to judge but could be as high as 25 pairs.

Eversholt — Up to 25 recorded at Washers and Daintry Woods in 1977 with records also from Palmers Shrubs, Kingshoe Wood, Briar Stockings, and Birchalls Wood.

Steppingley — Recorded at Priestley and Flitwick Plantations during the Atlas years and at the latter locality in 1983. Eight noted at Steppingley Wood in January 1986.

Millbrook — A population of 10–20 birds in the woodland complex west of Millbrook at Heydon and Jackdaw Hill, Blackfields Plantation, Moneypot and Breakheart Hill, and Fox Covert. Recent observations suggest this population had declined by the late 1980s.

Clophill — An established population of up to 50 birds at the Maulden Wood complex west of Deadman's Hill.

Haynes — A small population of about 10 birds at Chicksands Wood, with pre-1980 records from Exeter Wood, Warden Little Wood, and Rowney Warren. At Warden Great Wood six were noted in January 1983.

Old Warden — Presence noted in the 1970s at Palmers Wood, Warden Warren, and at Southill Park. Current status uncertain.

In the south of the county this species was released at Whipsnade Park Zoo during the 1930s and for a time bred ferally in small numbers within the park boundaries and in adjacent woodlands. By 1948 there were very few pheasants ranging freely within the zoo grounds, although a few pairs may have lingered into the early 1960s (Tack pers. comm.). Another isolated population still exists at the Luton Hoo estate where releases were made in the 1950s (Livett pers. comm.). Numbers on the estate have fluctuated between 50 and 100 birds and currently local gamekeepers have put the population at below 50. In 1987 a nest was found in thick cover containing a clutch of eight eggs. This is the only nest record in the county. The population at Luton Hoo seems likely to remain restricted due to the unsuitable habitat outside the estate. Isolated records have also come from Sharpenhoe (1972), Aspley (1981), and Wootton Wood (1981).

Bedfordshire's feral population of this spectacular Asiatic montane pheasant, numbering 100–200 individuals, may now be of international importance. It has found a niche in our Greensand woodlands and its status needs careful monitoring in the future if 100 years of colonisation is not to be wasted.

Naturalised it most certainly has become, confiding and easy to observe it is not. Little or nothing is know of its habits, breeding biology, population dynamics, or habitat preferences; in fact it is an avian enigma and certainly worth preserving and studying into the next century.

Water Rail

Rallus aquaticus

A regular autumn and winter visitor and rare breeder (**Map 23**).

Breeding season records from Luton Hoo and Southill led Steele-Elliott (1904) to believe that the Water Rail had probably bred in the county during the nineteenth century, although he could not positively claim it to have nested any nearer than the adjoining county of Cambridgeshire. Outside the breeding season he considered it a regular winter visitor whose numbers fluctuated considerably, depending upon the severity of the winter. Some interesting observations were recorded from the era by various sportsmen and taxidermists. 'Occasionally seen along the brooks at Elstow, the last I saw was perched in a thick hawthorn bush overhanging the water, I was particularly interested watching how quickly it wended its way through to the top to enable it to take flight' (H. Pestell). 'Fairly common around Langford and in fact along the Ivel generally' (J. King). '. . . one was brought in to me that had been found dead at Stanford; it had been choked in an attempt to swallow a Miller's Thumb' (J. S. Wright). 'Formerly their numbers were far more evident within the sportsman's bag than now-a-days. The most I have had at a time in recent years, was in the sharp frost we had in December, 1899, when fifteen were brought to me in about a fortnight' (A. Covington).

Studies from 1946 show Flitwick Moor as the only regular breeding locality for the Water Rail in the county. On 28 May 1956 a pair seen with two chicks was the first positive breeding record of this species in Bedfordshire. In 1957 a juvenile was seen on 17 August but there are no further confirmed records, although undoubtedly it has bred almost annually, in small numbers. It is thought likely that up to five pairs could be resident at this site. Elsewhere breeding season records have come from Marston Moretaine in 1952; Felmersham NR in 1964; the River Ouse at Clapham in 1966, where a pair was seen with an immature on 14 August; Dunstable SF, Bedford SF, Wyboston GP and Old Warden in 1969; Dunstable SF in 1970; Sandy Lodge in 1971; Luton Hoo in 1976; Luton Hoo, Harrold GP, and Toddington Manor in 1977; Toddington Manor in 1979; Houghton Regis ChP in 1980; Harrold GP, an immature seen on 21 August 1985; Harrold GP, five small chicks seen on 24 May 1986; and Battlesden Lake, Houghton Regis ChP, and Luton Hoo during 1987.

Harding (1979) recorded evidence of breeding in 11 (3%) of the county's 371 tetrads with probable breeding in five tetrads at Luton Hoo, Flitwick Moor, Wrest Park, Felmersham NR, and Ickwell Bury, and presence in a further six tetrads. A lack of suitable habitat was given as the reason for the paucity of records. The Moorhen-like nest is normally located in dense cover, amongst reeds or sedge interspersed with willow and alder scrub, where 6–11 eggs are laid from late March/early April. Incubation is for 19–22 days and there are usually two broods.

The small resident Bedfordshire population is augmented in the winter months by the arrival of migrants from Fenno-Scandia and central Europe from mid September to October. It then occurs much more widely across the county's wetlands and may haunt even the smallest pond or ditch until the return passage in March and April. River valleys and open water margins are particularly favoured and during sustained periods of cold weather several may be seen together. In 1959 seven were noted along a 400m stretch of the river Hiz on 6 December; and at Flitwick Moor on 30 December 1977 eight–nine were noted. At Cuttenhoe Road, Luton in February and March of 1955 one regularly visited a garden, feeding alongside Starlings.

Being a nocturnal migrant and an ungainly one at that this species is susceptible to fatal collisions with man-made objects such as over-head cables. Corpses have been recovered at the following: Pertenhall October 1948; Goldington 25 March 1952; Ickwell Bury 20 February 1954; Bedford SF 2 April 1955; Stratton School Farm 2 October 1961; Dunstable Library 29 August 1970; Girtford GP 17 April 1970; Priory CP 20 March 1986; and Manor Farm, Bolnhurst 28 March 1987.

Spotted Crake

Porzana porzana

A very rare, predominantly summer visitor.

This species was considerably more familiar in Bedfordshire during the nineteenth century judging by the correspondence to Steele-Elliott (1904). Mr A. Covington, a Bedford taxidermist wrote: 'altogether about two dozen Spotted Crakes have passed through my hands, the minority of which have been shot, the remainder were picked up along the railway, having killed themselves against the overhead wires. April and August are the months in which they are generally obtained, a few in September and one as late as November in 1894. The low meadows at Clapham and Oakley, and again Goldington and Fenlake seems to be the neighbourhood whence most are obtained.' Mr J. King used to shoot this species along the Ivel valley at Langford and Clifton, including one in 1867 on the late date of 11 November. A single was picked up under telegraph wires at Elstow on 11 June 1892, and several were obtained around that period from Leagrave Marsh, according to Mr Cole, a Luton taxidermist. The last records known to Steele-Elliott were at Cox's pit in 1898 and at Goldington on 3 November 1900, followed by one found dead at Milton on 24 August 1903 which is now part of the Steele-Elliott collection in Bedford Museum. Both Davis (1874) and Smith (1904) referred to the Spotted Crake as a rare visitor in the south of the county.

There have only been four post-war years in which this species has been recorded:

1946 One at Hockliffe on 13 August was found dead under telegraph wires.
1970 One seen at Fair View Farm, Edlesborough on 26 January.
1975 A single at Dunstable SW on 11–13 August.
1978 A male calling on 10–12 June at Houghton Regis ChP.

Little Crake

Porzana parva

A very rare vagrant.

The Little Crake is a rare vagrant to the British Isles and has under-
gone a general decline in numbers in recent years (Dymond *et al.*
1989). There is only one Bedfordshire record of this European summer
migrant, as recorded by Steele-Elliott (1904), one being caught by a
dog at Longholm, Bedford on 2 May 1901.

Corncrake

Crex crex

Formerly a regular breeder, now a very rare summer visitor.

The Land Rail, as it was formerly known, was described by Steele-
Elliott (1904) as a fairly abundant yet decreasing summer migrant
which arrived at the end of April to early May and nested in clover
fields and hay meadows throughout the county. An autumn passage
was noticeable in September with birds frequently encountered during
October. There were two winter records, both in 1899: at the Grammar
School grounds, Bedford on 3 January and at Henlow on 7 December.
Alexander (1914–15) mentions fluctuation in the Land Rail population in Hertfordshire and to a lesser extent in Bedfordshire. He
stated: 'for 20 years at least a decrease has taken place but a few pairs
still remain in various districts.' The acceleration in modern farming
methods, including intensive cereal growing, land drainage, and the
early cutting of grass for silage have all contributed to the Corncrake's
demise, not only in Bedfordshire but across the majority of the British
Isles.
Since 1946 it has been recorded in 11 years up to 1987, predominantly in the early part of the study period as follows:

1949 Two heard in the Toddington/Tingrith area on 1 June.

1950　A pair was seen displaying at Cranfield on 2 June with
　　　subsequent 'crekking' through the summer; a single calling
　　　near Flitwick in late May; and one shot at Lidlington on 2
　　　September.
1951　One seen at Stagsden on 18 August.
1953　One in a garden at Bromham on 12 October.
1954　One 'crekking' in an orchard in Kimbolton Road, Bedford
　　　6–18 May and again near Putnoe Wood in July.
1955　Four present at sandpits near Flitwick Railway Station on 4
　　　May, of which one died and was sent to the bird recorder.
1956　A single at Galley Hill on 19 May.
1966　One at Felmersham on 9, 16, and 17 September.
1974　One calling from a marshy area at Washers Wood in June.
1984　A single at Marston Moretaine from 30 May to 11 June.
1987　'Crekking' noted at Ickwell Bury on 5 May and at Astwick
　　　on 16th.

Moorhen

Gallinula chloropus

An abundant, widespread resident and winter visitor (**Map 24**).

The status of the Waterhen, as it was more generally known, as
a very common species, has altered little since Steele-Elliott (1904)
described it as such. However, the recent increase in quarry wetlands
may have caused a slight shift in distribution away from its preferred
habitat of riverine marshes and flood meadows that have so dimin-
ished this century. Despite this it is still a common breeding bird
along all the county's river systems, still waters, sewage treatment
works, ponds, and ditches; in fact any damp patch with rank emergent
vegetation is likely to attract a pair of Moorhens. Harding (1979)
recorded it in 259 of the county's 371 tetrads with confirmed breeding
in 189 tetrads, probable breeding in 25 tetrads, and possible breeding
in a further 45 tetrads. As the Moorhen usually stays close to its nest,
Harding considered that the majority of probable and possible records
undoubtedly referred to breeding pairs. In 1983 an independent survey
on riparian species breeding along the Rivers Ouse, Ouzel, and Ivel
was carried out by a team from Cambridge University. Along the
Bedfordshire section of the River Ouse 150 Moorhen territories were
found to be occupied, with 30 nests located resulting in 22 broods
raised. The River Ouzel held 22 breeding territories and 10 occupied
nests were found raising five broods, while along the River Ivel seven
territories were discovered.
　　The breeding season is a protracted one, from late March to mid
August, to allow for repeat egg-laying as a result of a high predation
rate, with up to three clutches of five to nine eggs being laid. Steele-
Elliott (1904) mentioned clutches of 11 and 12 at Oakley and Brom-

ham respectively and also some of 13 which probably refer to 'egg-dumping' when more than one female lays eggs in a single nest. Late breeding dates recorded are at Colmworth on 4 September 1964 when a bird was noted still sitting on four eggs and at Stagsden in 1950 where a brood of newly-hatched chicks was observed in early December. The nest is an untidy heap of dead or decaying aquatic plants and is situated amongst emergent or marginal vegetation, although in Bedford and Luton town parks nests may be more exposed and consist of a mixture of natural and man-made litter. Occasionally the nest may be sited several feet above the water line; one at Dunstable SF on 25 April 1962 was 10 feet above ground level and Steele-Elliott recorded a nest with eggs atop a hawthorn at Moggerhanger some 12 feet high, situated above an old Woodpigeon's nesting platform. The eggs are incubated for 21–2 days and the young remain with the adults for a further 40–50 days.

Our resident population is mainly sedentary but may move locally in winter when smaller waters are ice-bound. Loose flocks then form on more open sheets of water such as the clay pits and country park lakes where numbers are augmented by migrants from Fenno-Scandia and eastern Europe during November to March. A quantitative assessment of the wintering population is difficult to obtain because of the infrequency of data submitted for publication in the county bird reports. A gathering of c.500 during November and December 1951 at Bedford SW was the largest number ever recorded, followed by 200+ at the same locality in 1953. Counts at Luton Hoo have produced the following: c.110 on 9 January 1977; 78 in one field during November 1979; c.100 on 2 December 1980 and 14 January 1981; 150 in January 1984 and 115 in December; a maximum of 200 on 24 January 1985; and 205 in November 1986. At Blunham GP c.180 were counted on 14 January 1973 and 70+ were at Harrold GP on 19 January 1980.

Coot

Fulica atra

A widespread resident and winter visitor (**Map 25**).

Steele-Elliott (1904) considered the Coot's breeding range to be restricted to the larger lakes at the country estates of Woburn, Southill, and Luton Hoo where he found it 'in each instance exceedingly plentiful for the area of the waters.' Small numbers were then noted breeding along the slower reaches of the River Ouse, which contrasts markedly with today's status. When a survey on breeding riparian birds was carried out in 1983 the River Ouse was found to harbour 62 Coot territories of which 30 nests were located producing at least 14 broods.

It was not until large-scale mineral extraction began in the 1950s that the Coot began to flourish along the county's river valley pits and in the Marston Vale. Harding (1979) recorded this species in 105 (28%) of the county's tetrads with a high instance of confirmed breeding in 79 tetrads. Unlike the Moorhen, the Coot avoids small ponds, preferring to nest on the periphery of larger gravel or clay-pit waters and parkland lakes. At Wardown Park, Luton several pairs breed on the banks of an ornamental lake, where nests are constructed using a variety of man-made litter. More normally the nest is located amongst emergent vegetation where a clutch of 6–10 eggs is laid. The breeding season commences in late March and there are sometimes two broods.

During the winter months many of the smaller breeding waters are deserted as the Coot disperses to form large flocks on the larger more open clay and gravel pits. It is not known what proportion of our wintering population are resident birds or ones that have moved from neighbouring counties. Before large-scale mineral extraction began in the mid 1950s, the main wintering flocks were at Southill Lake and Luton Hoo, where about 200 birds were noted annually at each locality until the early 1970s. The maximum count at Southill was 317 on 25 December 1962 and at Luton Hoo c.250 were recorded several times during the late 1960s.

Unfortunately there have been few coordinated counts of this species in Bedfordshire and therefore much of the data is unquantifiable. What can be said however is that Coot flocks periodically move in response to the suitability of different waters. In the 1960s and 1970s Wyboston GP was a favoured location and flocks of up to 350 were regularly recorded. In 1974 536 were counted, the maximum ever recorded there. Similarly Barkers Lane GP formerly attracted large wintering flocks of up to 500, but numbers declined in the 1980s probably as a result of increased sailing and windsurfing activities (Kramer 1986). Other gravel pits which regularly record 200–300 birds per annum are Harrold, Radwell, Girtford, and Blunham. Bedford SF in the 1960s attracted flocks of 200+ and the lagoons at Dunstable SW have regularly attracted c.150 birds during the 1980s.

Coots began to utilise the Marston Vale clay pits as a wintering site in the 1960s as pits at Stewartby and Kempston Hardwick began to be flooded. By 1968 400+ and c.260 were the peak counts at Stewartby Lake and Chimney Corner ClP respectively.

Numbers at Stewartby Lake have subsequently declined following the increase in water sports but at Chimney Corner ClP flocks of 200–300 are encountered most winters. Elsewhere in the clay vale double-figure counts have been noted at Vicarage Farm ClP, Millbrook ClP, Coronation ClP, and Elstow ClP.

The most important clay pit for wildfowl in Bedfordshire is at Brogborough, where Coot numbers have dramatically increased during the 1980s with a flock now well in excess of 1,000 present most winters. A maximum of 1,820 was counted in January 1986, the highest concentration ever recorded at one site in Bedfordshire.

Great Bustard

Otis tarda

A very rare vagrant.

Centuries ago this species ranged across much of East Anglia, including nearby Royston and Newmarket Heaths in neighbouring Hertfordshire and Cambridgeshire, and may have been present in the more open areas of east Bedfordshire prior to enclosure. Steele-Elliott (1904) knew of only one record, a second-hand account from Mr P. Addington, a Wyboston farmer who referred to a Great Bustard that was killed on his farm about 1840 by Mr Martin George. The corpse was sold for £2 and passed into the possession of Dr Rix of St Neots, by whom it was sold again and unfortunately could not be traced by Steele-Elliott.

Oystercatcher

Haematopus ostralegus

A regular but uncommon visitor.

This very striking black and white bird with a large, powerful orange-red bill and pink legs is more associated with our coasts, both as a wintering bird in vast flocks and as a breeding bird in smaller numbers. The Oystercatcher was once a rare visitor to our county but has become more frequent in recent years due in some part to the creation of mineral extraction pits.

Steele-Elliott (1904) mentions just two definite records, one shot near Longholme, Bedford in either 1866 or 1867 and three at Great Barford about July 1880 after the river had flooded.

Between 1946 and 1987 the Oystercatcher has been recorded on 57 occasions and records have involved all months except November. There have been only two records in each of the months of October and December. Outside these three months occurrences have been fairly evenly distributed with slight peaks in May (nine) and August (10). Just over 75% of occurrences have involved single birds and 10% have involved parties of two. Apart from a flock of 10 over the River Ouse near Felmersham on 16 August 1984 all flocks of more than two have occurred during the winter months of December, January and February as follows:

1953 Five north over Bedford on 8 January.
1976 Eight at Brogborough Lake on 22 February.
     10 over Carlton on 17 December.
1982 21 at Grovebury SP on 2 January.

Six over Warden Lodge on 2 January.
1987   18 at Dunstable SW on 24 December.

There has been a change in status of this species in the county since the 1960s and, more particularly, from the mid 1970s. There were only four records from 1946 to 1960, eight between 1961 and 1975, and 32 between 1976 and 1985. This increase reflects a general increase in Britain particularly since 1940, thought to be due in part to less predation by man. Inland breeding in England has also increased with most of the new breeding sites being at gravel pits created at the end of the 1960s and early 1970s. The increase in Bedfordshire corresponds well with the creation of the new gravel and clay pits established during the 1970s. It has been suggested that a behavioural change has occurred in this species, not only resulting in more inland breeding but also in the eating of earthworms as a recently acquired habit.

Of the 57 records 22 refer to the gravel-pit areas (Barkers Lane GP, 11; Harrold GP, 4; Radwell, 2; Harrold/Radwell GPs, 1; Great Barford GP, 1; Roxton, 1; South Mills NR, 1; Wyboston, 1), 17 to clay pits (Stewartby Lake, 9; Brogborough Lake, 3; Chimney Corner 2; Vicarage Farm, Millbrook, and Rookery, 1 each), 3 to Grovebury Sandpit, 3 to Dunstable Sewage Works, and 12 to birds flying over. The creation of mown grass areas which border the newly formed country parks at Stewartby Lake, Barkers Lane (Bedford), and Harrold have resulted in a habitat which has attracted the Oystercatcher regularly in recent years.

Black-winged Stilt

Himantopus himantopus

A very rare passage migrant.

One was shot in about 1855 at Pinfold Hole, a disused sandpit between Chicksands and Shefford.

1978   One at Houghton Regis ChP 6–7 July (*British Birds* 72: 159).
1987   One at Chimney Corner ClP on 20 April (*British Birds* 82: 520).

Avocet

Recurvirostra avosetta

A rare passage migrant, mainly in spring.

Records from 1963 are as follows:

- 1963   One at Harrold GP on 30 May.
- 1971   One at Dunstable SW on 29 March.
- 1983   19 NE over Barkers Lane, 27 March.
- 1984   Two at South Mills GP on 19 April.
        Eight at Vicarage Farm ClP 18 November.
- 1986   Two at Stewartby Lake on 15 April were relocated on a flooded field north-east of Marston Moretaine later in the day. They reappeared at the same location on 18 April and remained there until 22 April, occasionally revisiting Stewartby Lake.

The origin of these birds is somewhat uncertain but the national status of the Avocet both as a breeding and wintering species has changed significantly in recent years. A large increase in the breeding population took place from the mid 1960s and a similar increase of birds wintering in Suffolk, Devon, and Cornwall occurred from 1979 onwards. Although most of the Suffolk population overwinter in their breeding area a few of these birds have been shown to winter in south-west England, but it is thought that the majority of birds there are from north-west European breeding populations. This seems to be supported by the occurrences in Bedfordshire as at the time when birds pass through the county on spring passage the Norfolk and Suffolk breeding populations are already at full strength. Birds leaving their breeding areas in this country have normally departed before the end of October and thus those which occurred in Bedfordshire in November would seem to be of continental origin. Whatever the situation it seems likely that this beautiful bird will be seen more frequently in the county and be a source of delight and surprise to bird watchers in future years.

Stone Curlew

Burhinus oedicnemus

A very rare passage migrant (**Map 26**).

A large almost plover-like bird with strong legs and an eerie 'Kur-lee' call note often uttered at twilight, the Stone Curlew was once commonly met with on the chalk downlands and sandy heaths of

England. Its old name of 'Thick-knee' is due to the swelling which is observable at its knee-joints, whilst its other name of 'Norfolk Plover' refers to its once comparative abundance in the Brecklands of East Anglia where a few still breed. It arrives in this country in March or April and departs for its wintering grounds in northern Africa during September and October.

Steele-Elliott (1904) states: 'Until the middle of the nineteenth century the Stone Curlew was a familiar migrant to the neighbourhood of the chalk hills running through the south of Bedfordshire. In other parts of the county, probably occurring more or less frequently during their spring or autumn movements.' He records it as being common around the Luton area in 1855 and frequenting Dunstable Downs, being commonest around Streatley. He also knew of their presence around Hexton and the Pegsdon Hills where, his friend and correspondent Mr J. King informed him, 'we generally flushed two or three pairs during the day'. Mr King also mentions finding eggs in this area on 5 May 1863, again on 22 May 1864, and of shooting a bird as it rose from a single egg on 13 June 1871. Mr C. F. Wood noted that between 1860 and 1870 a pair or two nested between Toddington and Houghton Regis where he once put up five. According to Mr J. Cole, a local taxidermist, they used to be more common on the Dunstable Downs than elsewhere and a year or two before 1884 he had two immature birds with some down still on them brought to him. They had been shot between Luton and Dunstable. Mr King also reported seeing them on two or three occasions at Langford.

Other records during the second half of the nineteenth century are: one shot at Wilden in September 1864; one shot at Milton in September 1884; and one killed on Dunstable Downs in 1894.

The Stone Curlew was obviously declining rapidly in the county by the end of the nineteenth century. Steele-Elliott (1904) wrote: 'My personal observation during the last ten years in all the Stone Curlew's once favoured haunts have failed the pleasure of even a sight of this bird, or a word of their nesting for at least within the last twenty years.' This decline he attributed mainly to the cultivation of its old haunts but also to the 'constant persecution such a fine bird would receive from the loafer with the gun.'

Steele-Elliott (1910–11) saw a single at Sandy on 15 May 1910 and stated that there had been only two records in the county since 1890.

This continued to be the situation and nothing more was written about the Stone Curlew until 1946 when H. A. S. Key wrote: 'The Stone Curlew has not nested, or even been observed for upwards of twenty years.' Since then the species has occurred in only nine years, mainly in the 1950s:

1951   Heard calling near Pegsdon and although a pair bred just over the county border in Hertfordshire they were not found to be breeding in Bedfordshire.

1953   Heard throughout the summer in the hilly areas of south Bedfordshire. (A pair bred just over the county boundary in Hertfordshire.)

1954   One and possibly two were heard calling in a potato field near Pegsdon on 11 July.

1955 Birds were heard calling near Pegsdon on 26 April and five or six were seen near Hexton on the Hertfordshire border on 20 August.

1956 Birds were seen and heard near Pegsdon in late April.

1959 One seen and heard on the Beds/Herts border near Hexton on 19 April.

1967 One was heard calling near Pegsdon on 23 April.

1968 One was heard near Pegsdon on 12 April.

1980 One at Whipsnade Zoo Park on 9 June.

Collared Pratincole

Glareola pratincola

A very rare vagrant.

The only county record was of one at Girtford GP 19–25 May 1983 (*British Birds* 76: plates 156–7; *British Birds* 77: 521).

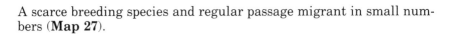

Little Ringed Plover

Charadrius dubius

A scarce breeding species and regular passage migrant in small numbers (**Map 27**).

Most breeding has occurred at gravel pits but this species has occasionally utilised exposed areas at or near to sewage works, sand pits, and less frequently the bottoms of worked out clay pits. It has been difficult to ascertain the true status of this species due to observers' secrecy concerning breeding sites in the early years of its presence and lack of accurate recording of the numbers of breeding pairs present and their success during more recent years.

Although the first British breeding record of this species was in 1938 at Tring in neighbouring Hertfordshire, it was not until 1951 that it was first observed and bred in Bedfordshire. A nest containing three eggs was found at Cople GP but unfortunately this attempt was unsuccessful as the eggs disappeared. One was present at Bedford SW on 10 May 1953 and in 1954 two were seen at Barkers Lane GP on 30 March. A juvenile was also at Dunstable SW from 26 August to 14

128

September. Singles again turned up at Bedford SW on 23 April and 1 May 1955. The first successful breeding took place in 1956 when birds nested at two gravel pits in the north of the county (probably at Wyboston) producing two young at one site and two or three young at another.

From 1956 this species bred more or less regularly in the county (with the exceptions of 1959, 1960, and 1964), but the difficulty in observing the presence of their well-camouflaged young has made accurate recording of successful breeding difficult. During the second half of the 1950s and the 1960s the gravel pits at Wyboston held the main breeding population with an estimated seven to eight pairs attempting to breed in 1962. However the hazards of nesting at sites which are being worked was well illustrated when earth-moving operations near the nesting area caused the desertion of all nests. (This occurred again at Heath and Reach in 1965.) At least 15 birds were present at this site in the following year and at least three young were seen. Breeding also took place at Barkers Lane GP, Blunham GP, City Fields GP (Henlow), Harrold GP, Heath and Reach, Houghton Regis ChP, Jones SP, Stanford GP, and Sandy GP. The number of breeding pairs in the county gradually increased during the 1970s with 13 pairs producing at least 17 young in 1977 and a peak of 18–20 pairs breeding in 1979.

The vast majority of breeding attempts have been at gravel and sand-pit sites with suitable habitat being available prior to or during the early stages of plant colonization. As succession continues, previously used sites become unsuitable and numbers gradually decline. A more abrupt change was brought about by the flooding of pits such as Wyboston and Harrold: at the latter site the 1979 breeding population of 10+ pairs was totally wiped out the following year. Obviously the population of the Little Ringed Plover is going to fluctuate as old sites become unsuitable and new pits are created.

Although the earliest arrival dates are 14 March 1986 (South Mills NR) and 15 March 1964 (Bedford SW), spring passage is very light and can be more easily observed in suitable non-breeding areas such as sewage works. It usually begins during the last week of March and the first week of April with the main arrival taking place during the rest of April tailing off in the first two weeks of May. Numbers recorded on passage during this period rarely exceed five at any one site.

Normally four eggs are laid in May in a slight hollow made in gravel or sand. The young are well camouflaged and tended by both adults who go to great lengths to distract any intruder, often feigning injury in order to lead one away from their offspring.

Return passage involves larger numbers and can be observed from the beginning of July, reaching a peak during the last week of July and the first two weeks of August. The largest parties noted during this period were 15 at Wyboston in August 1963, eight at Dunstable SW in July and August 1970, 11 at Dunstable SW 22 July to 25 August 1971, and eight at Houghton Regis ChP on 9 July 1972. Breeding birds usually leave their nesting areas in August and passage is normally over by the third week of September. Occasional birds, usually juveniles, pass through during the last week of September and the latest record is of one at Radwell on 4 October 1980.

Ringed Plover

Charadrius hiaticula

A regular but uncommon breeding species since 1971. Also a fairly common passage migrant and occasional winter visitor (**Map 28**).

Steele-Elliott (1904) noted this species as being more frequent in spring than in autumn with Newnham SF (Bedford) offering it a far greater attraction than any other area. Although he states 'I do not think that there is a month in the year but when this bird does not occur', he says that it was of somewhat unusual occurrence in other parts of the county. C. M. Prior in the 1879 *Zoologist* wrote: 'They were exceptionally abundant at Newnham in the autumn of 1878, no less than seven being sent to the local taxidermist in one week.' A party of six was recorded at Newnham SF on 26 May 1898 by Mr. A. F. Crossman (*Zoologist* 1898).

The status remained about the same until the end of the 1960s with small numbers passing through the county on spring and autumn passage with slightly more records during the spring. During the period 1946–65 there were 85 recorded occurrences, nearly all of them at the gravel-pit sites of Stanford, Willington, and Wyboston, and Bedford and Dunstable SW. Of these records 60% involved single birds and 20% involved parties of two. Flocks of more than five were recorded on only four occasions during this period with up to six at Willington GP between 6 and 11 May 1951, 11 at Stanford GP on 21 May 1958, nine at the same site on 9 May 1961 and eight at Bedford SW on 1 September 1962.

Spring passage may begin as early as the end of February but normally gains momentum from mid March and continues until the end of May. Autumn passage often commences during the second week of July and declines after the end of August. Passage is usually complete by the end of September and a few may pass through in October. 1971 proved to be an exceptional year, particularly during the spring when 21 were present at Dunstable SW on 26 May, 32 on 27th, and 12 on 30th. Houghton Regis ChP also provided good numbers with a maximum of 12 on 30 and 31 May.

After such high numbers it was not too surprising when, in 1971, a pair remained at Wyboston and provided the first breeding record for the county. Three eggs were laid but unfortunately it is not known whether they hatched. Autumn passage reflected that of the spring when numbers at Dunstable SW built up to 24 on 18 August, 24 on 22nd, 21 on 24th, 21 on 25th and then declined gradually to the end of the month. From 1971 the status of the species changed. Large parties became more frequent on passage with 14 at Vicarage Farm ClP on 20 May and 12 at Bedford SF on 9 August 1974, 15 at Harrold GP on 15 August 1981, 19 at Blunham/South Mills GPs 16 March 1985, and 16 at Radwell on 18 August 1985.

After the first attempt in 1971 breeding or attempted breeding took place in each successive year (Figure 3.7) and increased numbers were

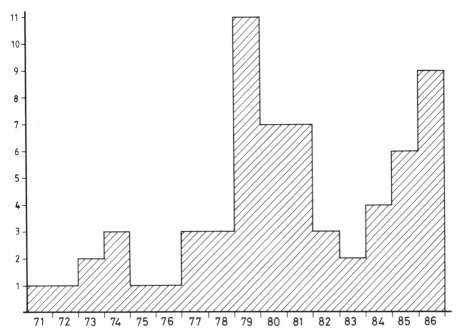

Figure 3.7 *Ringed Plover: annual totals of breeding pairs recorded, 1971–86*

involved in spring and autumn passage. Sites occupied during the breeding season were:

1971 Wyboston (1 pair).
1972 Wyboston (1 pair).
1973 Wyboston (2 pairs), Sandy (1 pair), Harrold (2 pairs).
1974 Wyboston, Vicarage Farm.
1975 Harrold (1 pair).
1976 Harrold.
1977 Harrold, Radwell.
1978 Girtford, Harrold, Radwell, Barkers Lane.
1979 Harrold, Girtford, Radwell.
1980 Harrold, Girtford, Radwell.
1981 Harrold, Girtford, Radwell.
1982 Barkers Lane, Chimney Corner, Harrold, Girtford, Radwell.
1983 Great Barford, South Mills.
1984 Cuckoo Bridge Pit, Girtford, Tempsford Airfield, Harrold GP, Chimney Corner, Radwell, Great Barford.
1985 South Mills, Harrold, Radwell.
1986 Harrold, Radwell, South Mills, Rookery ClP.

As with the previous species, the Ringed Plover occupies sites during and soon after gravel extraction but seems to tolerate a slightly greater amount of plant colonization before deserting a site. It has also bred on the bottoms of clay pits before they are flooded and as plant colonization takes longer at these sites, although not preferred, they may be used several years after extraction has been completed. It has also been suggested that it is competing with the Little Ringed Plover for sites and may be replacing it in some areas. These sites are subjected to many man-made changes and the number of sites and breeding pairs may fluctuate greatly.

Winter records, although increasing in recent years, have been scarce and apart from the reference by Steele-Elliott, there were none recorded until one visited Barkers Lane GP and Bedford SW between 24 and 25 February 1962. Further winter records are of one at Stewartby ClP on 3 November 1963, three at Wyboston GP on 6 November and one at Houghton Regis ChP on 20 November 1966, one at Vicarage Farm ClP on 27 November 1977, singles at Priory CP (Barkers Lane GP) on 30 January and 28 December 1982.

Kentish Plover

Charadrius alexandrinus

A very rare vagrant.

Mr A. F. Crossman writing in the *Zoologist* of 1898 says that whilst observing Ringed Plover and Dunlin at Bedford Sewage Farm on 26 May 1898, one differed considerably from the rest and he believed himself to be correct in identifying it as a Kentish Plover.

The only record in recent times is of a female and two juveniles which were reported from Bedford SF on 16 August 1967 (*Beds Naturalist* 22: 38).

Dotterel

Charadrius morinellus

A very rare passage migrant.

Steele-Elliott (1904) noted the gradual decline of this species after having once been a regular passage migrant. He mentions that 'formerly trips of Dotterel seemed to have frequently tarried awhile with us particularly along the chalk hill range running through the south of the county, seemingly occurring far more freely in spring than in their autumn movements.' Records mentioned in his work are as follows:

'It used to appear on Warden Hills every spring, I had six brought to me from there one morning; they also regularly visited the Dunstable Downs' (T. Cane). 'Three were shot by myself near Luton in 1891 and two others I obtained at another time' (J. Cole). 'Two were killed about 1875 on the high land known as Bandy-Knowles, between Clifton and

Shefford' (J. S. Wright). 'My Uncle shot a Dotterel on the Rectory Farm, at Wilden, about 1860' (W. J. Chalk).

Mr A. Covington, although never having a specimen 'pass through my hands in the flesh', recalls one in his possession being killed at Oakley prior to 1840, one shot at Milton, and another at Biddenham (no dates). His most recent recollection was of one shot at Bolnhurst about 1892. A specimen in Luton Museum was 'purchased locally' on 11 November 1933 but no additional details were given. There are two specimens in Bedford Museum from Warden Hills shot about 1895 and an immature male killed against telegraph wires at Biggleswade on 9 September 1907.

There have been only five other recorded occurrences since 1900:

1952   One at Maulden on 4 May.
1971   One at Pegsdon Hills on 8 May.
1982   One at Holme Green, Biggleswade on 12 May.
1986   Six at Blows Downs on 30 April.
1987   10 at Blows Downs on 18 April.

It appears that this species is occurring more frequently in recent years on the chalk downlands in the south of the county and continued searching may repay the diligent observer.

Golden Plover

Pluvialis apricaria

A common winter visitor and passage migrant.

Steele-Elliott (1904) gives the status of the Golden Plover as a common winter resident occurring in all parts of the county, frequenting the fields along the Ouse and Ivel valleys with great regularity. In his time it could be observed in thousands in the Newnham, Goldington, and Willington areas. Other areas frequented during the nineteenth century were the lands between Clifton and Langford, Stondon, fields along the roadside between Bedford and Bromham, Shefford, Wilden, and Clapham.

In a letter dated 15 September to the *Zoologist* of October 1871 W. J. Chalk writes: 'About a fortnight ago a large flock of golden plover – recognized as such by their note – passed over the town of Bedford, probably attracted by the lights. Their number must have been very great, as in the morning the streets and paths were marked by their excrement.'

Birds may begin to arrive in September, occasionally in August (there have been 14 August records between 1946 and 1986, the earliest being 1 August 1961, 2 August 1968, 4 August 1960, and 6 August 1948), and spring passage continues until the end of April. There are few records outside this period but A. F. Crossman did observe one between Bromham and Bedford as late as the beginning of June in 1888 or 1889. There have been only two July records, one on 22 July at Radwell in 1979 and another at Bedford SF on 21 July 1982.

The majority of records are associated with the deposits of alluvium and valley gravels found along the valleys of the Great Ouse, Ivel, Hiz, Flit, and Ouzel with further occurrences in areas of similar deposits between Kempston and Millbrook. Thus most of the records have been concentrated in the central, eastern, and northern parts of the county with some areas being used fairly regularly during the past 50 years. The regularity in the use of these sites is greatly influenced by habitat changes and changes in farming strategies and, as a result, some sites have fallen out of use and others are used intermittently. Traditional areas with approximate periods of use have been as follows:

Bedford SW	1946–68
Broom	1949, 1974, 1983–6
Kempston Hardwick	1949, 1960, 1983–5
Cardington	1949–86
Stewartby	1950–86
Clifton/Stanford/Henlow	1951–85
Luton (Copt Hall)	1952–78
Rowney Warren	1958–78
Ampthill	1967–85
Biggleswade Common	1974–85
Radwell	1985–87

Although Steele-Elliott (1904) mentions them being present 'in their thousands', this is no longer true, there having been only five records of 1,000 or over since 1946. About 1,000 were seen at City Field Farm during late March 1982, a party of c.1,850 was on Henlow Airfield in early January 1985, a large flock present in the Radwell GP area peaked at c.1,000 on 16 March 1986, c.1,000 were in the same area during January 1987, and c.1,250 were present there on 28 December of the same year. Most large flocks are 100–350. Flocks of larger numbers are as follows:

1957	500 near Clifton during February.
1958	500 near Rowney Warren on 29 December.
1959	500 at Houghton Conquest on 24 December.
1963	650 at Stanford on 12 April.
1964	600+ at Houghton Conquest on 8 March.
1967	500 near Stanford GP on 24 March.
1968	400 at Old Warden on 8 January.
	700 at Cardington on 27 March.
1972	400 at Rowney Warren on 13 January.
1973	400 at Copt Hall, January–February.
1974	600 at Rowney Warren on 24 November.
1975	400 at Luton Airport on 17 February.
1978	300–400 at Rowney Warren on 1 January.
1980	450–500 at Everton on 22 March.
	300–350 at Cardington on 2 November.
1982	389 at Cardington on 26 November.
1983	537 at Broom on 26 November.

382 at Cardington on 3 December.
400 at Willington on 29 December.
700 at Eaton Bray on 15 March.

1984 300–400 at Everton on 30 March.
700+ at Henlow Airfield on 22 December.
527 at Cardington Airfield on 27 December.

1985 550 at Cardington airfield.
500 at Henlow Airfield on 12 December.
600 at Radwell GP on 29 December.

1986 450 at Radwell GP on 20 December.
500 at Cardington Airfield on 20 December.

The results of the BTO Golden Plover Survey during the 1977–8 winter showed that about 43% of wintering flocks preferred pastures and 34% were found in areas of winter cereals whilst ploughed fields and stubble were used to a lesser extent. Of the three sample periods used for the survey, the total numbers of birds counted in Bedfordshire were 603 on 26/7 November, 1,867 on 31 Dec/1 Jan and 345 on 4/5 February.

Apart from the usual spring and autumn passage Golden Plover are subject to hard weather movements which can cause birds to depart altogether or bring large flocks into the county. This occurred in 1985 when hard weather further north resulted in the arrival of 1,850 at Henlow Airfield, 550 on Cardington Airfield and 200 on Biggleswade Common. There are few records of visible migration within the county, the largest being of c.1,000 passing north-north-east in one hour over Southill on 2 December 1962, but parties may sometimes be seen accompanying Lapwings during hard weather movements.

Grey Plover

Pluvialis squatarola

A rare passage migrant.

It was previously thought that the first record of this species in the county was in 1967 (Nightingale and Smith 1981) but there are two records in the Cople Game Book (1885–1909) of this species being shot on the Cople or Willington estates in 1900. The first was killed on 10 October and the second on 15 October. As both Lapwings and Golden Plover are also recorded under separate entries it seems probable that these are genuine records.

There are no records between 1901 and 1966, but they have been recorded in 15 of the twenty-one years between 1967 and 1987 and every year between 1976 and 1987, in all months except January. Although there are few records, they have been more frequent in spring from the end of March to the end of May, with 17 records during this period. There is a second smaller increase from July to October and only one November, two December, and one February record. Twenty-four of the 30 records have been of single birds, four of two, one of three, and one of five.

Thirteen of the 30 occurrences have been at gravel pits, 10 at clay pits, four at chalk pits and three at sewage works. The records are as follows:

1967   One at Dunstable SF 30 April.
1971   One at Dunstable SF and Houghton Regis ChP on 6 April.
1972   One at Bedford SF on 16 and 17 September.
1976   One at Harrold GP on 31 October.
1977   Two calling over Houghton Regis ChP on 23 March.
1978   One at Brogborough Lake on 9 August.
1979   One at Barkers Lane GP on 8 July.
1980   One at Radwell GP on 12 April.
      One at Stewartby Lake on 18 May.
      Two at Blunham GP on 18 May.
      One at Houghton Regis ChP on 30 May to 1 June.
1981   One at Radwell GP on 8 August.
1982   One at Stewartby Lake on 2 July.
      Five at Barkers Lane GP on 18 October.
1983   One at Barkers Lane GP on 8 February. This was found dead on 20 February and identified as a first winter male.
      One at Barkers Lane GP on 27 March.
      Two at Barkers Lane GP on 28 March.
      One at Houghton Regis ChP on 13 April.
1984   One at Harrold GP on 25 August.
      One at Stewartby Lake on 16 December.
1985   One at Stewartby Lake on 5 May.
1986   Three at Chimney Corner ClP on 18 May.
      One at Barkers Lane on 22 and 27 May.
      One at Chimney Corner ClP on 19 August.
      One at Cardington Airfield on 7 December amongst a flock of Golden Plovers.
1987   One over Priory CP on 9 May.
      One at Chimney Corner ClP 10–12 May.
      Two at Rookery ClP on 16 May.
      One over Rookery ClP on 1 November.

Lapwing

Vanellus vanellus

A fairly common resident, breeding species, common passage migrant and winter visitor (**Map 29**).

The Lapwing must be the one bird which we most associate with farmland, particularly with arable fields and damp pastures. In March it delights us with its leisurely manoeuvres as it wheels, twists, turns,

rises, and plunges over its breeding grounds uttering its 'peer-weet' call note from which is derived its other familiar name the Peewit. Its eggs, normally four, are laid from the first half of April onwards in a hollow on the ground which is lined with grass stalks. By the end of May and early June its well-camouflaged young are being tended by the female until fully fledged. There is perhaps no sight which gives greater pleasure to the birdwatcher than that of loose flocks of these birds flying high in the blue midsummer sky with their distinctive broad, rounded wings and deliberate flapping wing action from which it derives its name.

Steele-Elliott (1904) gives the status of this species as 'fairly abundant, but somewhat local as a resident; in the autumn its numbers being swelled considerably by continued arrivals'. In his time it was obviously a very common breeding species and he cites upwards of 20–30 pairs nesting in the neighbourhood of Bedford SF with Fenlake Marsh and the old racecourse along the Ampthill Road providing smaller colonies. Its status as a common breeding bird continued until about 1950 when a decrease in the number of breeding birds was reported. Harding (1979) recorded Lapwings in 257 of the 371 tetrads (69%). Breeding was confirmed in 97 tetrads (38%) and was probable in a further 63 (24%). The Lapwing will breed in a variety of habitats so long as vegetation is relatively short to allow feeding. It is mainly a farmland species nesting in scattered small groups in arable fields and pastures, particularly those which are damp or marshy, but in Bedfordshire it also has taken to nesting in the bottoms of disused clay and chalk pits. The results of the Bedfordshire survey followed the national trend in that there were large areas of apparently suitable habitat not utilised. The decline in breeding numbers has been attributed to the changes in land use and farming practice with some areas (such as the area bordering the River Great Ouse) being drained, whilst areas of waste ground have been reclaimed. The increased use of machinery, particularly in repeated rolling of cereal crops during the early part of the breeding season, may have frustrated attempts in otherwise suitable areas.

During June and July Lapwings leave their breeding areas and move south-west in post-breeding flocks. Most of these flocks are small but larger numbers are as follows: 70 at Luton Hoo on 28 July 1957,

200 at Wyboston on 26 July 1964, 650 at Wyboston on 28 July 1967, 500 in the same locality on 20 July 1968, and 2,000 at Great Barford in July 1987. These flocks become more frequent during August and early September.

Towards the end of June and, more noticeably, during the first half of July, there is also a westerly passage of birds which move into the country from Denmark, Holland, and north Germany. Parties nearly always number less than 25 and more usually contain less than 10. Flocks involved in this movement generally pass over in a steady stream during the early morning, suggesting that they have flown overnight. Hard-weather movements take place during any part of the day. Those birds involved in a south-westerly movement may also contain birds arriving from Scandinavia. Many of the birds arriving from the east are in active wing moult.

It is during the winter months of November to February that many of the largest flocks are present with flocks of over 1,000 recorded fairly regularly and several up to 3,000. The largest flocks recorded are of 4,000 near Tempsford at the end of December 1981 and 5,000 at Harrold GP in January 1983.

The onset of severe weather may cause almost complete desertion of the county. This occurred in December 1981 and again in January and February 1985. Occasionally spectacular hard-weather movements take place. In 1972 500 moved south-west in flocks of 50–150 over Pegsdon Hills in freezing weather whilst on 5 January 1976 3,120 moved south-south-west in 2½ hours. Flocks totalling 1,035 moved south-south-west over Priory CP (Barkers Lane) in two hours on 22 January 1984 and a second spell of freezing weather resulted in 1,144 passing south over the same site in two hours on 3 March. Although Lapwings had completely departed from the county in January and February 1985, 800 headed south over Priory CP on 9 February. Whereas the flight out of the county is often complete in one or two days the return passage is usually a much more casual affair often spread over a week or two. An exception to this took place in 1981 when 4,000 arrived near Tempsford at the end of December following a sudden thaw.

Knot

Calidris canutus

A rare passage migrant.

Many thousands of this coastal bird winter in the Wash after arriving from the high arctic islands of Canada or northern Greenland from August onwards. Its adherence to the coast is well illustrated by the relatively few occurrences in Bedfordshire.

Steele-Elliott (1904) cites just four records. One was killed from a brook at Ravensden, two others were found under telegraph wires at Elstow on 2 and 3 October 1884, one dead and the other with a broken wing. The fourth record is of a bird which was in the possession of Mr J. Wilkinson, killed in 1890, presumably near Chawston.

A further record was noted by the Duchess of Bedford (1927–8a) at Woburn Ponds on 28 November 1927.

Between 1946 and 1987 there have been 22 records in all months except April and July and distributed fairly evenly throughout the year. Six of the records have occurred in spring, three in summer, seven in autumn, and six in winter. Bedford SF provided four records, singles on 11 October 1954, 19 November 1961, 1 February 1962, and 15 March 1967. Singles also occurred at Wyboston GP on 14 October 1962, 1 September 1966, 26 August 1967, and 9 June 1968. Other records are of one at Dunstable SW on 10 August 1952, and one on 26 March 1967; singles at Stanford GP on 17 March 1960 and 2 November 1960; one at Ickleford 4–5 February 1956; one at Houghton Regis ChP on 29 November 1964; one at Tiddenfoot Pit (Leighton Buzzard) on 18 December 1964; one at Harrold GP on 23 January 1972; one at Chawston on 17 September 1976; one at Radwell on 29 March 1981; two at Girtford 14–15 May with one remaining until 16 May 1982; one at Brogborough Lake on 3 September 1983; two at Stewartby Lake on 19 January 1985; and one at Rookery ClP on 23 May 1985.

Sanderling

Calidris alba

A rare passage migrant and very rare winter visitor.

It is not surprising that there have been few occurrences of this species in the county as it is strictly a coastal species outside the breeding season. It is a very active bird probably best known for its characteristic running action as it chases the tideline like a clockwork toy.

Mr A. Covington writing to Steele-Elliott (1904) informed him: 'In January 1868 a large flock appeared in the neighbourhood of Fenlake and remained in the locality for two to three weeks, several were brought to me at this time, and one or two others were obtained much later. I have also received several odd birds from different localities bordering the Ouse. The last specimen that I was a witness to was one that was killed some years since, (January 1880), during a deep snow, from a ditch along the Kimbolton road, near Cleat Hill.'

One was shown to the Duchess of Bedford on 16 January 1912 which had been shot at Marston that morning and a bird in transitional plumage was present at Bedford SF on 9 August 1942.

Between 1946 and 1987 there have been 27 records of which 20 have occurred in the spring, six in the autumn, and only one in winter.

Of the spring records two have been in March, one in April, and 17 in May. The autumn records are one in late July, three in August, and two in September. The only winter record was of a very obliging bird which frequented the edge of the only ice-free pool on the River Ouse close to Bedford Town Bridge from 13–19 January 1987. Nineteen (70%) of the 27 records have been of single birds, five of two birds, one of three, and one of four at Vicarage Farm ClP in May 1974. Twelve records have been at gravel pits, seven at clay pits, six at sewage works, and two along the Ouse.

Gravel Pits:

Girtford	28 May 1982 (2).
Harrold	8 May 1979; 12 May 1984; 25 August 1984; 4 May 1985.
Radwell	1 August 1981; 20 September 1981.
South Mills	3 May 1984.
Stanford	11–12 May 1958.
Wyboston	20 April 1958; 17 May 1959; 25 March 1962 (2).

Clay Pits:

Chimney Corner	31 July 1986.
Rookery	19 May 1985.
Stewartby	21 May 1961 (2); 21 May 1984; 4 May 1985; 23 May 1985 (2).
Vicarage Farm	25 May 1974 (4).

Sewage Works:

Bedford	20–1 March 1962 (2); 8 September 1974.
Dunstable	21 May 1966; 14–16 May 1967 (2); 21 May 1975; 23 August 1971 (3).

River Ouse:

Bedford	13–19 January 1987.
Harrold	14 May 1950.

Little Stint

Calidris minuta

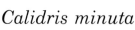

A scarce passage migrant, mainly autumn.

Steele-Elliott (1904) cites just five instances of this species in the county. One was killed at Langford on 29 September 1860; another was shot in the New Cut (Bedford) on 2 November 1889; an immature was shot on the irrigation farm at Newnham by Mr T. Harding on 21 October 1898; and two others were obtained from the same locality on 22 November 1902. One of the last two specimens is in the collection at Bedford Museum.

There have been 49 records between 1946 and 1987, all but three of them occurring during the autumn. Sewage works and gravel pits seem to provide the most suitable habitat requirements of this species with 27 of the 49 records at the former (11 at Dunstable SW and 16 at Bedford SW), and 19 at the latter (eight sites). The only other records have been at Houghton Regis ChP, Chimney Corner ClP, and Whipsnade Park. Most of the records (80%), have been of one or two birds but parties of four have turned up during autumn passage on two occasions, at Wyboston GP in September 1967 and at Bedford SW in October 1978. The highest numbers recorded were five at Dunstable SW on 26–7 September 1970 and five at Radwell GP on 13 September 1981.

There have been only three records during the spring, all of singles: at Whipsnade Park on 3 May 1953, at Stanford GP on 5 May 1961, and at Houghton Regis ChP on 30 May 1980. Birds may occur on autumn passage as early as July, the earliest being at Dunstable SW on 23 July 1979, but the main passage normally takes place during the second half of August and September with only five October records. In recent times the latest date was 16 October 1960 with two present at Bedford SW but two of the records mentioned by Steele-Elliott are much later than this.

Temminck's Stint

Calidris temminckii

A very rare passage migrant.

One was present at Bedford SW from 9 July to 2 August 1942.
   There have been four accepted records since 1946 as follows:

   1952   One at Bedford SW on 23–5 August.
   1978   One at Harrold GP on 4 June.
   1979   One at Dunstable SW on 19–20 August.
   1982   One at Girtford GP on 13 May.

Baird's Sandpiper

Calidris bairdii

A very rare vagrant. Only one accepted record.

   1961   One at Wyboston GP 13–24 September (*British Birds* 55: 372).

Pectoral Sandpiper

Calidris melanotos

A very rare vagrant with only five records.

1956   One at Dunstable SW on 14 October (*Beds Naturalist* 11: 44).

1973   One at Dunstable SW from 29 September to 6 October.

1978   A single present at Bedford SW from 15 September was joined by a second on 1 October, both remaining until 4 October and one until 8 October.

1981   One present at Dunstable SW 19–24 September.

Sharp-tailed Sandpiper

Calidris acuminata

A very rare vagrant.

1961   One at Bedford SW 4–11 September was the first county and sixth British record (*British Birds* 55: 573).

Curlew Sandpiper

Calidris ferruginea

Scarce passage migrant, mainly autumn.

Steele-Elliott (1904) records it as a 'rare migratory visitant' with the only records being of an immature shot by one of the old walls at Newnham (Bedford) on 12 October 1872 and a further six obtained from the same locality on 11 and 18 September 1902. Two of these are in the collection at Bedford Museum.

    Between 1946 and 1987 there have been 20 records of which 18 have occurred during the autumn and just two during the spring. The two spring records were of one at Wyboston GP on 24 April 1959 and one at Stewartby Lake on 11 May 1975. The earliest birds on autumn passage were recorded on 20 July 1961 at Barkers Lane GP (now Priory CP) and on the same date in 1972 at Harrold GP. Seven records have occurred in August, seven in September and two in October, with the latest being one at Stanford GP on 30 October 1960. As with others in this group of waders, most records have been at sewage works (nine at Bedford SW and two at Dunstable) and seven have been at gravel pits. The only records at clay pits were of two at Vicarage Farm ClP on 9 August 1974 and one at Stewartby Lake on 11 May 1975. A juvenile was seen at both Dunstable SW and Houghton Regis ChP on 27 and 28 August.

Purple Sandpiper
Calidris maritima

A very rare vagrant with only one record (*Beds Naturalist* 9: 35).

1954   One at Barkers Lane GP in May. (Nightingale and Smith 1981 gave the date as 1 May but the original record in Bedford School Natural History Society publication *Ousel* says '1, May 1954'.)

Dunlin
Calidris alpina

A common passage migrant and winter visitor.

This is one of our most familiar waders on passage and during the winter months. Birds of the race *C. a. schinzii* breed in Scotland and along the Pennines with a few other isolated pockets in Wales and the south-west. These birds winter further south, probably in West Africa. Our winter population consists of birds from the USSR and Scandinavia (*C. a. alpina*) whilst those from Greenland and Iceland (*C. a. schinzii*) pass through Britain on passage in spring and autumn.

Steele-Elliott (1904) mentions this species as occurring on passage in spring and autumn, being commonest in March and August, but being more or less regular from the end of July through to the following May. A few stragglers were also recorded in June. The valley of the Ouse and Newnham Farm (Bedford) are mentioned as being particularly attractive sites, the Dunlin occurring there with great regularity, with birds recorded there as late as 21 May 1899 and as early as 3 July 1900 at the latter locality. He writes that Mr A. Covington had nine adult males in perfect plumage brought to him after having been found under the telegraph wires near the New Cut (Bedford) on 28 July 1886 with several others 'considerably mutilated' also being found. During this period many were shot. Mr Covington mentions hundreds having been brought to him during a 36-year period when he was a taxidermist in Bedford. Three were killed at Fenlake in the winter of 1896. C. M. Prior in the *Zoologist* of 1878–9 mentions a small flock remaining for at least a week in December of 1878 and refers back to the winter of 1875–6 when, he says, 200 were killed locally. Two specimens shot from a party of four at Leagrave in December 1899 are in the collection at Bedford Museum.

Since that time the status of the Dunlin has remained very much the same, turning up at gravel pits, clay pits, and local sewage farms wherever there is a suitable shoreline for it to feed. Spring passage is usually on a much smaller scale than that of autumn and may begin as early as mid March, but the main passage is heaviest during the last three weeks of April and may continue until the end of the third week of May. Between 1946 and 1986 there have been only seven June records, all but one being during the first 10 days. Return passage commences during the second half of July, building up during August, reaching a peak during the last two weeks and continuing until the third week of September. During this period it occurs more than twice as regularly as in spring. Birds may occur from October through to March when spring passage begins and there is sometimes a slight increase during late October and early November.

Most records have been of less than five birds but larger flocks have been recorded on both spring and autumn passage and in winter. Flock of 10+ since 1946 are as follows:

1966   11 at Bedford SW on 20 April.
1967   12 at Dunstable SW in spring.
1969   16 at Bedford SW on 22 March.
1971   13 at Dunstable SW on 26 May.
1973   15 at Stewartby ClP on 25 March.
         14 at Wyboston GP on 6 August.
         12 at Vicarage Farm ClP on 21 October.
         14 at Vicarage Farm ClP on 30 December.
1974   20 at Vicarage Farm ClP on 12 May.
1977   10–15 at Harrold GP on 24 August.
1978   *c.*30 at Stewartby ClP on 26 March.
1980   24 at Barkers Lane GP (now Priory CP) on 20 December.
1981   13 at Radwell GP on 8 April.
1985   10 at Radwell GP on 27 April.

Ruff

Philomachus pugnax

Uncommon but regular passage migrant and winter visitor.

Before 1871 when the Ruff bred regularly in the Fen country of East Anglia it was probably a regular visitor to the county, but by the end of the nineteenth century its decline as a breeding species was reflected by fewer occurrences in Bedfordshire and Steele-Elliott (1904) gives its status as a 'rare straggler of the autumn'. In a letter to Steele-Elliott Mr A. Covington, when recollecting a reeve that was shot at Cardington in September 1877, writes: 'At one time this bird was evidently far from uncommon and I have heard our old local sportsmen speak of shooting male birds in the full spring attire'. Other records before 1900 are of one shot about 1870 near Shefford Mill; an immature bird killed about 1880 at Newnham; six or seven for a week at Newnham in the autumn of 1894 (one, a reeve, in this party was shot on 13 September) and on 23 August 1897 an immature was shot in the same locality. A male in the collection at Bedford Museum was shot at Bedford SW on 17 September 1902.

A male was present at Bedford SW on 8 and 9 August 1942 and one was also seen there on 30 April 1943.

It was as recently as 1934–5 that the Ruff was first recorded wintering in Britain and since that time it has steadily increased as a wintering species. Records in Bedfordshire have followed the same trend. The first published wintering record is of one which was present at East Hyde from 30 January to 14 February 1954. Up to 1975 there were only four additional winter records, in 1961, 1965, 1967, and 1973, all of single birds. In recent years occurrences in winter have increased. After only five winter records before 1976 there were 20 records between 1976 and 1987. Most winter records have been of single birds but four were present at Barkers Lane GP on 13 December 1981 and five frequented Stewartby Lake and Vicarage Farm ClP at the end of January and early February in 1985. There has been only one record during November (a single at Bedford SF 20–7 November 1965), seven in December, 12 in January and five in February. As Britain is on the northern edge of its wintering range, the numbers wintering in this country tend to fluctuate widely depending upon the weather conditions.

Spring passage takes place on a much smaller scale than that of the autumn with often only two to four records, mainly singles, and may begin from mid March onwards. Most occur during the last three weeks of April, trailing off in the first half of May. There have been only seven June records between 1946 and 1987. Return passage usually takes place from the middle of July reaching a peak during the last three weeks of August. Numbers involved during the autumn may be at least ten times greater than those in spring and tend to involve small parties of birds rather than individuals. Birds may continue to pass through in small numbers until the third week of September with the occasional bird being seen into October but between 1946 and 1987 there have been only eight records in this month.

This species has occurred primarily at the old style sewage farms and on the worked-out beds of partially flooded gravel and clay pits or, to a lesser extent, the margins of flooded pits. Flooded meadows may be used occasionally but are a scarce habitat in the county. The modernisation of sewage treatment and the consequent decline in sewage lagoons has removed one of its favoured habitats and the beds of worked-out clay and gravel pits now provide the main sites at which this species may be seen. Large numbers are rarely seen on spring passage, the highest being up to 11 at South Mills GP during May 1987. Parties of more than 10 were occasionally seen during the autumn in the 1960s and 1970s, all at sewage farms. The only large number observed between 1979 and 1987 occurred in August 1981 when a maximum of 20 were attracted to Radwell GP after it was drained, thus providing suitable habitat during the main period of passage.

Counts of 10+ during the autumn, 1946–87, are as follows:

1953   13 at Dunstable SW on 26 August.
1962   c.13 at Bedford SF on 22, 29 August and 3 September.
1963   11 at Bedford SF on 19–25 August.
1965   15 at Bedford SF on 11 September.
1966   27 at Bedford SF on 29 August.
1968   11 at Bedford SF on 14–15 September.
1970   11 at Dunstable SF on 26–7 August.
1971   10 at Dunstable SF on 31 August.
1978   11 at Bedford SW on 11 September.
1981   20 at Radwell GP on 9 August.

Jack Snipe

Lymnocryptes minimus

A regular winter visitor in small numbers.

This small relative of the Common Snipe inhabits boggy ground and prefers plenty of cover. Its cryptic plumage makes it very difficult to see and this is made more difficult by its habit of remaining prone until almost trodden on when it will rise silently, make a short erratic flight, and dive back to the ground to disappear again. Although it does feed during the daytime, it is mainly active at dusk or at night, which may result in it being under-recorded in the county.

Steele-Elliott (1904) notes it as being a regular winter visitor, in some years visiting in considerable numbers and in others being comparatively scarce. Its status today is very much the same and, as in his day, it usually arrives in October and remains until April. The earliest arrival is given by Steele-Elliott as 3 September 1893 and there have been only four other published records in this month, 18 September 1947, 17 and 19 September 1962, 28 September 1969, all at Bedford SW, and one at Dunstable SW on 21 September 1982. Most birds have departed by mid April. Occasionally birds may remain until the end of the month but in 1978 and 1984 single birds remained until 11 May.

From the latter part of the nineteenth century right up to 1974 Bedford SF was the most favoured site and was joined in 1953 by Dunstable SF. It was not unusual to record four or five birds in these localities in an average year and 10 or more in a good one. Modernisation in methods of sewage treatment resulted in a rapid decline of this species at both of these sites from 1979 and whilst a few are occasionally recorded at Dunstable SW, the sewage lagoons at Bedford SW gradually became overgrown and none have been recorded there since 1981. In 1975 the cessation of working at Houghton Regis ChP enabled a small area of previously disturbed marshy ground to be utilised and spring passage attained a maximum of 18 on 8 March of that year, the highest number ever recorded in the county. Since that time Houghton Regis ChP has been used annually and is now one of two major wintering sites in the county. Birds were recorded at Chalton SF between 1971 and 1973.

The increased extraction of sand and gravel during the 1960s created ideal conditions at some of the new pits with Wyboston GP being used from 1961 to 1979, Girtford and South Mills GPs from 1970 to 1987 (now the second major site), Harrold GP from 1978 to 1982 (occasionally since), and Radwell GP from 1980 to 1985. Records have been obtained from the clay pits at Kempston Hardwick, Brogborough, Chimney Corner, Vicarage Farm, and Stewartby but these, along with 19 other sites, have never been used with any regularity.

Although singles are usually recorded from the less frequented sites and up to five from these more regularly used, larger numbers have been recorded in good years. These are as follows:

1951 9 at Bedford SF on 14 November.
1953 13 at Bedford SF on 25 January.
1955 Up to 10 at Dunstable SF 20 November to 12 December.
1958 Up to 15 at Bedford SF November–December.
1960 12 at Bedford SF on 20 November.
1961 15 at Bedford SF on 19 November.
1974 10 at Bedford SW on 5 November.
1975 18 at Houghton Regis ChP 8 March.
      10 at Bedford SW on 25 October.
1978 10 at Bedford SW on 10 January.

Snipe

Gallinago gallinago

A scarce breeding species and common winter visitor, sometimes recorded in large numbers (**Map 30**).

During the winter months the Common Snipe is one of the most characteristic birds of wet meadows, boggy fields, sewage farms, and marshes but its skulking habits and cryptic plumage often make it difficult to see. It is reluctant to fly, often crouching until the last moment, but when disturbed its very long bill, zigzag flight and harsh 'scaap' call note leave its identification in little doubt. Whereas the Jack Snipe tends to land very quickly after being flushed the Common

Snipe makes a longer flight. Many of the birds which visit us for the winter are of Baltic origin. Although a scarce breeder in the county, the familiar drumming produced in a steep dive by the vibration of the outer pair of tail feathers may be heard from late March well into the early summer.

Steele-Elliott (1904) notes that this species was generally plentiful along our waterways, ditches, and other suitable places but there was evidence to suggest that once it was more plentiful than it was in his day. He attributed its decline to drainage and cultivation of some of its former haunts, giving Crawley Moor and a large portion of Flitwick Moor as examples. He knew of it possibly breeding from Flitwick Moor and Staughton Moor although in 1897 two pairs were heard drumming throughout the summer over Newnham Farm, Bedford. There is evidence to suggest that this species increased during the early part of this century but has declined again in recent years due to continued drainage of suitable habitats.

On May 2 1912 Steele-Elliott found two nests of the Common Snipe in some marshy meadows in Bedfordshire and at that time stated that there had been no previous satisfactory instance of this bird nesting in the county (*Zoologist* 1912).

Although the drumming display may attract the attention of the alert birdwatcher, the cryptic plumage and well-concealed nest site have made it difficult to prove breeding and this has undoubtedly resulted in its being under-recorded as a breeding species in the county. Henry Key (1950) assessed the county population as being 'a few pairs . . . in widely separated areas' and its status seems to be much the same today. Between 1950 and 1955 drumming was recorded from Bedford SF, Cowslip Meadow (Luton), and Flitwick Moor, with a pair actually proved breeding at Eaton Ford. There were no published records of drumming from 1956 to 1967 although it undoubtedly occurred in the breeding season during this period. Drumming was recorded again in 1968 from Biggleswade Common, Flitwick Moor, and Wyboston. The BTO Breeding Birds Survey (1968–72) stimulated a thorough search and as a result a more accurate assessment of the breeding status of this species could be made. In 1969 breeding was proved in four tetrads in the county with an estimated 6–10 pairs in TL14. Two pairs bred in 1972 near Grange Mill, Heath and Reach. The survey was continued until 1977 and during this period (1968–77) breeding was confirmed in only five tetrads, found to be probable in 18, and possible in a further 38. During the breeding season it was recorded from five localities in 1976 and from six localities in 1977 and 1978. Breeding was suspected from Luton Hoo and Houghton Regis ChP in 1980 and proved at Sandy in 1983, Houghton Regis ChP (two pairs) in 1984 and 1985, with one and possibly two pairs at that site in 1986. Between 1983 and 1986 drumming was heard at Brogborough ClP, South Mills GP, Linslade, Little Barford, Harrold GP, Biggleswade Common, Sandy Lodge, Vicarage Farm ClP, and Rookery ClP.

The population increases considerably in winter with birds arriving sometimes as early as August but more usually in September and October, departing again by the end of March and early April. Parties of 50–100 occur regularly in suitable areas such as flooded meadows and sewage works but numbers vary and may be much higher than this in good years. Another factor is the availability of suitable habitat and, apart from the most unusual occurrence of 500–600 at Felmersham NR in 1969 and two large flocks at Wyboston in 1969 and 1972, all records of large numbers before 1977 were at Bedford SF. The drainage of the fields and later modernisation in methods of sewage treatment have lead to the demise of this area. The fields of Fenlake have been used from 1980 but this area is subject to human disturbance from dog walkers, particularly in mild winters.

Great Snipe

Gallinago media

A very rare passage migrant.

Steele-Elliott (1904) gave its status as being 'an occasional winter visitant'. Mr A. Covington, in a letter to Steele-Elliott, mentions that the first within his knowledge was shot at Willington prior to 1860 and a second was shot in about the same year on the Renhold side of the river. In September 1866 he handled his first 'in the flesh' which had been shot at Biddenham by James the keeper. This was too mutilated to be set up except as a prey for a Merlin. Two were shot at Newnham Farm in about 1878 and on 3 October 1885 one was shot in the same locality. In 1887 an immature was taken to Mr Covington after killing itself against the telegraph wires by the New Cut (Bedford). Another record, supplied to Steele-Elliott by Mr P. Addington, is of one out of 18 snipe which he shot between Wyboston and Tempsford in about 1860. Unfortunately this bird was not preserved. One was said to have been obtained from Newnham by Mr Bennet, a well-known gunner with considerable experience in river shooting, but again, this record is unsubstantiated.

Henry Key (1946) mentions this species as being a winter visitor but the only accepted record from 1890 is of one recorded at Stanford GP on 24 March 1967 (*British Birds* 61: 340). There have been two other possible records, one at Bedford SF on 20 August 1947 and a second at Coronation ClP on 3 February 1955 but insufficient details were obtained.

Woodcock

Scolopax rusticola

A local resident breeding species, mainly confined to the Greensand Ridge. Also a regular winter visitor (**Map 31**).

The Woodcock inhabits open woodlands with some ground cover and open spaces or rides as well as young forestry plantations. Outside the breeding season its cryptic plumage and crepuscular and nocturnal feeding habits make it difficult to observe unless it is flushed. Usually it occurs singly and during the daytime will roost in a crouching position close to the ground, almost impossible to see. When flushed it will fly with a rather slow wavering flight with the bill held in its characteristic downward position. During the breeding season however, one may observe two or three at dusk taking part in their display flight which is called 'roding'.

Steele-Elliott (1904) describes its status as being thinly distributed from October onwards and says that 'there is little doubt that it is a gradually decreasing species'. Although it did breed within the county Steele-Elliott could only give four instances: Chicksands Priory Woods in 1828, Charle Wood in 1868, Southill Estate (no date), and one other (no site and no date).

Information concerning the breeding status of this species is scarce but by 1950 it had been established that the main breeding areas were confined to the woodlands along the Greensand Ridge and, to a lesser degree, the primary woodlands in the north of the county which are situated on Boulder Clay. Further observations during the 1960s showed that woodland in the Clay-with-Flints area in the south of the county also provided suitable habitat where breeding took place. The BTO Breeding Survey (1968–72) confirmed this as being the true situation and breeding was proved in 16 tetrads, was probable in 45, and possible in 18.

An indication of how difficult it can be to see the nest of the Woodcock and an example of the fidelity of the adults at this time is shown by an occurrence in 1958 when a machine cutting grass along a ride in Rowney Warren went over a sitting bird without injuring it. The bird was flushed from the nest, which was then exposed, but later returned to it and successfully hatched the eggs.

There has been at least one recent record in the county of this species carrying its young.

It might be expected that with a decline in primary woodlands the Woodcock would decline as a breeding species but this may to some

TABLE 3.6 *Woodcock tetrad breeding records by habitat*

Habitat	Confirmed	Probable	Possible
Boulder Clay	2	6	4
Greensand	10	28	10
Clay-with-Flints	3	7	1
Others	1	4	3
Totals	16	45	18

extent have been counteracted by the management of coniferous plantations, particularly along the Greensand Ridge, where felling followed by replanting has provided additional suitable habitat. Although it is difficult to obtain accurate information for the whole county it does not seem to be declining.

Additional birds visit us during the winter from Norway, Sweden, Finland, Denmark, and possibly Russia, arriving from October onwards. Numbers vary considerably from year to year with very few seen in some years. Higher numbers than usual were reported by keepers in 1974 when up to five were shot in a day at Luton Hoo Park. High numbers were again reported in 1975, and in 1983 25 were flushed during a shoot in Warden Great and Little Woods on 15 January. Birds also turn up, sometimes exhausted and in uncharacteristic habitats, after hard weather. Two examples of this are of singles which turned up in Luton gardens, one in December 1980 and another in 1986.

Black-tailed Godwit

Limosa limosa

A scarce but now regular passage migrant.

This taller, more elegant species than the closely related Bar-tailed Godwit is though to have bred widely in East Anglia until the early nineteenth century but drainage, egg-collecting, and shooting resulted in its extinction in England by the 1930s. The recovery of this species really began in the early 1950s, since when it has gradually increased as a breeding bird due mainly to the efforts of the RSPB and the Wildfowl and Wetland Trust in the Ouse Washes. When in flight it can easily be distinguished by its broad white wing-bar and long legs which project well beyond the tail.

The earliest record of this species in Bedfordshire is of one mentioned by F. O. Morris (1860) which was shot at Cardington but no further details are given. Steele-Elliott mentions two further records; one shot near The Park at Luton and an immature male which was shot by Mr G. Pestell near the osier-bed at Goldington during the first week in September 1897. This was accompanied by a second bird which was wounded 'but not secured'.

A party of six was observed at Bedford SW on 8 April 1942, four of which were in almost full breeding plumage whilst the other two were immature (Miller 1943–4).

During the 42 years 1946–87 the Black-tailed Godwit has occurred on 35 occasions in all months except October, November, and December. A gradual increase has taken place from three occurrences in 1946–55 to 13 in 1976–85, which correlates with the increase in the breeding population at the Ouse Washes.

Spring passage may begin as early as the end of February but mainly takes place during March, April, and May. There has been only one June record. Slightly fewer birds have occurred during the autumn with passage taking place from July to the third week of September. Totals observed by calendar month 1946–86 are:

Jan.	Feb.	Mar.	Apr.	May	Jun.	Jul.	Aug.	Sep.
1	1	9	6	4	1	4	4	5

Up to the end of the 1960s most were recorded at Bedford SF with single records from Felmersham GP, Stanford GP, Wyboston GP, Stewartby ClP, and Kempston SF. Since 1970 the change in habitat around Bedford SF has resulted in only one further record there in 1971, and 10 out of 17 records have been at gravel-pit sites. Of the remaining seven records three were at clay pits, two at Dunstable SW, and one flying along the River Ouse west of Bedford.

Twenty-eight of the 35 reports (80%) have involved single birds and five have involved two birds. Three birds were present at Harrold GP on 21–2 July 1979 and a party of 10 circled over Barkers Lane GP (Priory CP) on 15 August 1982.

Bar-tailed Godwit

Limosa lapponica

A rare passage migrant.

The Bar-tailed Godwit is shorter legged than the Black-tailed Godwit giving it a dumpier appearance. It has a more upturned bill and lacks the conspicuous white wing-bar. In winter it appears more streaked along the back in contrast to the rather plain back of the Black-tailed. Birds arrive in Britain from arctic Russia and western and central Siberia in August when many gather in the Wash to moult. Many continue to arrive during late autumn and winter from the Dutch Wadden Sea. It is very much a bird of the coast in winter so that it would be unusual to find it in the county during this season.

Steele-Elliott (1904) notes seven records: two shot at Goldington on separate occasions during the winter of 1866–7; one killed on 21 May 1870 near Ampthill; one shot at Wyboston in 1870; one in full breeding plumage obtained near Stanford about 1877 (now in Bedford Museum); one from Ampthill, May 1887; one killed at Newnham, no date.

Between 1946 and 1987 the Bar-tailed Godwit has been reported on 24 occasions in only 14 years. Nineteen of these records have occurred on spring passage during the last week of April and the first three weeks of May. There have only been five records outside this period, two in March, one in August, and two in September. All of the five records between 1946 and 1956 occurred at Bedford SW. During the first week of May 1957 a party of eight, the largest party recorded in the county, flew north-east over Colesden and one of these was shot. There was then a period of 15 years when this species was not recorded, the next being two at Luton Hoo on 16 September 1973. From this time the bird appeared more frequently in the county, annually 1981–6, but it is not certain why. The increase in suitable habitats in the form of clay and gravel-pit sites could be a factor as could be the increase in observer coverage.

Nearly all records have been of one or two birds but, apart from the party of eight over Colesden in 1957 mentioned above, five were at Vicarage Farm ClP on 27 April 1974, three at Radwell GP on 28 April 1984, three over Priory CP, Bedford on 3 May 1984, three at Stewartby Lake on 10 May 1984, and a 'small flock' passed over The Lodge, Sandy on 8 August 1986.

Godwit

Limosa sp.

1980 Eight over Radwell GP on 27 July.
1981 Three over Harrold GP on 22 August were thought to be Bar-tailed.

Whimbrel

Numenius phaeopus

A regular but uncommon passage migrant and very rare winter visitor.

The Whimbrel is a smaller bird than the Curlew with a shorter bill, distinctive head markings, and tittering flight call. Over 450 pairs nest in the north of Scotland, particularly in Shetland. These birds winter in Africa south of the Sahara. Birds which breed in Finland

and the USSR pass through Britain probably on a broad front on spring and autumn passage with relatively few staging-posts and winter on the coasts of southern Africa.

The status given by Steele-Elliott (1904) is that of 'a regular passing migrant in small flights during the spring and autumn; seldom alighting, and flying overhead', much the same as its present status.

The earliest record in the county is of a bird killed at Tingrith in 1868 which was in the possession of Col. H. Barclay. Mr A. Covington, in a letter quoted by Steele-Elliott, says that he received six locally but gives very brief details of only five. All were shot in May or

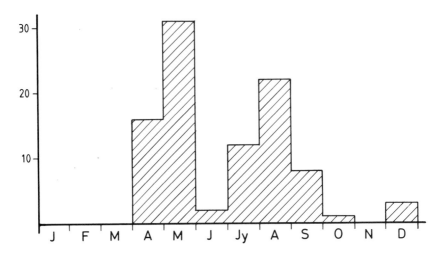

Figure 3.8 *Whimbrel: total monthly counts, 1946–87*

September with records from Harrold, Kempston, Turvey, and Cardington accounting for four of them. The fifth had killed itself against telegraph wires in 1896. Mr J. Wilkinson also wrote that 'One year we obtained a Whimbrel from a flight that passed over us whilst we were Rook shooting at Roxton', but no further details were given. One other record by Steele-Elliott is of one killed at Streatley in 1894 by Mr Osborne.

Between 1946 and 1987 there have been approximately 102 records. There have been 11 years in which the Whimbrel has not been recorded, 10 of those being between 1947 and 1967, the other being in 1971.

Occurrences are split almost equally between spring (51 records) and autumn (44 records) with two June (1975, 1985) and two October records (1957, 1987). Spring passage may begin as early as the first week of April, the earliest record being of one at South Mills GP on 5 April 1985, but the main passage builds up during the third week of April to reach a peak during the last week of April and first week of May. A few birds may pass through in the second half of May. Autumn passage begins during July with most passages taking place during the second half of July and the first half of August and is nearly complete by mid September.

Most reports involve less than five birds, usually one to three, but occasionally larger numbers are seen, for example:

1963 22 over Bedford SF on 7 September
1969 19 over Sandy on 3 August.
1980 15 over Whipsnade Downs on 6 May.
1983 13 over Everton on 30 July.
1985 23 over Priory CP, Bedford on 25 August.

Much passage takes place at dusk, dawn, or during the night. A large northward passage was noted over Bedford early on 12 May 1949 intermittently for over one hour and a similar movement took place over Bedford on the night of 30 April/1 May 1952, when many were heard calling during a period of several hours.

Up to 1987 the Whimbrel has not been recorded in November, January, February, and March. All three winter records occurred in 1953 with a most unusual report of c.30 at Bedford SF on 11 December, a party on water meadows at Oakley 'heard in fog' on 15 December, and one seen there on the following day. These are all exceptional records and must be treated with caution, particularly the former record, when one takes into account that the present total winter population for the whole of Britain is estimated not to exceed 30 birds (Lack 1986).

Curlew

Numenius arquata

A fairly common passage migrant and scarce winter visitor.

Many were reported to Steele-Elliott (1904) but without particulars. Those where details were supplied are as follows:

1878 Nine in company with three Dunlins in the middle of December.
1894 A few frequented Newnham Sewage Farm.
1895 One picked up dead at Sandy after a severe winter.
1896 One shot at Little Staughton in September.
1897 One in December 1897 over the old racecourse, Elstow.
1901 One shot at Roxton on January 4.
       One picked up dead at Kempston on 5 January.
       Three at Langford on 8 January of which two were eventually shot.
       On 15 and 24 July Curlews were reported passing over Bedford and Langford during the night.

Other records prior to 1946 are of one at Bedford SF on 8 and 20 March 19452 and one at the same locality on 2 April 1943 (Miller 1943–4).

Although the Curlew may be seen during all months of the year it is mainly a bird of spring and autumn passage with the first few passing through in spring from mid March, sometimes a little earlier. Passage remains at a low level until the second half of April when the main passage takes place and continues until the first week of May. Numbers decline during the rest of the month. Autumn passage starts during the second half of June but does not build up to any extent until the second week of August with the main passage taking place during the last week of that month. Autumn passage is on a slightly larger scale than that of spring and continues to a much lesser degree to the first week of October. A few birds are observed after this date and may be seen occasionally throughout the winter.

As with the Whimbrel, the Curlew is usually seen flying over and is often heard migrating at night. Ornithologists noted nocturnal movements regularly in the county during the 1940s and 1950s but less frequently in recent years. This may be due to the increased use of the motor car for the nocturnal movements of birdwatchers! Flocks of 20+ noted since 1946 are:

1953   28 north over Whipsnade on 8 August.
1957   21 at Stewartby on 28 August.
1959   25–30 west over Bedford on 15 March.
1980   c.30 over Blunham on 23 August.
         40+ over Harrold GP on 25 August.

Spotted Redshank

Tringa erythropus

A scarce passage migrant.

The Spotted Redshank is a more elegant species than the closely related Redshank with longer legs, a longer, thinner bill, and lacking a broad white trailing edge to the wing. It only occurs in the county on passage to and from its breeding grounds in northern Scandinavia and the USSR and often draws attention to itself in flight by its characteristic 'chew-it' call note.

Steele-Elliott (1904) gives only two known occurrences, the first of which was a pair, one of which was shot at Langford on 17 September 1856 by Mr J. King. In his diary Mr King made the following entry: '17 September, 1856, shot a Spotted Redshank this evening down the meadows along the river, two in company flew past, one of which I secured, the other returned and whistled loudly but it was some distance away and too dark to obtain a second shot with any chance of success.' This specimen is in the collection at Bedford Museum. The second record is of one mentioned in a letter by Mr T. Cane to Steele-Elliott in which he writes: 'From the Bogs now known as Aramica, I once had a Dusky Redshank brought to me, about 1870.'

J. A. Miller (1943–4) recorded one at Bedford SF on 13 April 1943.

Since 1951 the species has been recorded on about 74 occasions during 26 of the 37 years to 1987.

During the early 1950s most occurred at the sewage farms of Bedford and Dunstable. These continued to be used into the 1970s but as new methods of sewage treatment were introduced, the habitat created at gravel pits and, to a lesser extent, clay pits during this period provided a suitable but not ideal substitute. Birds can also be seen and heard passing over.

Spring passage is on a much smaller scale than that of the autumn and may take place from early April (earliest record, one over Priory CP on 3 April 1988), but most occurrences have been during the last week of April and first week of May. The latest spring record is of one which visited Willington GP 13–17 May 1951. There have been no June records.

Autumn passage has involved about four times as many records as spring and may start in July though there have been only two records up to 1987. The first was at Bedford SF on 21 July 1959 and the second, the earliest, was of one at Blunham GP on 9 July 1982. Passage, although small, normally builds up from the second week of August reaching a peak during late August and early September. The latest record was of one at Wyboston GP on 30 September 1967. Eighty per cent of records have involved single birds. Parties of four birds have been recorded on three occasions: at Bedford SF on 2 September 1962, at Wyboston GP on 18 August 1969, and over Priory CP (Barkers Lane GP) on 12 August 1984.

Redshank

Tringa totanus

A common passage migrant and scarce breeding species wintering in small numbers (**Map 32**).

This noisy and restless bird with bright red legs and distinctive white trailing edges to its wings is rightly called the 'sentinel of the marsh' as it is usually the first to signal the approach of any danger by its repeated liquid alarm call. By March it has established itself in its favoured breeding haunts, and its attractive display flight with quivering wings and yodelling song forms an essential part of any marshland scene. The nest is on the ground and eggs are laid from the middle of April. During this time it may often be seen perching on fence posts or even the branch of a tree calling its defiant warning to any potential predator.

Steele-Elliott's assessment (1904) of the status of the Redshank was very much the same as it is today, which is a little surprising as there was more suitable habitat in the form of flood meadows at that time. The first published record is of one shot at Langford on 22 March 1855, with a second shot in the same locality by Mr J. King on 5 October 1880. Before this time the taxidermist Mr A. Covington said in a letter to Steele-Elliott that 'sportsmen that have known our county from the early part of the century, have spoken of the Redshank as at one time nesting regularly in various of our marshy meadows.' Towards the end of the century sewage water was dammed up at Newnham SF and 'rapidly formed a swamp many acres in extent.' It was in this area that, in 1896, two or three pairs of Redshank bred, and despite at least one nest being robbed of its eggs, one pair reared young. Breeding again took place there in 1897 and in the same year one or possibly two pairs probably nested on Fenlake Marsh. Breeding was again proved at Newnham in 1898 with two pairs in the following year at Newnham and one at Fenlake. In 1900 after the fields at Newnham had once again passed under cultivation Steele-Elliott was unable to find any trace of this species at this site.

In more recent times a pair bred near Silsoe in 1937 and doubtless bred at Bedford and Dunstable SFs during the 1940s, though information from that period is very vague. However in 1953 at least five pairs bred at Bedford SF and in 1957 seven pairs were recorded there during the breeding season and six pairs at Dunstable SF. In the same year one pair was reported at Steppingley Marsh. By 1956, in addition to the previously mentioned sites, two pairs probably bred at Stewartby ClP. From this time we see the effect of increased mineral extraction on the breeding status of this species. In 1957 two pairs bred at Bedford SF, three to four pairs were present at Dunstable SF, two pairs bred at Stewartby ClP, and one at Wyboston GP. Worked-out beds of clay and gravel pits continued to have a positive influence and by 1959 there were breeding or probable breeding records from nine sites involving 13–14 pairs as follows: Bedford SF (four to five pairs), Vicarage Farm ClP (two pairs), Stewartby ClP (one pair), Brogborough ClP (one pair), Barkers Lane GP (one pair), Sandy GP (one pair), Stanford GP (one pair), Wyboston GP (one pair), and Jones SP (one pair).

A further increase in the number of sites used took place in 1971 with the addition of Coronation ClP, Bromham GP, Harrold GP, and Houghton Regis ClP, making a total of 12 localities for that year.

During the 1970s most breeding occurred at various gravel pits and at Houghton Regis ChP but by the mid 1980s growth of vegetation at several gravel pits made them unsuitable as breeding sites and Houghton Regis ChP and South Mills GP became the main breeding areas. In 1983 at least five pairs were present at Houghton Regis ChP and three at South Mills with the same numbers the following year. South Mills became the main stronghold in 1986 with at least six pairs breeding, but only one at Houghton Regis ChP where human disturbance resulted in a less successful breeding season. In 1987 seven to eight pairs bred at South Mills with a further five pairs at Rookery ClP; three at Chimney Corner ClP; two pairs at Houghton Regis ChP; two pairs at Radwell GP; and one pair at Vicarage Farm ClP.

The BTO Breeding Survey (1968–77) showed that birds were recorded in 31 tetrads (8%). Breeding was confirmed in 11 tetrads, was probable in 8, and possible in a further 12.

TABLE 3.7 *Redshank, probable breeding pairs, 1971–87*

Year	Pairs	Localities
1971	14	12
1972	8–9	4
1973	13	17
1974	17	–
1975	14	–
1976	9	9
1977	15	12
1978	4	10
1979	3	5
1980	2	8
1981	9	7
1982	2	4
1983	8	5
1984	8	2
1985	9	4
1986	7	5
1987	20	6

A few birds occur during the winter months at suitable sites but spring passage usually begins in early March (sometimes February) and continues to late April. During this period numbers up to 10 are not infrequent but 45 at Bedford SF on 24 March 1949 and 50 at the same locality on 18 March of the following year were quite exceptional. Flocks of 11+ on spring passage 1946–87 are as follows:

1946 12 at Bedford SF on 21 March.
1949 45 at Bedford SF on 24 March.
1950 50 at Bedford SF on 18 March.
1960 18 at Bedford SF on 10 April.
1967 22 at Bedford SF on 16 March.
      15 at Stewartby ClP on 29 March.
1974 21 at Bedford SF on 22 February.
1984 14 at South Mills NR on 24–6 March.
      20 at South Mills NR on 18 April.
1985 14 at South Mills NR on 4 April.
      15 at South Mills NR on 5 April.
1986 16 at South Mills NR on 26 March.
1987 24 at South Mills NR in April.

Autumn passage takes place on a much smaller scale than that of spring, becoming evident during the second half of July and the first half of August. Numbers dwindle during the second half of August and passage is almost complete by mid September. No large numbers have been recorded during this period.

Greenshank

Tringa nebularia

A scarce passage migrant in spring, regular and fairly common in autumn. Rare winter visitor.

The Greenshank is one of our most graceful waders, greyer and a little larger than the Redshank with longer greenish legs and slightly upturned bill. Its flight is swift and straight, and it shows a striking white lower back and rump and legs projecting beyond its tail. Its clear 'tew, tew, tew' call is one of the most distinctive wader cries. The Scottish breeding population may begin to leave their breeding grounds during late June or early July, passing through Britain from mid July to late October, but many which occur on the eastern side of England are of continental origin.

Steele-Elliott (1904) noted this species as being a regular passage migrant in autumn occurring annually at Newnham Farm when this area was flooded with sewage water towards the end of the nineteenth century. The earliest record recollected by Mr A. Covington was of a pair flushed from a pond at Putnoe (Bedford) in August 1868, one of which was shot. Other records mentioned by Steele-Elliott are from Goldington (1878), Stanford (*c*.1880), and Turvey (1896). Mr Covington states that upwards of a dozen local birds, which in every instance were killed in the month of August, passed through his hands. The Stanford specimen is in the collection at Bedford Museum.

W. B. Alexander (1943–4) noted one at Bedford SF on 21 August 1939 and J. A. Miller recorded one on 24 May and three in August 1942 at the same locality (1943–4).

Spring passage through the county is on a very small scale indeed but the Greenshank may turn up at sewage works and clay, gravel, or chalk pits in the county where suitable habitat exists. Of 22 spring records 11 have been at gravel pits, five at clay pits, three at chalk pits, two at sewage works and one at sand pits. Between 1946 and 1986 this species has been recorded in spring in only 18 of the 41 years with 11 years being between 1974 and 1986.

The earliest record was of two at Bedford SF on 28 March 1959 and a few birds may begin to pass through during the first three weeks of April, but there have only been five records during this period. Most have occurred during the last week of April and first two weeks of May with passage coming to an end by the end of the month. There have been three June records, one on 2 June 1977 at Houghton Regis ChP and one on 1 June 1980, with an unusual record at Harrold GP

160

on 15 June 1985. Nearly all records at this season have been of singles. The highest number recorded was a party of three at Harrold GP on 9 May 1971.

Autumn passage takes place on a much larger scale than that of spring with the first birds passing through the county as early as the first week of July. Passage begins to build up during the second half of July and becomes quite steady during the first two months of August reaching a peak during the second half of the month. Although flocks are still small, parties of up to five are not infrequent during this period and occasional larger flocks have occurred. A party of 46 passing south-west over Priory CP (Barkers Lane), Bedford on 27 August 1985 was quite exceptional. Passage continues at a steady rate during the first half of September and in most years is complete by the end of the month. There have been only four October records: one at Wyboston GP on 9 October 1966; one at Harrold GP on 1 October 1972; one at Radwell GP on 4 October 1981; and one which remained at Blunham GP from 13 September to 14 December 1975. Apart from this last record there have been only six other records of this species in winter: one in January 1946; one on 27 December 1961; one on 24 February 1962; one on 2 November 1980 (all at Bedford SF); one at Stewartby Lake on 4 November 1984; and one at the same locality on 19 January 1985.

Autumn passage groups of 5+ since 1948 have been:

1954 Up to six at Dunstable SF 13–29 August.
1962 Nine 18–26 August at Bedford SF.
1963 Six at Bedford SF on 26 August.
1974 Eight at Bedford SF on 8 September.
      Seven at Bedford SF 10 September.
1979 Six+ at Harrold GP on 12 August.
1980 Eight at Radwell GP on 24 August.
1981 11+ at Radwell GP on 23 August.
1984 Eight at Brogborough No. 2 ClP on 14 August.
      Eight at Bedford SW on 21 August.
1985 Six at Radwell GP on 18 August.
      17 at Radwell GP on 19 August.
      10 at Radwell GP 21–4 August.
      46 over Priory CP (Barkers Lane GP) on 27 August.
1986 Nine at Chimney Corner ClP on 20 August.

Green Sandpiper

Tringa ochropus

A common passage migrant, more frequent in autumn. Uncommon winter visitor.

This species has occurred in every month of the year and may be encountered in any damp habitat from river banks, ditches and small pools to gravel pits, chalk pits, clay pits, and sewage works. Steele-Elliott (1904) give the status of this species as being 'most regular in its appearance with us' and in autumn frequently appearing in some numbers, together with solitary birds 'not infrequently met with throughout the winter months' – very much the same as it is today. The earliest records were passed on to him by Mr J. King who shot specimens at Langford on 28 August 1853, 1 December 1854, 31 January 1855, 11 September 1857, and 19 December 1860. Other places given are Elstow, Clifton, Shefford, Fenlake, Leagrave, Luton Hoo, Southill Lake, and Newnham where 'upwards of a dozen were about the farm on 6 August 1899' and 15 on 9 August of the same year.

Several records are mentioned by W. B. Alexander (1943–4) and J. A. Miller (1943–4) for the years 1938–43 which indicate that the status as given by Steele-Elliott was still applicable during that period.

Birds on passage may turn up at any suitable habitat such as edges of gravel or clay pits, small ponds, muddy pools, and ditches but sewage farms, particularly those of Bedford and Dunstable, are the most favoured.

Spring passage may begin as early as the first half of March but more usually takes place during the last week of March and the first two weeks of April then declining until the end of the month. It is usually very light, involving mainly singles, but up to five were seen together at Bedford SW on 29 March 1979. In 1951, 1964, and 1966 there were no spring records and in most years reports have been confined to five occurrences or less. In 1982 this species was recorded from six sites during the spring and 10 in autumn. Records in 1983 involved eight sites during the spring and 15 sites in the autumn whilst in the following year it was recorded from 22 sites in all.

Although singles occasionally may be seen during May and June, return passage normally takes place from mid July, becoming a steady passage from the last week of July and reaching a peak during the second half of August. A record of up to nine at Bedford SF in June 1954 was quite unusual. Passage gradually declines and is normally more or less complete by the end of September. Small parties of five or more occur fairly regularly in autumn and in good years much larger numbers are involved. Numbers of 10 or more have occurred at Bedford SW as follows:

1959 22 on 12 August.
1960 10 on 27 August.
1962 12 on 23 July.
      c.14 on 29 August.
1963 25 on 4 August.
1964 11 on 15 August.
1968 15 on 6 August.
1969 11 on 19–21 August.
1970 10 on 26 August.
1971 16 on 21 August.
1974 10 on 8 September.
1980 16 on 21 August.
1982 11 on 14 August.

A few birds, mainly singles, remain to spend the winter in the county but five were present at Bedford SW on 13 November 1978.

Wood Sandpiper

Tringa glareola

An uncommon passage migrant, mainly autumn.

The only record cited by Steele-Elliott (1904) is of a male shot from a pond at Thurleigh in May about 1875 and taken to Mr A. Covington, the taxidermist.

In view of the status given by Steele-Elliott and the subsequent status of this species, a record by J. A. Miller (1943–4) of 'about 20 seen on June 7 1942' at Bedford SF seems very doubtful.

The Wood Sandpiper has been recorded in 37 years between 1946 and 1987. During this period it has occurred on spring passage in 13 years providing a total of 19 records. The only record during the spring involving more than a single bird is of two at South Mills NR on 3 May 1984.

There have been only six occurrences in April, the earliest being one at Dunstable SW on 19 April 1975. Most records have been during the second half of May and the only June records during this period under consideration were at Dunstable SW on 4 and 17 June 1971 and at Harrold CP on 20 June 1987.

The Wood Sandpiper has been recorded in autumn in 30 of the 42 years from 1946. Autumn passage is heavier than spring and may begin as early as July, the earliest being at Bedford SW on 7 July 1962, but more usually takes place during August and early September. Again most records have involved singles but larger parties of two or three may occur at this time. The largest number was a party of seven at Bedford SW on 11 August 1968.

Common Sandpiper

Actitis hypoleucos

A common passage migrant and occasional winter visitor. Has remained during the breeding season with display noted, but breeding has not been proved in recent years.

The Common Sandpiper occurs frequently on passage at any suitable site and may be observed at gravel, sand, and clay pits, sewage farms, and waterways during spring and autumn. Its characteristic bobbing action makes it easily recognisable as it feeds. When flushed it will fly low over the water with very distinctive flight, progressing by flicking its straight wings before a short glide on bowed wings, usually uttering its 'twee-wee-wee' flight note.

Although this species has been recorded on spring passage towards the end of March, the earliest 19 March 1983 and 24 March 1972 (may have been wintering birds), the main passage usually begins during the second or third week of April and continues into May. Numbers in spring rarely exceed five together although up to 10 have been recorded. By mid May passage is more or less complete and just a few birds can be seen to the end of the month. There have been very few records in June, nearly all during the first week. A party of 11 at Stanford GP on 25 June 1958 was most unusual.

The first possible breeding record is recorded in a letter by Mr A. Covington to Steele-Elliott (1904) where he writes: 'I have known the odd bird to occasionally stay with us the summer through at Goldington, and in the neighbourhood of the Biddenham Rapids a pair once remained throughout their nesting period. James, a well-known gamekeeper at that time (a man with a knowledge of bird-life far above the average), first gave me information of the fact, and I frequently saw the birds thereabouts. During July he brought two young birds to me that he had shot to satisfy my incredulity of their having actually nested there; both had down still upon the head and neck.' Unfortunately no date is given but it must have been during the second half of the nineteenth century. Another instance is cited in 1970 when up to three were present during May at Girtford GP and two birds appeared to be paired. Song was heard on several occasions during the first half of May but unfortunately the possibility of attempted breeding was not followed up and thus remains unconfirmed.

The first birds on return passage may be recorded in early July, but more frequently it begins around the middle of the month with the main passage taking place during August and early September when some large flocks may be seen. Numbers then dwindle towards the end of the month with the occasional bird being seen during October.

Maximum autumn counts of Common Sandpipers for the period 1946–87 are:

1963   15 at Bedford SF on 8 August.
1966   15 at Wyboston GP on 1 September.
1968   15 at Bedford SW on 3 August.
1969   15 at Harrold GP on 17 August.
1978   12 at Harrold GP on 10 August.
1980   20 at Radwell GP on 15 August.
1981   15 at Radwell GP on 26 July and 1–2 August.
       16 at Radwell GP on 11 August.
1984   19 at Bedford SW on 20 August.
1986   12 at Radwell GP on 12 August.
1987   12 at Bedford SW on 4 September.

There have been a few winter records as follows:

1926   1 at Woburn on 14 January.

1949 1 at East Hyde 19 November to 18 December.
1961 1 at Bedford SF and Tiddenfoot SP 5 November.
      1 at Linslade 24 December.
1963 1 at Bedford SW on 20 January.
1970 1 at Wyboston GP on 5 December.
1974 1 at Girtford GP on 10 November.
1978 1 on River Ivel at Blunham 1 January.
1983 1 at Stewartby ClP 16–22 January.
1984 1 at Blunham GP on 2 December.

Turnstone

Arenaria interpres

A scarce passage migrant.

The first bird for the county was recorded as recently as 1955 when one was present at Bedford SF 8–10 May. It has occurred on 41 occasions in 24 of the 32 years since that first record but in some cases records may have involved the same birds. Although still scarce it has been recorded more regularly in recent years and between 1971 and 1987 it was recorded in all years except 1975 and 1985.

This species has turned up at sewage farms, gravel pits, clay pits, and chalk pits in the county, showing a slight preference for sewage farms until the early 1970s when modernisation of sewage treatment and the resulting alteration in habitat made them less suitable. Since 1974 all records but one have occurred at gravel or clay pits.

There have been 26 spring occurrences of which seven have been in April, 18 in May, and one in early June. The earliest April record was of one at Stewartby Lake on 20 April 1983.

Of the 17 autumn records only six have been in July, all during the last week, 10 in August, and one in early September. Three-quarters of all records have involved single birds but during the spring passage there have been six records of two birds and four of three. The highest number recorded was in 1961 when a party of five to six was present at Bedford SF 7–10 August.

Wilson's Phalarope

Phalaropus tricolor

A very rare vagrant.

There have been only two county records. A female in summer plumage was present at Stanford GP from 10 to 13 May 1958. This was only the second European record (*British Birds* 52: 385).

The second county record was of one at Bedford SF from 12 to 16 September 1972 (*British Birds* 16: 342).

Red-necked Phalarope

Phalaropus lobatus

A very rare vagrant.

Steele-Elliott (1904) mentions that a female was shot on the glebe pond at Houghton Conquest on 1 June about 1890 and was in the possession of Revd E. W. Boling.

Grey Phalarope

Phalaropus fulicarius

A rare vagrant.

Steele-Elliott (1904) mentions one which was killed from the Elstow Brook on 22 September 1866 and a second which had been killed while swimming about on a farm pond at Beeston on 2 October 1879. One was killed in about 1875 by a keeper at Tempsford. Another was observed about 1885 swimming about on a flooded meadow at Langford by Mr J. King. Davis (1874) mentions that two or more specimens had been killed near Luton but unfortunately no further details are given.

H. W. Finlinson (1928–9) reported one present on 21 October 1928 on 'an artificial lake' in Bedford with 40 Mute Swans but it was not present on the following day.

The only recent records occurred in 1987 when a moulting male was present at Stewartby Lake 21–2 July and, after severe storms, an adult in non-breeding plumage was present at Blunham Lake on 17 and 18 October.

Phalarope

Phalaropus sp.

Two phalaropes were seen at Stewartby ClP on 12–13 September 1969 but adverse weather conditions and distant views prevented specific identification.

Pomarine Skua

Stercorarius pomarinus

A very rare vagrant.

Steele-Elliott (1904) knew of only one record of this seabird in the county, a male which was shot at Ravensden on 18 October 1879 and is now at Bedford Museum.

There has been only one recent occurrence, at Stewartby Lake, when an immature was noted on 14–18 November 1985, briefly appearing at Brogborough Lake on 16 November. Both records coincided with large influxes of skuas along the eastern coastal counties of England.

Arctic Skua

Stercorarius parasiticus

A very rare vagrant.

The only record is of a flock of eight, probably all adults, flying south-west over Willington GP on 23 August 1987 (*Beds Naturalist* 42: 46–7).

Great Skua

Stercorarius skua

A very rare vagrant.

One was caught alive, with a large sea-fishing hook in its throat, by

Mr J. Cole on Bankey Park pond near Leagrave on 11 May 1902 (Steele-Elliott 1904), and is preserved at Bedford Museum.

More recently this species has occurred in three years as follows:

1969   One at Wyboston GP on 14 September.

1984   A single at Stewartby Lake 17–30 November.

1987   Following storm-force westerlies six were found at Brogborough Lake on 16 October declining to two later in the day; two at Stewartby Lake on 16 October remained until 17th; one flew south along the River Ivel near Blunham Lake on 21 October.

Skua

Stercorarius sp.

Due to the difficulties in specifically identifying this genus the following records are worth noting:

1962   One dark-phase bird flew along the River Ouse in Bedford on 11 December.

1968   An Arctic/Pomarine was seen flying south over Bedford on 16 September.

1987   A probable Arctic was at Sandy on 14 August.

Mediterranean Gull

Larus melanocephalus

A very rare, mainly winter visitor.

This species has only recently been recorded in the county and has occurred in four years as follows:

1982   A first-winter at Pirton Hill School playing field, Luton on 6 February.

1984   One at Brogborough ClP on 29 March.

1986   An adult at Luton Hoo on 17 February.

1987   A first-winter at Elstow Tip 6–11 January; an adult at Elstow Tip on 22 January; an adult in full breeding plumage at Houghton Regis ChP on 29 March; a first-winter at South Mills NR on 3, 11, and 13 September.

The Mediterranean Gull's range is expanding in Europe and together with an increasing observer interest in gulls, it is considered likely that it will be recorded regularly in the county in the future.

Little Gull

Larus minutus

Formerly scarce but now a regular, mainly spring and autumn passage migrant.

From the mid 1950s this species has increased markedly as a passage migrant across the wetlands of central and southern England, *en route* to its breeding grounds in the Low Countries and the Baltic states. The apparent increase in records correlates with the emergence of many new reservoirs and mineral lakes across our region, thereby making available suitable habitat for this dainty gull to pause and feed whilst on migration. Little is known of its distribution outside the passage period and breeding season, but the majority are considered to winter at sea along the west coast of Europe and north-west Africa.

The first documented occurrence of the Little Gull in the county was an adult at Bedford SF on 7 May 1942 (Miller 1943–4). This species then went unrecorded until 1957 when two adults and an immature were noted at Stewartby ClP on 28–30 April. From 1957 to 1987 it occurred in 24 out of the 31 years; the blank years being 1958, 1959, 1963, 1964, 1965, 1977, 1979. Prior to 1980 it was generally a scarce passage migrant during the spring and autumn period with usually no more than one to three individuals annually, except in 1967 when up to 16 were recorded. The majority of records were from Stewartby ClP/Lake which was then, significantly, the only substantial expanse of open water in the county. Other occasional records came from gravel and sand pits in the Ivel and Ouzel Valleys respect-

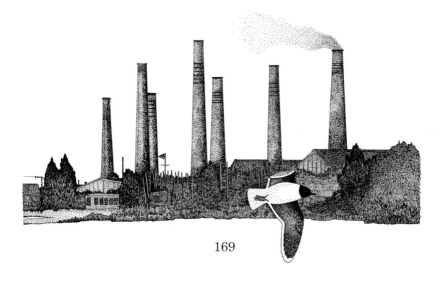

169

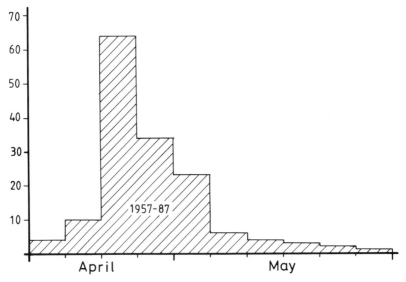

Figure 3.9 *Little Gull: numbers observed on spring passage, 1957–87, using European standard five-day periods, beginning 11–15 April*

ively, and from Dunstable SF, Luton Hoo, and Southill Lake. Between 1980 and 1987 Little Gull sightings increased dramatically to an average of 30 birds annually, predominantly from Stewartby Lake and the adjacent Marston Vale clay pits, but also at Priory CP and to a lesser extent from the Ivel and Ouzel mineral pits. It remains a rarity in the south of the county with singles noted at Dunstable SW on 9 August 1982 and at East Hyde on 18 October 1987 being the only records.

Ten seen together at Priory CP on 27 April 1983 was then the largest flock recorded in the county, until 1987 when unprecedented numbers passed through during the spring. On 22 April 29 were counted at Priory CP, followed by at least 41 at Brogborough Lake

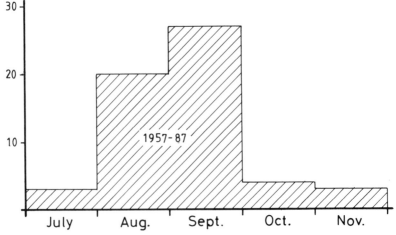

Figure 3.10 *Little Gull: numbers observed on autumn passage, 1957–87, by month*

the same day, the majority of the latter flock remaining until 23 April. In total during 1987 about 150 individuals were recorded in the county; but even this figure is an approximation due to the difficulties of counting birds that are actively migrating. The majority of spring records relate to adult birds in breeding plumage, whereas during the autumn there is a more diverse mixture of juveniles, immatures, and adults.

It is apparent that spring passage (Figure 3.9) is of shorter duration but more intense than in the autumn (Figure 3.10) and may begin about the middle of April reaching a peak during the last week of April and the first week of May, after which a few may pass through until the end of May, but it is then only rarely recorded during June and July. Autumn passage occurs mainly during August and September and is a fairly protracted affair with a slight peak in mid September, but may last until the end of the month. There have been only four October records, three in 1987 and one in 1974. All winter records have been at Stewartby Lake and have involved single birds as follows: 2 November 1982, 9 November and 16 December 1984, and 5 November 1985.

Sabine's Gull

Larus sabini

A very rare vagrant.

This species has a circumpolar breeding range and passes down the western seaboard of Britain during the autumn, sometimes in large numbers as in 1987.

There is only one Bedfordshire record, a second-winter bird at Stewartby Lake on 17 October 1987, which coincided with hundreds more scattered across south-east England in the wake of near hurricane-force westerlies on 15 October (*Beds Naturalist* 42: 48).

Black-headed Gull

Larus ridibundus

An abundant autumn, winter and spring visitor, and recent localised breeding bird (**Map 33**).

Although Steele-Elliott (1904) describes the status of this species as 'perhaps the commonest of the Sea-Gulls that one may so frequently

171

observe as far inland as with us', it was by no means as common as it is today. For example he gives a flock of 16 at Newnham in February 1900 special mention. Another indication of its winter status is given by him when he writes: 'A favourite haunt being the flooded grounds of the Newnham Farm where at times several may be seen together, and not infrequently staying for several days.' During the middle of the nineteenth century there was a marked decline in the Black-headed Gull population in Britain, due mainly to egg collecting and shooting, which led to fears of it becoming extinct as a breeding species. Following this period numbers steadily increased but during the late nineteenth century it was still mainly a winter visitor, departing before summer plumage was attained. Its scarcity during the summer caused Steele-Elliott to comment: 'I have notes of two in perfect plumage being seen at Newnham on 21st May 1898 and a single bird that I observed on three successive days, 6–8th August 1899; and again a party of four were together on 31st July 1900.'

Its status as mainly a winter visitor continued until the early 1950s when increasingly it was noted to summer in small numbers at several localities. This led to the discovery of the first recorded breeding colony in Bedfordshire at Dunstable SF in the spring of 1955. On 29 May two nests were located, each containing one egg, but at a later date the colony was found to be composed of 11 nests with eggs and one without eggs. The nests were in clumps of twitch grass and contained a maximum of three eggs per nest which hatched in early June followed by a successful fledging in mid July. Due to subsequent modernisation work at Dunstable SF breeding did not take place again. In 1956 a colony of 10 nests was discovered at Stewartby ClP increasing to over 100 nests in 1957 with attempted nesting at Coronation ClP the same year.

Conditions which are ideal for nest sites occur in the Marston Vale soon after the clay pits have been worked out, when shallow pools and islands are present. However, water soon permeates into the pits and as the water level rises the islands eventually become submerged. This occurred at Stewartby ClP in 1962 when the islands were washed away, thus removing any potential nesting sites. Often the pits have been deliberately flooded for reasons of safety or to provide suitable open water for recreation, resulting in frequent changes in the locations of breeding colonies. Suitable nesting sites have continued to be available, mainly in the clay pit areas, but at no time has the county breeding total exceeded c.500 pairs. Harding (1979) recorded this species in 11 (3%) tetrads, with possible breeding in five tetrads and confirmed breeding in six tetrads. During the 1980s small colonies of less than 100 pairs each have been recorded at Millbrook ClP, Chimney Corner ClP, Coronation ClP, Rookery ClP, and Brogborough No. 2 ClP.

In the early 1950s some of the gravel pits which had been excavated during the Second World War, such as Willington, became exhausted and were then used for dumping domestic refuse. These and other rubbish tips provided an ideal food source which attracted increasing numbers of Black-headed Gulls to feed. About 200 were observed feeding at Willington and a smaller number at Luton refuse tip in February 1951, increasing to c.500 at the latter site in March 1953.

From the late 1950s the increase in the extraction of clay resulted in more clay pits, providing safe roosting, and later, as some were filled with refuse, feeding places. By 1958 *c*.1,000 Black-headed Gulls roosted at Stewartby during the early months of the year, steadily increasing to 6–7,000 in 1961, 15,000 in 1967, and reaching a peak of 38,000 in 1968. Accurate counts were made in 1973 and 1983, as part of a BTO Gull Survey, when 22,500 and 27,000 were present respectively. Unfortunately there is no accurate data for the mid 1980s but many thousands of this species roost and feed at Brogborough, Stewartby, and Elstow Lakes, and adjacent refuse tips. Elsewhere in Bedfordshire during the winter months this highly adaptable gull can be encountered almost anywhere from town parks and gardens to arable farmland. There seems to be a constant interchange in roost sites, as surrounding counties also offer safe open sheets of water. A steady stream of birds can be witnessed following the southern chalk escarpment, towards Tring Reservoirs, Hertfordshire and likewise there is a daily movement along the Ivel and Ouse valleys towards Grafham Water, Cambridgeshire.

The number remaining within the county during the summer months is fairly low until late June and July when there is a small but significant increase due to birds arriving from the Low Countries. A classic example of this movement, extracted from ringing data, was in 1978 when an immature was found dead at Wrest Park on 21 July having been ringed as a pullus on 15 June at Reeuwyk, Zuid, Netherlands. Low numbers are recorded in August: Gladwin and Sage (1986) considered that the decline in August is due to a change in diet from domestic refuse to invertebrates gathered from fields which have been recently ploughed after the harvest. During September there is a fairly rapid build-up of birds arriving from north-east Europe. Depending upon the weather conditions a peak is usually reached in January. The main return passage occurs during March and continues into early April.

Of the 12 ringing recoveries of Black-headed Gulls in Bedfordshire all relate to birds which have been ringed in Fenno-Scandia, the Baltic region, and the Low Countries. One ringed at Espoo, Finland on 21 April 1984 was recovered at Stewartby on 25 January 1986 having moved 1,789km west-south-west. Of the remaining recovery records three originated from Poland, two from Norway, five from the Netherlands, and one from Belgium.

Common Gull

Larus canus

A common winter visitor and passage migrant.

Steele-Elliott (1904) commented 'It does not seem to appear in the county with any regularity in the spring or autumn as several other of the Gull family. . . . hence their visits seem more particularly in the nature of winter records, and at this season evidently under conditions of stormy weather only.' In the south of the county it was then so scarce that when one, which had been killed at Barton in the winter of 1900–1, was received by Mr J. Cole, a Luton taxidermist, he remarked that it was the only one of this species he had seen that had been obtained locally.

H. A. S. Key (1947) noted that 'During the severe weather of the early months of the year many gulls passed over the county, often along the valley of the river Ouse where Black-headed Gulls were commonly seen and with them a number of Common Gulls.' Even so in 1948 the Common Gull was recorded on only three occasions and in 1949 only once. In 1952 several were noted feeding at a Luton rubbish tip in February and A. R. Jenkins (1955) wrote of this species, 'It appears in small numbers during the winter months on fields around Arlesey.' From the mid 1950s numbers steadily increased at the Bedford clay pits and in 1961 a roost of 1,250–1,500 had become established at Stewartby Lake with 2,500–2,800 birds present in January 1973. Quantitative data on this species as a winter visitor throughout the 1970s and 1980s is non-existent, probably because it is now so commonly seen that it is seldom reported to the county bird recorder. At present large numbers are known to occur during the winter period at Stewartby, Brogborough, and Elstow land-fill sites and associated roosting lakes. Elsewhere it can be encountered on its preferred feeding habitat, open grassland, particularly where livestock are grazed, but even in town parks and on playing fields where it feeds mainly on earthworms.

A. R. Jenkins (*op. cit.*) was the first to document the migration of the Common Gull in the county when he noted approximately 400 at Streatley on 10 April 1954. On 24 April 56 were counted in an open field. The following year Jenkins observed 150–200 Common Gulls in a field near the Hertfordshire border rise and fly off in a north-easterly direction and commented: 'This is the first time I have been able to observe the actual migration of this species on such a scale inland since I began making notes nearly 20 years ago.' After this date increasing numbers were noted on passage during March and April, especially in the south of the county where birds following the line of the Chiltern Hills enter the county at Whipsnade, pass north-east through the Pegsdon Hills and on into Hertfordshire and Cambridgeshire. Due to intensive fieldwork during the 1980s at Blows Downs this species is particularly noticeable from mid March to mid April when parties of up to 200 can occur.

The autumn passage is less dynamic with birds generally starting to arrive from late September onwards. During the summer months the population is scarce, with just the occasional individual or small group in non-breeding plumage summering at the Bedford clay pits. The majority of our birds originate from the Baltic region and one found dead on 26 June 1964 at Cardington had been ringed as a nestling on 10 July 1960 at Lake Kohaja, Pueta, Estonia, USSR.

Lesser Black-backed Gull

Larus fuscus

An abundant passage migrant, a common winter visitor and occasional rare breeder (**Map 34**).

The status of this species has changed somewhat since when Steele-Elliott (1904) knew of it as primarily a passage migrant. Today it is also commonly recorded during the winter months, particularly at the county's waste disposal tips in the Marston Vale. From 1946 to 1956 there were very few winter records until the expansion of earthworkings for the brick industry provided safe roosting areas and a constant supply of food from adjacent refuse tips. Numbers began to increase and in November 1961 500–600 were counted at roost on Stewartby Lake. There has been a steady build-up of birds since the early 1960s, and although there is little accurate data available it is probable that well over 1,000 individuals regularly winter in and around the Bedford Basin, primarily at Stewartby, Brogborough, and Elstow, with smaller numbers at Sundon waste disposal site and along the county's river valleys.

As a passage migrant the Lesser Black-backed Gull is a far more widespread species within the county; although the complexities of these movements are not fully understood. In general migration usually begins in mid June and lasts into November, comprising mainly birds of the western race *L. f. graellsii*, which breeds in Britain and parts of the near continent, some of which eventually winter as far south-west as the Iberian Peninsula and along the coast of north-west Africa. This movement is partially corroborated by Bedfordshire's two recoveries of birds ringed in the Netherlands as nestlings as follows: one ringed at Groede on 11 July 1983 was recovered at Stewartby on 12 July 1984; one ringed at Maasvlakle on 9 June 1985 was recovered at Melchbourne on 22 August 1985. During the autumn passage period 'dark mantled' birds of the nominate race *L. f. fuscus* from northern Scandinavia have been known to visit the county in small but increasing numbers from the early 1950s. Documentation of these records is further complicated when it became apparent during the mid 1980s that birds of the intermediate race, *L. f. intermedius*, from southern Scandinavia, are also occurring in the county and may even be quite common during the winter. Unfortunately there is little detailed information on the movements of these sub-species.

The first recorded flocks of any appreciable size were 52 at Luton on 6 October 1958, and in 1960 30 at Barkers Lane GP on 27 July, 60 on 10 August, and c.100 on 30 October. Passage was again noted at Barkers Lane GP in the autumn of 1961 when flocks of c.250 were seen on 31 August increasing to c.500 6–13 September. Good numbers continued to be recorded on autumn passage with localities such as Dunstable SF attracting c.600 in October 1969 and c.800 on 25 October 1974. At Brogborough ClP 2 June 1984 was an early date for a large concentration of 600 and, typically, comprised mainly immature birds which predominate in the autumn. On 18 October 1984 c.500 were at the gull roost on Stewartby Lake and c.1,000 at Brogborough Lake.

Return passage is noted throughout the Bedford clay pits from mid February to the end of May, and can be particularly noticeable along the chalk downlands at Dunstable where a steady stream of birds is often recorded heading north-east along the Chiltern escarpment. Elsewhere in the county, where visible migration is not as obvious, birds can be found resting on farmland or on parks and open spaces in built-up areas. There seem to be fewer individuals relating to the Scandinavian races involved in the spring movements of this species, probably as a result of the British race being more numerous and therefore more apparent at this time of year. This is probably due to a slight shift northwards of its winter range, rather than any alternative migratory route in the Scandinavian sub-species. As a result of the constant migratory interchange of this species there is rarely a month when it is not now present in Bedfordshire.

The deep excavation quarries in the Marston Vale have proved to be attractive breeding sites for the commoner Black-headed Gull, especially just after clay extraction has ceased, and also to the Lesser Black-backed Gull in limited numbers. On 30 May 1966 a pair was seen displaying at Brogborough ClP and in 1968 three pairs bred, constituting the first breeding record of this species in the county. In 1970 two pairs held territory at Chimney Corner ClP followed by a pair that nested in 1971. Seven pairs bred at Brogborough ClP in 1973 but only managed to raise one young, followed by suspected breeding in 1974 and 1975. A nest was occupied at Brogborough ClP in May 1977 but there were no further records until two pairs bred at Coronation ClP in 1987. During the 1968–77 fieldwork for the Breeding Bird Survey (Harding 1979), possible breeding was recorded from three tetrads outside the Bedford clay pits, at Harrold and Odell GP in the Ouse valley and at Heath and Reach. Inland breeding records of the Lesser Black-backed Gull in England are quite unusual, particularly in the southern half of the country.

Herring Gull

Larus argentatus

A common winter visitor and regular passage migrant (**Map 35**).

This highly vocal and aggressive gull is a familiar bird along the English coastline, where it has adapted particularly well to man-made environments, utilising buildings as nest sites and feeding on human waste. To Steele-Elliott (1904) this species was primarily known as a passage migrant through the county. It was regularly recorded along the Ouse Valley in small groups in Spring and Autumn, the majority being immature birds, with greater numbers passing through in August and September and only the occasional records of solitary birds throughout the winter months.

Due to an absence of records for 1904–46 it is not possible to assess whether or not its status has changed, although as Gladwin and Sage (1986) categorised the Herring Gull as a rare bird in Hertfordshire prior to 1930 it seems reasonable to assume that this also applied to Bedfordshire. During the late 1940s it was still scarce, with a party of 11 at Bedford SF on 9 February 1947 worthy of note. In the hard winter of that year up to four were seen feeding in gardens at Flitwick following heavy snow falls.

The first major increase in numbers occurred in 1949 when *c*.25 were observed at a Luton rubbish tip on 10–30 December, increasing to *c*.100 by 1 January 1950, which was regarded as 'a remarkable number'. Approximately 400 were present at the same tip in Luton on 7 February 1951, and refuse being used to infill Willington GP attracted 50 on 25 February. Numbers continued to increase and in December 1960 *c*.1,000 were reported from Barkers Lane GP. In January 1961 a roost of *c*.3,500 was established at Stewartby ClP and *c*.3,000 were present in November. Numbers at the Stewartby roost remained at about this level until 1968 when *c*.3,000 were counted at Stewartby on 9 March, but after this numbers declined to a maximum of 1,215 on 22 January 1983, as recorded by the BTO Gull Survey. A similar decline was noted in neighbouring Hertfordshire about this time and the closure of nearby waste tips was put forward as a possible reason (Gladwin and Sage 1986). However this seems unlikely in the case of Bedfordshire birds as the tipping of domestic refuse in the county has, if anything, increased. As with other members of the gull family, birds feeding on the clay-pit tips during the day roost mainly at Stewartby and Brogborough Lakes, where they are joined by birds feeding away from the Marston Vale or outside the county.

As a passage migrant there is little quantifiable data on this species in Bedfordshire and all that can be said is that it migrates through the county during April and May and August to September, although it is rarely recorded at Blows Downs and along the chalk escarpment during April. Between May and August it is very scarce with only occasional, mainly non-breeding birds present at the Bedford clay pits. Gladwin and Sage (1986) noted that numbers on spring passage in

Hertfordshire now outnumber those on autumn passage. Whether or not this is true of Bedfordshire's Herring Gulls is uncertain. An increase in sightings during October 1987 was as a result of gale-force westerly winds.

The Herring Gull would seem an unlikely candidate as a breeding species in the county but at Brogborough ClP in 1971 a pair successfully raised young, followed by suspected breeding at the same locality in 1974 when a pair was observed mating. Breeding again occurred in 1977 when an occupied nest was found in May at Brogborough ClP, though whether this was successful is not recorded. In 1978 a pair was observed displaying on 9 April without any subsequent breeding. Harding (1979) considered breeding possible at two sand pits near Heath and Reach and at Wyboston GP in the Ivel Valley. There has been no more local attempt at breeding by this species since 1978 of what is a very rare event in inland England.

As with the previous species, the taxonomy of the Herring Gull is confused and uncertain, but in 1982 10–30 'dark mantled' types that were regularly attracted to Deepdale refuse tip showed the typical features of the nominate race *L. a. argentatus* from Fenno-Scandia. In 1983 *c*.200 birds at Elstow Tip were mainly large dark types, and were almost as big as Great Black-backed Gulls. Further identification and distribution studies need to be carried out on these various forms which could be further complicated by the northwards expansion of the yellow-legged Mediterranean race, *L. a. michahellis*, which was first recorded in Bedfordshire as recently as 13 October 1987 at Brogborough Lake.

Iceland Gull

Larus glaucoides

A very rare winter visitor.

This rare visitor from the sub-Arctic region of eastern Greenland has occurred in Bedfordshire on only three occasions during the period 1946–87:

1962 A second-winter bird at Bedford SF on 18 March.
1985 A bird in first-winter plumage was at Brogborough Tip and Lake 16–30 November.
1987 A first-winter bird was seen at Elstow Tip on 5–6 January.

All the forecasts are that, with the increase in suitable wintering conditions for gulls in the Marston Vale, this high Arctic species will continue to be recorded in the county.

Plate 5 (*Top*) Dunlin (Dunstable SW). Regularly noted throughout the
summer months. © *Bill Drayton*
(*Bottom*) Redshank's nest (Houghton Regis ChP, May 1984).
© *Paul Trodd*

Plate 6 (*Top*) Common Sandpiper (Dunstable SW). A common passage migrant. © *Bill Drayton*
(*Bottom*) Turnstone (Brogborough No. 2 ClP, May 1984). An irregular passage migrant © *Andy Tomczynski*

Glaucous Gull

Larus hyperboreus

Formerly a very rare winter visitor which now appears annually.

This species has a far wider circumpolar breeding range than the previous polar gull and breeds as close as Iceland, although the origins of birds visiting eastern England are unclear. From the first two Bedfordshire sightings in the 1970s the Glaucous Gull has been recorded annually from 1983 involving a total of approximately 20 individuals. This recent dramatic increase in records is probably due to a greater awareness by observers, coupled with suitable feeding and roosting sites at the Bedford clay-pit tips and lakes. The majority of records occur between December and March with extreme dates on 19 November and 15 April. A most unseasonal record was one at Stewartby Lake on 25 August 1987.

This species has occurred in the county from 1972 as follows:

1972 One adult at Harrold GP on 19 November.

1974 An adult at Biggleswade on 1 December.

1983 A first-winter bird seen flying over Priory CP on 19 November was relocated the following day at Elstow Tip.

1984 A first-winter bird stayed in the Brogborough area 14–25 February with a different one at Stewartby Lake on 30 March. A first-winter bird was present at Stewartby Lake on 2 November.

1985 A first-winter and a third-winter plumaged bird were at Brogborough Lake on 12 January followed by many reports of a first-winter bird, possibly a different individual, in the Brogborough/Stewartby area from 13 January to 20 February and also at Elstow ClP on 22 February and Vicarage Farm ClP on 13 March. A bird in second-winter plumage was noted at Stewartby and Brogborough Lakes 22–6 January.

1986 A first-winter at Houghton Regis ChP and Sundon Tip on 5 and 11 January respectively followed by a single over Blunham on 12 January. A third-winter bird was seen at Stewartby Lake on 10 January and a second-summer plumaged bird was noted there on 15 April.

1987 An adult at Brogborough Lake on 14 January was seen at Stewartby Lake the next day. Similarly a first-winter bird at Elstow Tip on 14 January was probably the same bird seen going to roost at Stewartby Lake on 25 January. An adult in breeding plumage was at Stewartby Lake on 25 August. At Brogborough Lake an adult was seen on 13, 28, and 31 December with two first-winters on 30th and one on 31st, totalling three individuals in all.

179

Totals of Glaucous Gulls by calendar month observed in Bedfordshire 1972–87:

Aug.	Sep.	Oct.	Nov.	Dec.	Jan.	Feb.	Mar.	Apr.
1	0	0	3	4	9	3	2	1

As with the previous species, the Marston Vale seems set to harbour increasing numbers of this Arctic gull.

Great Black-backed Gull

Larus marinus

A regular winter visitor and passage migrant.

This large, powerful species of gull breeds mainly around the western coastline of Britain and is absent as a breeding bird down the east coast of England. The British population is predominantly sedentary and most of the wintering individuals in eastern England originate from Norway.

It was described by Steele-Elliott (1904) as 'very rare'. He quoted an adult shot at Hockliffe in the spring of 1849, and three which were received by Mr A. Covington the Bedford taxidermist, the last of which was shot near the New Cut at Goldington in the winter of 1892–3.

Between 1946 and 1960 this species was still a rare winter visitor to the county with no more than four being seen together and no more than five records during any winter.

In early 1960 there was a slight increase in the winter population when c.10 were seen regularly at Stewartby Lake during January and February and this increased to c.20–30 in early 1961. There were few records after this until 1967 when c.100 were seen at Elstow ClP on 10 January 1967. A further increase occurred in 1973 when c.200 were present at Brogborough Tip on 16 December and numbers have fluctuated between 100 and 200 since then. The Great Black-backed Gull remains relatively scarce in the county, being attracted to the larger clay-pit lakes and refuse tips during the winter months. It is rarely recorded in the summer, but a few are noted on spring and autumn passage.

Kittiwake

Rissa tridactyla

A mainly uncommon winter visitor and passage migrant.

The Kittiwake is a common breeding seabird around the coastline of Britain where it nests predominantly in large, noisy cliff-face colonies. Outside the breeding season it is highly oceanic and disperses into the North Atlantic from where it is occasionally 'wrecked' inland in large numbers following winter storms.

It is interesting to note that Steele-Elliott (1904) describes the status of the Kittiwake in Bedfordshire as 'Almost as plentiful a species locally as the Black-headed Gull, not particularly noticeable during any migrating season of the year, but appearing freely from November until the following February. It generally occurs inland in the wake of every storm that beats upon our coasts'. The comparison with the status of the Black-headed Gull is more a reflection of that species than of the Kittiwake, as the Black-headed Gull was not a common bird inland during the nineteenth century.

The status of the Kittiwake is similar today to that of Steele-Elliott's time, though it also appears during the spring: and in his day, reports normally involve solitary birds. It usually occurs at the larger clay-pit or gravel-pit lakes and may occasionally be seen in fields in company with Black-headed Gulls. As birds are often blown inland by severe gales some are found dead, moribund, or in an exhausted condition.

The Kittiwake has been recorded in 20 years from 1946 to 1987 on 46 occasions involving c.210 individuals. It occurs throughout the year but is mainly reported during the winter months of January and February and on passage in March, April, and May. Immature birds are more frequently seen during the autumn and winter periods whilst adults are noted more often on spring passage. Of the 46 occasions during the study period, 38 have involved single birds, two birds have been recorded together on five occasions, and three birds only once. Large flocks have been observed on three occasions: on 6 January 1981 a flock of at least 42 was seen at Blunham GP and later the same year a flock of 16 adults was noted at Stewartby Lake following severe north-easterly gales. The latter movement was part of a large influx of seabirds into central and southern England, as documented by Nightingale and Sharrock (1982). On 27 April 1985, during a similar period of strong north-easterlies a flock of c.100 Kittiwakes was observed over Priory CP being blown in a south-westerly direction during a snowstorm! Again the flock was composed mainly of adults. It appears that the main passage of birds returning to their breeding grounds along the east coast occurs during the last week of April and any prolonged period of north-easterlies at this time is likely to blow large numbers deep into central England.

Total occurrences of Kittiwakes by calendar month in Bedfordshire from 1946–87:

Jan.	Feb.	Mar.	Apr.	May	Jun.	Jul.	Aug.	Sep.	Oct.	Nov.	Dec.
5	6	7	11	6	2	1	2	1	1	2	2

Caspian Tern

Sterna caspia

A very rare vagrant.

This near cosmopolitan, but everywhere localised, species breeds closest to us along the Baltic coastline and is recorded almost annually in East Anglia and southern England when on migration (Dymond *et al.* 1989).

There is only one Bedfordshire record, at Harrold GP on 18 July 1976 (*British Birds* 70: 427).

Sandwich Tern

Sterna sandvicensis

A scarce passage migrant.

The nearest breeding colonies to Bedfordshire of this large, vocal tern are among the East Anglian coastal dunes of North Norfolk at Scolt Head and Blakeney Point. Birds on overland passage in eastern England are probably bound for this area, or further east across the North Sea to the Baltic region. Autumn migrants will be *en route* to wintering grounds along the Ivory Coast and south along the western seaboard of southern Africa.

The Sandwich Tern was first recorded in the county in 1967 when two were present at Wyboston GP on 8 July followed by 'one or two', there on 23 July. Coincidentally these first sightings occurred at a time when the breeding population in Britain had reached a peak (Lloyd *et al.* 1975). From 1967 to 1987 it was recorded in 12 years, being annual from 1981 and involving *c.*68 individuals. April is the peak month during the spring with August and September the most favoured during the autumn period. First and last dates were singles at Houghton Regis ChP and Grovebury Farm SP on 4 April and 20 September 1987 respectively. The majority of records are of single birds, and all refer to birds which have only remained for one day and in many cases for just a few hours. Apart from the first two birds in 1967, multiple sightings are as follows: Stewartby Lake, two on 9 September 1982; Priory CP, two on 19 September 1982; Radwell GP, eight on 28 April 1984; Priory CP, two on 20 August, 1984; Harrold CP, two on 7 April 1985; Stewartby Lake, two on 7 June 1985; South Mills NR, three on 26 April 1987. On 22 August 1987 an unprecedented flock of 29 immatures was recorded at Priory CP for five minutes before moving off south-east.

The majority of records have come from the Ouse Valley gravel pits at Wyboston, Harrold, Radwell, and Bedford, and from Stewartby Lake in the Marston Vale. Elsewhere there has been one occurrence each in the Ivel Valley at South Mills NR, in the Ouzel Valley at Grovebury Farm SP, and in the south of the county at Houghton Regis ChP.

Totals of Sandwich Tern by calendar month observed in Bedfordshire 1967–87:

Apr.	May	Jun.	Jul.	Aug.	Sep.
18	2	4	4	32	8

Common Tern

Sterna hirundo

A common passage migrant and regular but localised breeding species (**Map 36**).

It must be remembered that during Steele-Elliott's time the Common Tern and Arctic Tern could not readily be distinguished in the field and thus most of the definite records of these species are of those which were either shot or picked up dead. Even so it seems that the Common Tern was noted fairly regularly, usually singly and occasionally in small parties, as it passed through the county along the Rivers Ouse and Ivel on spring and autumn passage. Mr A. Covington writing to Steele-Elliott (1904) in the late nineteenth century says, 'When I was living in St. Paul's Square I remember seeing a Tern during the whole of one bright August afternoon circling around the spire of that church. The following morning I saw a company of seven Terns, and they remained in the vicinity for more than a week, two being shot near the Old Common.' Again in a letter Mr J. King writes, 'I have frequently seen the Sea-Swallow along the Ivel down my meadows here, but of course it is impossible for anyone to say which species they were, this or the Arctic Tern. I remember shooting a Tern as late as 23rd September in 1858.'

The status of the Common Tern as a regular passage migrant in small numbers appears to have continued until 1963 when for the first time in Bedfordshire a pair nested at Wyboston GP, successfully rearing three young. A pair bred there again in 1964, then as follows: two pairs in 1965, three in 1966, six in 1967, five in 1968, 10 in 1969 (all nests were robbed), five in 1970, four in 1971, three in 1972, two in 1973, and one in 1974. Wyboston GP was flooded in 1974 thus reducing the number of available nesting sites and eventually destroying the colonies, although possible breeding was noted in 1975, before one pair finally bred successfully in 1978. Subsequently this species has bred or attempted to breed annually elsewhere along the chain of gravel pits in the Ouse valley at Harrold, Radwell, Barkers Lane, Bedford, Great Barford, Roxton, and Tempsford. Currently Harrold GP and Radwell GP attract a small number of breeding pairs. Similar conditions exist in the Ivel Valley where breeding has occurred at Blunham GP and Sandy GP in 1973, Girtford GPs in 1981 and 1982, with attempted nesting at South Mills NR in 1986 and 1987. In the Ouzel Valley possible breeding occurred at Grovebury Farm SP in 1982, 1983, and 1984 and was confirmed in 1987 when a pair hatched three young from a nest on an artificial nesting platform.

Away from the river valleys breeding was suspected at Vicarage Farm ClP in the Marston Vale clay pits in 1973 and 1974 followed by subsequent breeding at Stewartby Lake in 1978, Brogborough No. 2 ClP in 1984 and 1987, Rookery ClP in 1985–7, and Millbrook ClP in 1987.

At all localities the nest is on an island where a hollow is scratched out to receive the clutch of typically three eggs which are laid in late May. Following a 20–8 day incubation period the young fledge after a further four weeks.

The breeding status of the Common Tern in the county is dependent upon suitable breeding sites. As most gravel or clay pits are flooded or filled after mineral extraction and as islands become overgrown the number of breeding pairs will continue to fluctuate. It is regrettable that no action has been taken to preserve a suitable area to allow a colony to become established, or to create floating islands as in neighbouring counties, so that a bird so typical of the county's wetlands may remain with us as a breeding species (Figure 3.11).

As a summer migrant it is a far more widespread species. Spring passage commences in mid April, peaking towards the end of the month and lasting until late May. Numbers consist mainly of small parties of less than 10 birds although the following larger numbers are of note: 58 at Stewartby Lake on 25 April 1980; 22 at Stewartby Lake on 5 May 1984; 30 at Priory CP on 5 June 1983 and 23 May 1985; and 20 at Radwell GP on 28 April 1986. The autumn movement is more protracted and lasts from late July to late September with

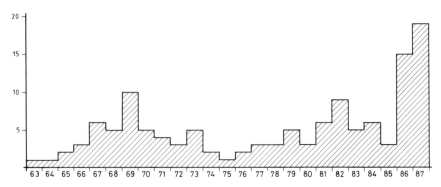

Figure 3.11 *Common Tern: annual totals of breeding pairs recorded, 1963–87*

occasional October records. Flocks of 10–20 are often noted at Stewartby Lake during this period and the highest autumn counts were 40 at Radwell GP on 20 July 1987 and 36 at Barkers Lane GP on 21 August 1980. The earliest recorded migrant was at Priory CP on 4 April 1985 with the latest passage birds on 26 October at Priory CP and Stewartby Lake in 1985 and 1984 respectively.

The Common Tern winters chiefly along the coast of tropical west Africa, where a nestling ringed at Wyboston GP on 20 August 1967 was found dead on 11 December 1967 at Abidjan on the Ivory Coast.

Arctic Tern

Sterna paradisaea

A regular, predominantly spring, passage migrant, occasionally in large numbers after gales.

The status of this species has, until recently, been uncertain due to the difficulties of identifying Common and Arctic Terns in the field. This problem prompted Steele-Elliott (1904) to write, 'It is owing to the impossibility of distinguishing these two terns upon the wing – even at close quarters – that observation only upon such must remain unsatisfactory as to their proportionate numbers with us, and that again also, even if procured, so few people would know the distinguishing features of this and the Common Tern'. The taxidermist, Mr A. Covington, writing to Steele-Elliott says, 'Once I remember I had five brought in during one week, shot near the Common Bridge over the river just above Bedford. I believe it was in August, 1866. In later years it appears more rarely than I think it used to do. The last I set up was one from Bletsoe, 19th September 1894.' Steele-Elliott also mentions one being picked up dead out of the Ouse at Clapham in May 1893 and one being killed at Luton Hoo in May 1899. Lord Lilford (1895) mentions an adult shot near Sharnbrook in August 1885.

An overall analysis of the modern records since 1946 reveals, on average, a slightly later passage during the spring for the Arctic Tern compared with the Common Tern. It normally involves parties of three or less during the last week of April and the first week of May but when north-easterly gales occur numbers can be substantially larger. The most likely localities for recording this species are the open aspect clay-pit lakes at Brogborough and Stewartby and along the River Ouse gravel-pit lakes, notably at Priory CP near Bedford, where the earliest spring migrant was noted on 11 April 1983.

The number of Arctic Terns occurring in the county on return passage is normally much smaller than in spring and takes place over a longer period with records from the end of June to the end of September and rarely into October. In many years it has not been seen at all during this period. The latest record was one at Stewartby Lake on 26 October 1984.

From 1946 to 1979 this species was recorded on passage in small numbers in 10 years, with the exception of 22–7 April 1974 when a remarkable movement of at least 64 birds was recorded at Blunham GP. The increase in the number of records since the beginning of the 1980s is in great part due to better-known identification criteria, along with much improved optical aids and a vast increase in the number of observers. This is partly borne out by the corresponding decline in 'Commic' Tern records during the 1980s.

From 1980 the Arctic Tern has occurred annually with the following high counts of note:

1980 40 at Dunstable SW on 3 May with 30+ at Radwell GP the same day.

1981 30 on 4 May at Stewartby Lake.

1985 A remarkable influx took place involving exceptionally large numbers at Stewartby Lake and Priory CP as follows:

	Stewartby Lake	Priory CP
25 April	17	–
27 April	6	2
28 April	183	8
29 April	50–60	126
30 April	3	4
2 May	14	15
3 May	–	84
4 May	31	–
5 May	45	20
7 May	–	3
8 May	7	–

Common/Arctic Tern

Sterna hirundo/paradisaea

As has already been mentioned it is sometimes very difficult to determine the composition of mixed flocks of these two terns, resulting in the popular name of 'Commic' Tern. Many more Commic Terns were recorded prior to the mid 1970s when optical equipment was less sophisticated, but since the advent of the modern telescope positive identification has much improved.

Probably the majority of these records were of the Common Tern, especially during the autumn when Arctics are quite scarce. Two large flocks have been noted at Stewartby Lake, 32 on 28 April 1981 and 35 on 29 April 1982, although the majority of occurrences are of single birds or groups of less than 15. Two early records came from Bedford on 11 March 1967 and 24 March 1965 and a late straggler was noted at Stewartby Lake on 5 November 1962.

Little Tern

Sterna albifrons

A scarce, predominantly spring, passage migrant.

It is difficult to know whether this species passed through the county in greater numbers during the time of Steele-Elliott (1904) than today. It might be expected that as it nested more frequently around the East Anglian coast then, it may well have been a more regular visitor, but as the number of man-made lakes during that period was very few and their size very small it probably passed through without staying for any length of time.

Before 1900 it was certainly very scarce and Mr A. Covington could only remember five specimens being brought to him in 37 years experience as a taxidermist. These specimens were obtained from Fenlake, Willington, and Harrold and were all 'taken' on spring migration. In addition two were shot near Willington Church in June about 1865 and Mr R. J. Cawse shot one on the River Ivel at Biggleswade in 1883. Steele-Elliott observed one on 11 May 1899 in a flooded field at Newnham Farm.

From 1947 to 1987 the Little Tern has occurred in 15 years involving approximately 42 individuals and has been noted annually from 1982. The majority of records have come from Stewartby Lake and Priory CP with further sightings at Kempston Hardwick ClP, Wyboston GP, and Harrold CP. A single at Grovebury Farm SP on 6 June 1982 was the only record for the Ouzel Valley and at Dunstable SW one was noted on 23 May 1983. Probably the most remarkable record of this species in the county, and the only occurrence away from the wetlands, was a party of three over Blows Downs on 6 May 1986. The largest group ever noted were 10 at Felmersham GP on 17 May 1948. There has been one party of four birds at Kempston Hardwick ClP on 23 May 1947 and two double bird sightings at Stewartby Lake on 22 May and Priory CP on 17 July in 1984.

As in Steele-Elliott's day most birds occur on spring migration, with 32 of the 42 individuals seen in May, with the earliest atWyboston GP on 20 April 1958. Autumn records are rare and a single at Stewartby Lake on 7 September 1987 was the latest recorded bird. On only one occasion, at Stewartby Lake on 12–13 August 1983, has this species been known to stay for more than one day.

Totals of Little Terns by calendar month observed in Bedfordshire 1946–87:

Apr.	May	Jun.	Jul.	Aug.	Sep.
2	32	3	2	2	1

Black Tern

Chlidonias niger

A regular spring and autumn passage migrant, occasionally in large flocks.

During the early part of the nineteenth century the Black Tern was a regular breeding bird in the Fenlands of East Anglia. According to Lilford (1895) it was known to nest at Whittlesea Mere, until about 1843, approximately 30km from the northern borders of the county. During this era it must have been fairly abundant along our river valleys in spring and autumn. Mr A. Covington, a Bedford taxidermist, in correspondence with Steele-Elliott (1904) wrote, 'I might add, that I have been assured by old sportsmen, that not only used Redshanks to nest in our marshy meadows in company with Lapwing, but also a few pairs of Black Sea Swallows.' However by the turn of the century Steele-Elliott knew of this species only as a fairly common passage migrant, although he considered it to have declined in numbers probably as a result of human persecution. It was regularly recorded along the rivers Ouse and Ivel, from where there were numerous references of its demise on spring and autumn passage. Flocks of 30 and 32 were recorded on the River Ouse in May 1870 and at Newnham SF in August 1896 respectively. Elsewhere in the county it was noted at Woburn Park and Luton Hoo.

Passage migrants continued to be noted at Woburn Park, with entries in *British Birds* from 1910 and 1911, and at Bedford SF in 1942. A. R. Jenkins (1958) recorded one shot at Stondon on 30 April 1914, eight over Arlesey Pit on 9 May 1934, and one at Arlesey Pit on 2–8 October 1938.

As the Black Tern occurs at wetland localities, which are well watched by birdwatchers, this species has fortunately been one of the best recorded passage migrants in the county. From 1946 to 1987, there was only one year, 1955, when it was not recorded and, as with many other species, throughout the 1980s, due to the growth in observer coverage there has been a quite staggering increase in records.

The earliest migrant was at Felmersham GP on 12 April 1947 but the main spring passage (Figure 3.12) begins towards the end of April and continues throughout May with a peak in mid-month. Passage is lighter during the first half of June with only stragglers noted towards the end of the month. Before the expansion of the clay pits in the Marston Vale the majority of records were from the river valley gravel pits along the Ouse and Ivel, and also at Bedford and Dunstable Sewage Farms, prior to modernisation. Although passage is still recorded along the river valleys, particularly at Priory CP, more recently the clay pits at Stewartby and Brogborough have attracted the majority of birds. It is rarely noted in the south of the county at Dunstable SW, Houghton Regis ChP, and Luton Hoo. Black Terns normally arrive singly or in small parties of up to 10. The following

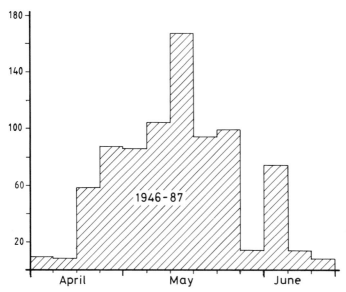

Figure 3.12   *Black Tern: numbers observed on spring passage, 1946–87, using European standard five-day periods, beginning 11–15 April*

double figure counts have been noted during the spring: 10 at Felmersham GP on 30 April, 1952; 18 at Bedford SF on 9 May, 1954; 17 at Barkers Lane GP on 12 May, 1954; 36 at Stewartby Lake ClP on 2 May, 1958; 15 at Houghton Regis ChP and 13 at Arlesey ChP on 24 May, 1959; 40+ at Stewartby ClP on 13 May, 1961; 12 at Stewartby Lake on 12 May, 1965; 24 at Vicarage Farm ClP on 4 May and 10 on 18 May, 1970; 10 at Stewartby Lake on 25 May, 1971; 16 at Brogborough Lake on 15 May, 1977; 14 at Brogborough Lake on 13 May, 1979; 11 at Priory CP on 25 April, and 10 on 6 May 1983; 30 at Brogborough Lake on 28 April 1987; and 10 at Harrold CP on 29 April 1987.

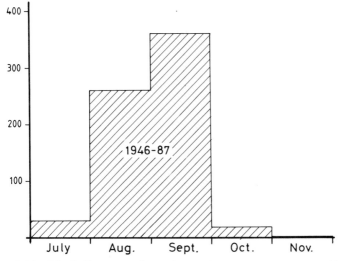

Figure 3.13   *Black Tern: numbers observed on autumn passage, 1946–87, by month*

189

The autumn passage (Figure 3.13) is more protracted and lasts from late July to early October with a peak in August and September. Although never as intense as the May passage, birds tend to stay longer, and sites such as Stewartby Lake often have periods of continuous presence from mid August to mid September. There have been two November records, both at Stewartby Lake on 5 November 1984 and 10 November 1976. The following double figure flocks have been recorded during the autumn at Stewartby Lake: 13 on 22 September 1957; 11 on 29 August to 3 September 1967; 11 on 22 August 1968; 11 on 16 August 1970; 10 on 12 August 1972; 10 on 4 August and 15 on 15 September 1974; 10 on 10 September 1981; 12 on 23 September 1983; 51 on 30 August 1985; 18 on 14 August 1986; and 18 on 25 August 1987. Elsewhere in the county 12 were at Harrold GP on 4 September 1977 followed by 14 at Barkers Lane GP/Priory CP on 16 September 1980 with 20 on 19 September 1987, when 21 were also noted at Dunstable SW.

White-winged Black Tern

Chlidonias leucopterus

A very rare vagrant.

This elegant marsh tern occurs annually in very small numbers in southern and eastern England during the spring and autumn whilst on migration to and from its breeding grounds in eastern Europe and central Asia. It winters mainly in tropical Africa, southern Asia and Australia. There have been only three Bedfordshire records as follows:

1961   An adult in breeding plumage at Stewartby Lake on 16–17 May coincided with others around the country (*British Birds* 55: 575).

1967   An adult in non-breeding plumage at Stewartby Lake on 28 and 29 August and 2 and 4 September (*British Birds* 61: 344).

1983   A juvenile at Stewartby Lake on 10–12 August (*British Birds* 78: 561).

Guillemot

Uria aalge

A very rare storm-blown vagrant.

Although the Guillemot is an abundant breeding species around the British coastline it is seldom seen inland, even after strong gales. Steele-Elliott (1904) referred to one at Renhold on 26 November 1893 and others at Sharnbrook and Goldington. An old specimen was passed to Mr A. Covington 'some years ago that had been shot close to Milton Mill', and there were two more records from that locality, one in November 1893 and an adult in 1894.

The only record this century was one picked up moribund at Pulloxhill on 15 September 1973, which died the same day.

Razorbill

Alca torda

A very rare storm-blown vagrant.

The rarest of the auks to have occurred in the county and known to Steele-Elliott (1904) from an old stuffed specimen bought at a local sale by Mr A. Covington. On the rear of the case was a label, 'Razorbill from Fenlake'.

There is only one subsequent record, of a corpse found at Stewartby Lake on 23 February 1983 which had been dead for about a week and coincided with other storm-blown birds driven inland by strong north-easterly gales.

Little Auk

Alle alle

A very rare storm-blown vagrant.

Steele-Elliott (1904) considered there to be 'many instances of this little arctic visitor being storm driven into our county.' Davis (1874) refers to four in the Luton area 'in the last thirty years' and gives details of one found at Barton in January 1870. The other known records are listed below:

1861–2   One picked up near Bedford during the winter.
1878   A single recovered after severe gales on 8 December on allotments at Husbourne Crawley (the *Field*).
1882   One killed at Turvey on 22 November 1882 (the *Field*).
1894   One picked up dead on 21 November near Colmworth Woods.

1895 One received by Luton taxidermist Mr T. Cane, from Cad-
     dington in the last week of January.
     One picked up moribund on 2 February in Haynes Park is a
     part of the Steele-Elliott collection housed at Bedford
     Museum.
1901 A male recovered near Hangers Wood, Stagsden on 19 Feb-
     ruary.
1950 One found dying on the Luton–Markyate Road on 11 Feb-
     ruary.
1983 A 'wreck' of five 9–22 February: one at Luton on 9th died
     later; one at Keysoe on 9th, was later released alive; one
     at Potton on 16th, released alive; singles at Flitwick and
     Greenfield were both found dead on 22nd.

Puffin

Fratercula arctica

A rare storm-blown vagrant.

As with the previous species, Steele-Elliott (1904) describes instances
from Mr A. Covington who received several specimens towards the
end of the nineteenth century from Clapham Wood, Castle Mills,
Willington, Turvey, Harrold, and Kempston, the last in March 1901.
One record of particular interest was a leucistic individual recovered
at Girtford in the autumn of 1880, described by him as 'a uniform
cream-coloured specimen.' Other occurrences were recorded by Steele-
Elliott in Tingrith Park in November 1893, and a female at Park
Farm, Marston on 5 January 1895, followed by 'a male in the same
parish two or three days later.' The Duchess of Bedford (1925–6a)
recorded the following note: 'The remains of a young Puffin which
had been partially eaten by rats were found at Woburn Lake on 23
September 1925. The weather had been very strong.'
     Since 1946 the Puffin has occurred in six years, more so than any
other species of auk:

1953 One recovered at Moggerhanger Sanatorium in early Febru-
     ary died later.
1954 An immature at Honeydon on 28 December.
1964 One picked up alive on 7 July at Goldington Power Station.
1974 A juvenile picked up at Leighton Buzzard on 17 September
     was released at Heath and Reach SP on 18th but died on
     22nd.
1979 An immature found at Millbrook on 15 February died on
     20th. One picked up in a garden at Cotton End, also on 15
     February, was released on the coast, along with another two
     found walking along the A5140 between Wootton and
     Kempston on 17 February. An immature picked up alive at

192

Roxton Park on 18 February was also successfully released on the coast.

1983   One found dead at Woburn on 17 February had been ringed at Sule Skerry, Orkney on 28 July 1982.

Pallas's Sandgrouse

Syrrhaptes paradoxus

A very rare vagrant.

This central Palearctic sandgrouse is native to the Steppes of the Aral–Caspian region of the USSR, and eastwards to north-west Manchuria. It is an irruptive species and in the great invasion of May 1888 'many honoured us with their presence', as documented by Steele-Elliott (1904). A flock of about 14 stayed for three weeks in May 1888 at Cople with records of 18 at Goldington and Ravensden probably relating to the Cople group. Other birds were reported from Cranfield and Kempston; at the latter locality one was taken alive on 3 July and subsequently released. One was picked up dead at Thurleigh on 11 June and another was killed in the Luton area during the same year. Steele-Elliott considered these records to be an incomplete picture of their occurrence in the county during 1888, and Hine (1934) referred to many being shot in 1863 and 1888 in the Hitchin region.

Feral Pigeon

Columba livia

A very common resident.

This descendant of the Rock Dove may be observed in most town centres and large villages. The plumages are very variable due to hybridisation between different forms of racing pigeons, those from dovecotes, and collections. A large flock of several hundreds used to roost in Goldington power station after it ceased to be used until its demolition during the late 1980s. The droppings of town centre populations have had a deleterious effect on buildings and some, such as those at Bedford, have been controlled.

Stock Dove

Columba oenas

A fairly common resident (**Map 37**).

Confined to the south and east of England at the beginning of the nineteenth century the Stock Dove has expanded its range greatly since then. By the end of the nineteenth century Steele-Elliott (1904) gave its status as 'Fairly abundant and resident, but slightly decreasing rather than increasing in numbers'.

A species of arable land, open parks, woodland, and semi-rural areas, it has been overlooked in recent years possibly due to it resembling the feral pigeon at a distance. As a consequence changes in status noted in neighbouring counties, such as that caused by pesticides during the late 1950s and 1960s, have gone unrecorded in Bedfordshire. Flocks begin to form from early August but only attain any size in the winter, with 300–400 at Turvey on 7 January 1984, and a flock of 100–50 at Luton Hoo from 1965, which increased sharply in 1986 to 500 by 5 December but had declined to 200 by early January 1987.

This species now has a rather patchy breeding distribution throughout the county, being absent from some quite large areas of what would appear to be suitable habitat. It normally nests in trees and buildings but has also been recorded breeding in crevices of the chalk faces of some disused chalk quarries. Harding (1979) showed that breeding was confirmed in 58 of the county's 371 tetrads, was probable in 48, and thought possible in 105.

Woodpigeon

Columba palumbus

A very common resident (**Map 38**).

The increase in this species seems to be related to the development of more modern methods of agriculture during the nineteenth century.

Plate 7 (*Top*) Kittiwake (Barkers Lane GP, Bedford, 18 April 1982). An uncommon winter visitor and passage migrant. © *Andy Tomczynski* (*Bottom*) Woodpigeon. A common bird of town and countryside.
© *Bill Drayton*

Plate 8 (*Top*)   Cuckoo, juvenile (Dunstable SW).   © *Bill Drayton*
(*Bottom*)   Snow Bunting (Blows Downs, January 1987).

© *Paul Trodd*

By 1904 Steele-Elliott gives its status as being a common resident, 'considered by many to be far too common – causing damage to grain and pea crops during the summer and to root crops in the winter'.

Despite the attempts by farmers to control this species it is still a considerable pest. It is common and widespread throughout the whole of the county occurring in woods, parks, hedgerows, and larger gardens. Large cold-weather movements take place in hard winters. Mr J. King, in a letter to Steele-Elliott (1904) wrote, 'I must tell you of the amazing flight of Ring Doves we have observed this winter [1895]. It was from the 5th to the 8th of December that, not thousands, but hundreds of thousands, were passing over, going from NE to SW. . . . They were passing each morning from daylight until ten or eleven o'clock.' A similar movement took place during the hard winter of 1962–3. After severe frosts in November and December 7,000 moved south over Bedford on 11 November and more than 14,000 flew north-north-west in just over one hour on 23 December with smaller flocks of up to 4,000 moving in the same direction during the following four days. On 8 January 1963 flocks totalling 6,000 passed east over Bedford and during the same month vast flocks devastated brussels fields in the Shefford and Biggleswade area in order to keep alive. In 1967 a flock feeding on brussels near Howbury Hall, Bedford, was estimated to be more than 10,000.

Harding (1979) showed that it occurred in all 371 tetrads during the breeding season and was confirmed breeding in 234 (63%), thought probable in 76 (20%), and possible in 61 (17%).

Collared Dove

Streptopelia decaocto

A common resident (**Map 39**).

Although this species first appeared in Britain in 1955 it was not until 9 August 1961 that a bird at Stagsden provided the first county record. There were no records in 1962 but in the following year singles were seen at Sandy on 10 and 31 January. A notable increase took place in 1964 with birds being recorded from Leagrave, Willington, Bushmead Priory, and three sites in Bedford. Spilt grain at Jordan's grain silo in Mile Road, Bedford, attracted up to 13 in December. The increase was then quite rapid with up to 50 observed at Dunstable in 1966, and it was reported as 'widespread' in the county by 1967. By 1971 SP93 was the only 10km square with no records. Larger flocks were seen from the early 1970s with 44 at Dunstable SW in 1973, 150 at Sewell, and 250 on the outskirts of Dunstable in December 1974. Feeding flocks of 50–100 were recorded fairly regularly whilst winter roosts at Blows Downs, County Hall (Bedford), Dunstable Downs, Stewartby, Warden Hills, and Wootton Green became regular features in the 1980s. The largest and most regular roost has been at Well

Head, Totternhoe which contained maxima of 360 in November 1981, 80 in 1982, 120 in 1983, 250 in 1984, 300 in 1985, and 110 in 1986.

The first breeding record in the county was at Bushmead Priory in 1964 and by 1977 it had been recorded in 68 of the county's 371 tetrads, was thought probable in 71, and possible in 94 (Harding 1979). It was unrecorded in 37% of the county, showing a tendency to avoid large areas of open country and a preference for sites near human habitation such as farm buildings, parks, villages, and large gardens.

Turtle Dove

Streptopelia turtur

A fairly common summer visitor and passage migrant (**Map 40**).

Steele-Elliott (1904) gives its status at that time as increasing year by year after having been a scarce breeder in the previous 20 years. At the beginning of this century he says that it was 'by no means an uncommon incident to find it breeding in any neighbourhood' with it nesting very commonly in the small plantations between Wootton and Marston, and in Moggerhangar Grove. Flocks of about 30 were noted by him feeding in a field at Notting on 17 May 1899 and similar sized flocks were observed feeding amongst stubble and in clover and turnip fields during the autumn.

The Turtle Dove usually arrives from mid April onwards, usually towards the end of the month, but the earliest record is of one at Sandy on 5 April 1973. It occurs throughout most of the county in agricultural areas where there are trees and hedges, woodland edges, parks, and large gardens but avoids areas of high density building and even agricultural areas which are devoid of trees. Harding (1979) recorded it as a common breeding bird with breeding confirmed in 88 of the 371 tetrads, probable in 120, and possible in a further 81. Until recent years large post-breeding flocks used to form during July and August with flocks of c.100 at Pegsdon during July 1951 and 1953. Similar flocks were a feature at Wyboston GP from 1964 to 1967 and c.100 were observed at Shelton in June 1978.

There have been no large flocks recorded since that date. This reflects a decline in the breeding population in the 1980s. After recording 30 pairs in a CBC census plot at Old Warden in 1975, B. J. Nightingale noted a decline to 16 pairs in 1981, 15 in 1982, five in 1983, five in 1984, four in 1986 and two in 1987. Although there have been fluctuations in previous decades this recent decline may be more permanent. It might be related to a combination of factors such as the change from hay crop to silage involving earlier and multiple mowings which limit seeding by grassland herbs, and the increased use of herbicides and fertilisers on grasslands, both of which reduce plant diversity. The impact (if any) on our breeding population of the annual massacre of Turtle Doves which takes place as they move across Europe on their spring and autumn migrations is not known.

Ring-necked Parakeet

Psittacula krameri

A rare visitor, feral in origin.

This noisy green parrot was added to the British List in 1983 as a category C species after escapes and deliberately released birds established feral but self-maintaining breeding populations, particularly in south-east England.

Before this time little attention was paid to them and the first published county records are of singles over Luton in April 1978 and Streatley in June. Four took up residence in the Harlington area in June of that year with three remaining until the end of the following year, after one was found dead in March. In 1980 this population again increased to four but had declined to two when last observed at the end of November.

Other records during this period were of singles over Kempston on 18 November 1979, one by the River Ouse a mile from Bedford centre on 1 December, and a pair present in the Risely area from September to the end of the year. In 1980 evidence was received of two having been released from an aviary in Luton and, apart from the Harlington birds, two were seen feeding on a bird table in Toddington in January and singles were seen in March and July in Kempston.

There have been 13 other records as follows:

1981 One at Wardown Park Luton on 11 August.
1982 One at Harrold CP on 9 September.
      One at Priory CP on 8 and 11 September.
1983 One at Houghton Regis ChP from 31 July through most of August.
      Two over Tebworth in December.
      One over Tempsford in December.
1984 One near Pulloxhill from mid to end May.
      One joined a Starling roost at Totternhoe from early August to mid September.
1985 One at Pavenham on 23 July.
1986 Two at Houghton Regis on 22 December.
1987 One over Cotton End on 26 October.
      One over Chicksands Wood on 26 October (possibly the same as the Cotton End bird).
      One at The Lodge, Sandy, on 4 December.

Cuckoo

Cuculus canorus

A common summer visitor (**Map 41**).

This well-known summer visitor from Africa usually arrives in the county during the third week of April, the earliest record being of one at Whipsnade on 7 April 1955. The only dates to rival this are 8 April 1894 at Kempston and 9 April 1895 at Langford. Many birds depart in July and early August with only a very few remaining into September, rarely until the third week. The latest was a record of one at Wrest Park on 7 October 1951.

Unfortunately the great interest shown in the arrival date of this species and its association with the beginning of spring has resulted in little else being recorded. It is difficult to assess whether there has been any change in its status as it has always been recorded as being common throughout the county. It is apparent that the spread of urbanisation has resulted in some reductions whilst the removal of hedgerows may have reduced the availability of potential host species in agricultural areas. To counterbalance this, the recent development of marginal vegetation around the county's man-made lakes and consequent increase in some Reed and Sedge Warbler populations, both host species, has resulted in local increases, with up to six birds being observed at one time in such places as Harrold CP and Priory CP. This shift is reflected by the observations of host species feeding young Cuckoos. Between 1961 and 1977 the Dunnock (Hedge Sparrow) was reported most frequently as the host species with Meadow Pipit and Pied Wagtail also being recorded. Since 1977 the Reed Warbler has been the only host species reported. The prevalence of egg collecting during the nineteenth and early twentieth centuries enabled Steele-Elliott (1904) to give perhaps a more accurate assessment of that period: 'More freely the Hedge Sparrow's is chosen to that of any other bird . . . Following in commonness to the Hedge Sparrow the nests selected by the Cuckoo are those of the Robin, Pied Wagtail, Reed and Sedge Warblers.' He also gives instances of Cuckoos' eggs being found in the nests of the Willow Warbler, Greenfinch, Chaffinch, Chiffchaff, and Yellowhammer, and he observed a young Cuckoo being fed by a pair of Whinchats at Roxton.

Harding (1979) showed that breeding took place in 51 out of the 371 tetrads, was probable in 151, and possible in a further 59, although the difficulty of proving breeding must be taken into account. The species was well distributed throughout the south of the county but there were some surprising gaps in the north.

Barn Owl

Tyto alba

A rare resident (**Map 42**).

Even by the end of the nineteenth century Steele-Elliott (1904) indicated that the population of the Barn Owl had begun to decline. He attributed this to the more healthy state of farming in former years, when more barns were required to store grain, and to their being more valued by farmers when 'in the construction of the barns an "Owl hole" would frequently be left at the top corner of the gable end to allow the Barn Owls an entrance, so that they could do their welcome share of keeping in check the Rats and Mice.' Even so, despite this possible cause of decline and the shooting of Barn Owls by keepers, it was, by recent standards, a common bird with at least one pair of Barn Owls breeding in the vicinity of most of the villages in the county, and was found never far from the habitation of man. They nested in old timbered parks such as those at Ampthill, Bromham, Silsoe, Warden, and Woburn whilst ivy-covered buildings, barns, church belfries, and the gable ends of houses provided other sites in which 'the snorings of the young awaiting their food in the evening cannot fail to attract the attention of the passer-by'. A pair even nested in a decayed tree along the Cardington Road, Bedford, despite the constant traffic. In January 1894 a pied variety was shot at Harrold, the tail and the whole of the wing feathers being pure white.

The species continued to decline during the early part of this century and by 1945 had become quite rare in some areas. An increase was noted in 1946 and H. A. S. Key, the county recorder, wrote that 'After many years of comparative absence the White Breasted Barn Owl is now being seen regularly and is fairly well distributed as a breeding species'. This state of affairs continued until the mid 1950s but in 1967 there were only six reports in the county. Although this did not give a true picture, it did alert observers to the scarcity of the species. Harding (1979) revealed that it bred in only 19 of the 371 tetrads during this period, with breeding possible in a further eleven. In 1983

The Hawk Trust estimated the county population to be 20 pairs whilst in 1987 it is probably no more than 15 pairs.

There have been few ringing recoveries of this species, most being recovered within a few miles and in the same year as they were ringed. Two recoveries indicate longer movements: one ringed in south Lancashire in July 1974 was recovered in Bedford in November of the same year having moved 234km south-east and one ringed on the Isle of Wight in June 1977 was recovered in Bedford nine months later having travelled a distance of 176km north-north-east.

[Eagle Owl]

[*Bubo bubo*]

Davis (1874) mentions 'one shot some three years ago near Harpenden' and says that it was kept in the possession of Mr Cane, of Luton. Presumably this bird found its way into the collection of Mr G. P. Cane and is now in Bedford Museum. This specimen is not mentioned by Steele-Elliott (1904) and much doubt must exist about its authenticity.

Little Owl

Athene noctua

A fairly common but widely distributed resident (**Map 43**).

Davis (1855) gives the status of this species as rare and mentions in the 1874 edition that the last recorded specimen taken near Luton was in 1838. Steele-Elliott (1904) mentions that one was caught alive at Woburn in 1862 and kept alive for three months before it escaped.

Witherby and Ticehurst (1907–8) say that the bird was first discovered breeding at Lilford, Northamptonshire, in 1889 but for several years Lord Lilford had made a practice of liberating Little Owls in various parts of his grounds. From 1889 the birds appear to have multiplied in a remarkable way.

By 1892 Lord Lilford recorded how the bird had spread to Woburn in the south-west of Bedfordshire and the keepers there said that it existed prior to this date. This indicates that the Woburn birds must have come from Lord Lilford's introduction and not from Tring, where birds were introduced at a later date. There is no truth in the idea, prevalent in the early years of this century, that imported birds were introduced at Woburn. By 1909 the Duchess of Bedford reported that there were a great many of them at Woburn. It was seen at Chawston in the north-east of the county in 1894 and apparently made a stronghold in that neighbourhood. By 1899 it was more generally distributed throughout the county and had reached Luton by 1900. In 1901 it was reported breeding in Great Barford and Southill and by 1907 Steele-Elliott (*Zoologist* 1907) estimated its numbers in the county at between 200 and 300 pairs, being at that time the commonest owl in the county and its population still increasing. Whiteman in the Hexton parish survey (1936) stated that it was common around Hexton.

The status of this species seemed to stabilise during subsequent years to common and widespread in suitable localities – 'the easiest owl to see in Bedfordshire' (BHNS 1979). Harding (1979) confirmed this species as breeding in 55 tetrads, probable in 18, and possible in 80.

One ringed at Turvey on 28 June 1914 was recovered at Sharnbrook on 22 May 1918, having moved 9km in four years. This must be one of the earliest ringing recoveries. A bird ringed at Cardington in June 1983 was recovered in July 1987 in Essex (63km south-east). Most other recoveries have been local and within two years of being ringed.

Tawny Owl

Strix aluco

A widespread fairly common resident (**Map 44**).

Davis (1855) gives its status as common around Luton but in 1903 Steele-Elliott found it to be far less so saying that it was 'by no means so common a species with us as the Barn Owl'. He implied that the reduction in numbers was due to the activities of gamekeepers who considered that they ate young game birds.

By 1950 it was widespread and the BNHS bird report 1967 gave its status as 'distributed plentifully throughout the county'. This was confirmed in 1976 when the increase in the nocturnal activities of the county's birdwatchers taking part in a Nightingale survey resulted in it being recorded in at least 50 localities. By 1986 it was still the most abundant owl, being noted in many woodlands as well as urban and suburban areas with mature trees such as town parks, cemeteries, and large gardens. The obligation of local authorities to remove any damaged trees or those with cavities which might be a danger in public areas, reduces the availability of possible breeding sites in potentially suitable habitat. The erection of nest boxes in Bedford has had a limited success with three out of 21 boxes being occupied in 1987. Two of these were in rural areas and one in the urban fringe.

Harding (1979) showed that breeding was confirmed in 69 of the county's 371 tetrads, was probable in 80, and possible in a further 64. Nine of the 10 recoveries of birds ringed in the county have been controlled or found dead within a few kilometres of where they were ringed. Two other recoveries are of birds ringed in Hertfordshire and recovered a few kilometres inside the Bedfordshire county boundary. One exception to this was of a bird ringed at Whipsnade in May 1985 and recovered in Ettington, Warwickshire in March 1987, having moved 77km west-north-west. In view of this site tenacity it is therefore probable that the birds recorded as 'probable' or 'possible' breeders during the survey did breed locally.

Long-eared Owl

Asio otus

A rare resident and scarce winter visitor (**Map 45**).

Steele-Elliott (1904) found this bird to be locally distributed and particularly associated with fir and spruce plantations where it was to be found breeding. It was not rare in the fir woods of Warden, Southill, Clophill, Ampthill, Flitwick, Aspley, and Woburn. He considered that it was probably as common in similar habitats in the north of the county where it was frequently shot in many localities.

A great decline took place during the following 40 years and in 1948 a diligent search throughout the county failed to reveal any at all. This state of affairs continued in 1949 and 1950.

A pair bred in the Flitwick area in 1945 and a nest containing three young was found in the Flitwick/Millbrook area in May 1951 but breeding was not proved again until 1968 when a pair produced four young at Sandy. There have been seven further breeding records as follows: one in SP93 in 1972; an injured juvenile was found at Millbrook in 1981; one pair bred in TL13 in 1984 and again in 1986; two pairs bred in TL14 and one pair reared three young in TL13 in 1987.

Adult Long-eared Owls tend to roost near to their breeding haunts but in some years birds arrive from northern Europe, occasionally in large numbers, following crashes in the populations of small rodents on their continental breeding grounds. This was well illustrated during the first winter period of 1976 when 15 roosted in the Tempsford area and 12 near Dunton. Five were observed roosting on Dunstable Downs in the following year and this roost has occasionally been utilised on subsequent occasions. Other roosts of smaller numbers have been recorded from other areas in the south and east of the county. A roost at Priory CP contained up to three birds during the first winter period in 1987. There is no doubt that this scarce species is under-recorded both as a wintering and breeding bird. There has been an increasing tendency for eager birdwatchers to visit both breeding and roosting sites, thus endangering the very tenuous hold which this species has in the county. Recent signs of a more sensitive attitude by some birdwatchers may help to ensure that this bird continues to occur in the county. It would be a pity if the activities of a few, merely in order to tick it off on an annual list, jeopardised the future of the Long-eared Owl.

Short-eared Owl

Asio flammeus

A fairly regular, but scarce, winter visitor. Has bred.

Steele-Elliott (1904) recorded the status of the Short-eared Owl as being a fairly regular winter visitor, 'by no means rare'. Their habit of frequenting open fields to roost resulted in many of them being shot and during his time they were commonly found at the local taxidermists. A party of nine or ten was recorded during mid November 1894 at Cople by a party out shooting Partridges. They occurred regularly at Langford where the earliest specimen was shot on 17 October 1878 and the latest on 3 April 1895.

Although this species has been recorded wintering in every year since 1960, except 1969, it has been an uncommon, but regular, winter visitor occurring in rough areas around clay and gravel pits, on old airfields, arable farmland and the chalk downland in the south of the county, particularly Warden and Pegsdon Hills. The Vauxhall test-track at Millbrook has been utilised regularly in recent years. Most are reported from early December to the end of March but the earliest can arrive in October and may remain until the end of April. Nearly all records are of four birds or less, more usually one or two, but six were at Coronation Pit in December 1982 and up to eight in the Pegsdon Hills area in 1987. The number arriving from the continent varies from year to year with at least 26 being recorded from 17 localities in 1979 but, apart from 1969 when there were no records, there have been five years with only one record.

In 1949 the first and only proven record of breeding took place at a locality on the Greensand Ridge (probably Millbrook), when five to six young were hatched. A pair was present at the site in the middle of the county in 1976 and almost certainly bred.

Nightjar

Caprimulgus europaeus

A rare summer visitor (**Map 46**).

At the end of the nineteenth century Steele-Elliott (1904) noted that this was a decreasing species in most of its haunts. However it was still far more numerous than it is now. He knew of it nesting at Aspley Woods, the fir plantations at Sandy, especially Sandy Warren, Ampthill, Clophill, Maulden, and fairly commonly in many of the fir woods around Leighton Buzzard. He writes of it as being far less plentiful at Warden, Southill, and Rowney Warrens than it was formerly and of having been known to breed at Flitwick and Turvey and probably in Odell and Clapham Woods. Mr A. Covington told him of an instance of eggs once being found in a field of standing beans at Milton whilst at Rowney Warren Mr J. King found as many as five or six nesting pairs in a day's ramble over this area and was 'kind enough' to present several clutches of eggs to Steele-Elliott. Davis (1855) gave the status of this species as being scarce around Luton whilst in the 1874 edition he describes it as being a 'regular visitant to Luton Park and other open spaces'. R. L. Hine (1934) records it as being fairly certain to be heard calling on Pegsdon Hills and apparently nesting on chalk areas where it was once commonplace.

After the breeding season there are undated records from Bolnhurst, Great Barford, Clapham, and Shefford. A very late immature bird was shot from some turnips at Biddenham in early October 1900.

This summer visitor has been recorded in the county as early as 20 April (1948) but usually does not arrive until mid May, during which time it may be recorded at any suitable site. An unusual record was of a party of 12 on 11 May 1953 between Flitwick and Eversholt. It is rarely observed after the first week in August, the latest record in recent times being of one at Warden Warren on 12 August 1980.

In recent years it has declined greatly as a breeding bird with the main stronghold being the Greensand Ridge. Between 1940 and 1970

TABLE 3.8 *Summering records of the Nightjar, 1974–84*

	74	75	76	77	78	79	80	81	82	83	84
Chicksands Wood	x	x	x	x	x	x		x			
Charle Wood	x	x			x						
Gastlings								x			
Keepers Warren							x	x			
The Lodge, Sandy				x							
Maulden Wood	x	x									
Old Warden	x					x		x			
Tingrith Wood			x								
Warden Warren	x		x	x	x	x					
Warden Wood		x									
Wavendon Heath											x

it was proved to have bred at Aspley Heath (1956, several pairs), Clophill (1956), Maulden Woods (1956), Rowney Warren (1956, at least three pairs, 1958, at least three pairs, 1962, 1967), Sandy Lodge (1963, 1965, at least four pairs, 1967), Tingrith (1960), Woburn Sands area (1958, at least seven pairs). Pairs were also present during this period at Luton Hoo, Wavendon Heath, and Heath and Reach with an estimated 10–20 pairs in TL14 in 1968. In 1974 seven pairs were present in the county during the breeding season and the county population remained at about this level until 1980 when summering was known from only one site. A slight recovery took place in 1981 but the following year was the worst on record with only two sightings. A pair observed feeding young at Wavendon Heath in 1984 was the only record for that year whilst in the following year none was recorded for the first time in memory. Summering occurred again in 1986 but there was only one record during 1987.

Swift

Apus apus

A common summer visitor and passage migrant (**Map 47**).

Recorded as a common summer migrant by Davis (1855) this continued to be the state of affairs when Steele-Elliott wrote about this species in 1904. At that time he noted the 'Devilin', as it was called by country folk, breeding in Bedford, particularly in the older parts of the town, whilst also inhabiting the more ancient of the county's villages.

C. M. Prior writing in the *Field* (1877) mentions that numbers of this species, having perished during a spell of cold weather, were found by masons in May of that year, whilst Steele-Elliott noted that especially cold windy weather resulted in a total absence of birds seen on the wing.

During the last 50 years the Swift has remained a common summer visitor, usually arriving during the last week of April and first week of May and staying with us until most birds depart during mid August to early September. The earliest arrivals were in 1961 and 1981 when the first birds were observed on 12 April. It is possible to see late birds towards the end of September but October records are uncommon, the latest being one on 29 October 1948.

The older parts of towns and old villages provide the main breeding sites with most of the breeding records occurring in the south and east of the county and around Bedford, reflecting the distribution of built-up areas. The design of modern buildings does not provide suitable places for breeding and although there has been little demolition of old buildings in recent years due to the need for housing, the addition of new roofs has, in some cases, removed suitable sites. Old churches are frequently used and about 20 pairs nested under the eaves of St Andrew's Church at Langford in 1987. Harding (1979) confirmed breeding in 74 of the county's 371 tetrads (20%).

Large feeding parties may gather over open water areas in cold or wet weather. Numbers of 500 or more have been seen regularly at places such as Stewartby Lake, Radwell GP, and Dunstable SW. Larger numbers noted elsewhere were 1,500 at Chalk Hill on 26 July 1978 and 5,000 south over The Lodge, Sandy on 7 July 1980.

Kingfisher

Alcedo atthis

A fairly common bird in suitablè habitat but subject to rapid fluctuations in population due to its susceptibility to hard winters (**Map 48**).

Both Davis (1874) and Steele-Elliott (1904) described this species as being a common or fairly common bird in the county. The status of the Kingfisher has remained about the same during the last 150 years, possibly being less frequent during the eighteenth and nineteenth centuries due to its persecution by man. Now, as then, its population is subject to marked fluctuations as a result of extreme winters which have on occasion caused its near extermination in the county. In such times ice over water cuts off its food supply and birds may die of starvation or move to seek the open waters of the coast. After these depletions in its population it is fortunately able to make a fairly rapid recovery due to it having two, sometimes three, broods in a year.

Steele-Elliott (1904) records it as being seen at Kempston, Newnham (Bedford), Cardington, Great Barford, and Langford. Its distribution follows closely the rivers Great Ouse, Ouzel, Ivel, Flit, and Lea, whilst also occurring at the complex of clay-pit lakes around Stewartby and Brogborough. Declines in population were noted during the severe winters of 1962–3 and 1981–2 but good recoveries were made after each. Although the Kingfisher is a noisy bird during the breeding season it is difficult to find its nest as it often utilises the quieter reaches of the river systems and the first signs of breeding are often the sightings of parties of young. Harding (1979) confirmed breeding in 23 tetrads, thought it probable in 15, and possible in 43.

The young disperse soon after fledging, and outside the breeding season birds have frequently been seen in Bedford near the Town Bridge, in gardens of Luton and Bedford, and occasionally in woods well away from any suitable habitat.

Areas where the Kingfisher has been seen are as follows: Arlesey, Bedford SF, Blunham (bred), Biggleswade Common, Brogborough Lake, Bromham Mill, Cardington, Chalton SF, Clapham (bred), Cople (bred), Dunstable SW, East Hyde (bred), Eaton Socon, Eversholt Lake, Felmersham NR (bred), Flitwick Moor (bred), Grange Mill (Heath and Reach, bred), Great Barford (bred), Harlington, Harrold GP (bred), Howbury Hall, Kempston (bred), Langford GP (bred), Leagrave, Linslade, Luton Hoo Park, Luton SF, Oakley, Odell, Priory CP (bred), Radwell GP, Renhold, Rowney Warren (bred), Roxton, Sandy (bred), South Mills NR (bred), Southill Lake, Stewartby Lake (bred), Woburn (bred), Wrest Park (bred), Wyboston GP (bred).

There have been seven ringing recoveries, six within 15km of where they were ringed. Nearly all birds were found dead, five within three months of being ringed. One found dead at Willington on 23 July 1985 had been ringed in September of the previous year at Hounslow, Middlesex, having travelled 76km north.

Bee-eater

Merops sp.

A very rare vagrant.

One was present at Manor Farm, Upper Stondon on the afternoon of 4 September 1971 (*British Birds* 65: 339).

Hoopoe

Upupa epops

A rare passage migrant.

All the records mentioned by Steele-Elliott (1904) were, in every case, of birds which had been shot: one at Thurleigh 'many years ago', one at Haynes in the autumn of 1876, one between Luton and Dunstable about 1885, and one at Melchbourne on 5 October 1890. Hine (1934) mentions one at Shillington in 1892.

Since 1946 when H. A. S. Key noted it as being a 'rare or former visitor' it has occurred on 20 occasions, of which most have been during the spring. The earliest date is one at Sandy on 27 March 1964 with seven further records in April and five in May. In some years a bird has stayed in an area for some time; one remained around a garden in Poddington from late July for about a fortnight in 1947 and another stayed in the Flitwick/Greenfield area for a similar period from 26 April 1953. One which was observed in Stockgrove Woods on 14 June 1964 was seen on several subsequent occasions until 1 August, with possibly two on 21 June. It was thought that the possibility of breeding could not be ruled out although no firm evidence was obtained. The bird's preference for the more open habitat of parkland and gardens is reflected by records from a garden in Biddenham on 8–9 April 1947, one on a lawn at the Willbury Hotel on the Herts/Beds border on 18 September 1957, one on the lawn of a nursing home at Woburn Sands in 1959 (no date given), one on the lawn of 'The Barns', Fenlake on 4 May 1975, one at Dunstable Downs on 15 April 1980, and one at Cuckoo Bridge near Great Barford on 12 May 1980.

Wryneck

Jynx torquilla

A rare passage migrant.

The Wryneck was first mentioned by Davis (1855) as a common summer visitor around Luton. Steele-Elliott (1904) notes that it was one of the earliest of the summer migrants arriving a full fortnight earlier than the Cuckoo and not at the same time as its other name, the 'Cuckoo's mate', suggests. Some of the earlier dates given by Steele-Elliott are as follows: 7 April 1865, Maulden; 26 March 1871, Wilden; 4 April 1877, locality not given; 9 April 1893, locality not given; 12 April 1895, Elstow; 1 April 1899, one killed at Clifton was said to have been heard several days earlier.

By the end of the nineteenth century this species was already on the decline and Steele-Elliott makes the comment that although it 'may still be heard more or less frequently about the county, it is unfortunately now-a-days becoming with us a decreasing summer migrant'. He mentions that 20 years previously this species was looked on as 'by no means a rarity' and recalls frequently finding its eggs in holes in old pollarded willows. Dr Sprigge (in Steele-Elliott) mentions that a pair nested annually in a hole in one of the plum trees in his orchard at Great Barford until they were ousted by a pair of Tree Sparrows. Mr J. King also recalls hearing it commonly at one time at Langford and of its nesting every year in the pollarded willows in his meadows alongside the River Ivel. On one occasion he found a clutch of 12 eggs in a Sand Martin's hole. It was once common around Flitwick but by the end of the century was declining in numbers. A pair nested in the hole of a dead apple tree in an orchard in Turvey in 1905.

By 1946 Key gives its status as 'rare or former visitor'. Since then there have been 27 records in 13 of the 41 years. Recent records have occurred in parks, gardens, and woods in widely scattered localities throughout the county, with five of the 27 records being of injured or dead birds, four observed in gardens, and two flying into windows.

The earliest recent record is of a bird at Old Warden on 20 April 1987 and the latest is of one at The Lodge, Sandy on 11 October 1985. The vast majority of records (21) have been during the autumn with 11 during the last week of August and six during the second week of September. Although most birds have been seen on only one or two days one frequented a garden in Aspley Guise from 30 August to 14 September in 1974.

Green Woodpecker

Picus viridis

Fairly common in suitable habitat (**Map 49**).

The largest of our three species of woodpecker, its laughing call was the origin of its other name 'Yaffle'. However, in the Bushmead area it was better known as the 'Laughing Lady' and around Silsoe it was known as the 'Whetile'. The latter name possible came from 'Wet-tail' as it was thought that its call preceded rain but another possibility is that it had its origins in the Saxon word *'thwitan'* to cut.

During the nineteenth century the Green Woodpecker was by far the commonest of the three species of woodpecker in the county, presumably due to the greater abundance of mature timber. Steele-Elliott (1904) knew of it occurring at Bromham, Stagsden, Turvey, Odell, Colmworth, Ampthill, Flitwick, Woburn, Southill, Warden, Renhold, Moggerhanger, Tempsford, Roxton, and Bushmead whilst Davis (1874) mentions it as being common around Luton. An increase took place in Bedfordshire during the latter part of the nineteenth century, whilst in neighbouring Northamptonshire Lilford recorded it as being far less abundant during the same period. Mr A. Covington, the Bedford taxidermist, in Steele-Elliott (1904), mentioned that for every bird 25 years ago he now had eight or nine brought to him. During the very severe winter of 1894–5 he had 37 brought to him during a three-week period, the great majority being females, most having been picked up dead, apparently killed by the severity of the weather. There has been no such occurrence in hard winters of recent times.

Little has been recorded about this species during the last 80 years. H. A. S. Key (1946) noted it as being 'resident' in 1946 and a decline undoubtedly took place after the 1962–3 winter. It is probable that the 1947 winter also took a heavy toll but unfortunately no records from this period are extant. In recent times the areas around the clay pits have been utilised during the winter months as feeding grounds, presumably providing a plentiful supply of ants.

Harding (1979) showed that breeding was mainly concentrated in the woodlands along the Greensand Ridge and in a few areas of the Clay-with-Flints in the south of the county. The same survey revealed an interesting number of possible breeding records along the Ouse Valley which may be attributed to small areas of woodland linked by mature trees bordering the river. Breeding was confirmed in 34 tetrads, was probable in 31, and thought possible in a further 52. In 1968 it was estimated that 10–20 pairs bred in TL14.

Great Spotted Woodpecker

Dendrocopos major

A fairly common resident in suitable habitat (**Map 50**).

Davis (1855) says that this species was common in the Luton area but in the edition of 1874 it was noted as being rare. Steele-Elliott (1904) mentions it as being by no means an abundant bird in Bedfordshire, being far less common than the Green Woodpecker.

The present population is only slightly greater than that of the Green Woodpecker but it has almost the same breeding distribution, being mainly confined to the larger deciduous and coniferous woods of the Greensand Ridge, the Clay-with-Flints, and the Odell/Souldrop areas. Harding (1979) confirmed breeding in 40 tetrads, showed that it was probable in 37, and possible in a further 42. In recent years it has become a more frequent visitor to garden feeding stations.

During the winter months Steele-Elliott (1904) observed that it becomes more generally distributed and this continues to be the case today. He also suggested that, in some years, the winter population may be considerably increased by migratory birds. It is interesting to note that, although there have been no subsequent records of winter influxes and no definite records of continental birds in the county, a bird trapped in neighbouring Hertfordshire in 1968 was considered to be of the Scandinavian race *D. m. major* and birds of this race occur regularly on the east coast particularly in years when irruptions take place.

Lesser Spotted Woodpecker

Dendrocopos minor

An uncommon resident (**Map 51**).

The smallest and least obvious of the woodpeckers, the Lesser Spotted has never been a common bird in the county. Davis (1855) mentions it as being rare around Luton, but in the 1874 edition revises this to 'occasionally seen'. Steele-Elliott (1904) knew of it from seven woods in the north of the county – Turvey Park, Bromham, Roxton Spinnies, Henlow Grange, Kempston, Warden and Southill.

Low observer coverage from the beginning of the century until the mid 1960s resulted in only a few records in most years with no reports in 1957, three in 1961, and two at Sandy and Northill in 1965. A truer picture emerged after the Breeding Birds Survey 1968–77 (Harding 1979), when most were found to inhabit the woodlands of the Greensand Ridge, the Clay-with-Flints, the older woodlands along the line from Harrold to Kimbolton in the north of the county, and those which stretch from the north of Bedford SW to Marston Thrift. With an increase in the number of experienced observers this species was recorded from 15 to 23 sites annually from 1970 onwards and these included two urban sites, one in Biggleswade and the other at Putnoe, Bedford where breeding was also recorded. Breeding was confirmed in 23 tetrads, thought probable in 21, and possible in 29.

Woodlark

Lullula arborea

Formerly a scarce breeder, now a very rare visitor (**Map 52**).

Due to a lack of suitable habitat it seems likely that the Woodlark has at best been only a scarce species in the county, breeding in limited numbers along the Greensand Ridge. Steele-Elliott (1904) knew of only one positive occurrence from a specimen which had been shot at Oakley in 1867. Mr C. F. Woods, who resided at Woburn during the middle of the nineteenth century, recorded the Woodlark at Milton Wood, Speedwell Belt, Lowes Wood, and Charle Wood. He also mentioned that it was sometimes parasitised by the Cuckoo. The only Victorian reference from the south of the county came from Davis (1855) who considered it uncommon.

The first documented report of this species during the twentieth century came in the Bedford School Natural History Society Bird List (1941–3). It was classified as a 'Rare Resident' having bred at Clophill in 1941 and 1942 with one noted near Bedford Park on 26 April 1942. Annual bird reports published since 1946 recorded the Woodlark in 11 years with the final record in 1970.

1948   Present at Kings Wood, Heath and Reach.

1949   A pair in the Southill area during June and again resident at Kings Wood, Heath and Reach.

1950   Reported from a single small breeding area, site unknown.

1951   A singing male at Clophill on 29 April.

1953   Two at Galley Hill on 19 May.

1957   A singing male at Rowney Warren on 31 May followed by two birds at Woburn Sands on 8 June.

1965   A singing male at Tingrith on 27 May.

1966   One at Sandy Lodge on 27 February.

1967   Two at Sandy Lodge on 6 and 8 May. A single at Whipsnade in June and two at Rowney Warren on 13 July.

1969   Noted on two occasions in the breeding season in the 10km square TL03 and one heard at Charle Wood on 4 May.

1970   A single at The Lodge, Sandy on 1 and 13 December followed by three on 15th.

The national fluctuations as discussed by Sitters (1986) correlate with the decline in records in Bedfordshire. The suggestion that the East Anglian Breckland population is partially migratory could account for records outside the breeding season.

Skylark

Alauda arvensis

A widespread resident, abundant autumn passage migrant, and winter visitor (**Map 53**).

The Skylark is a species very much at home in Bedfordshire's open aspect farmland, both as a common breeding bird and as a winter visitor. Its sweet lilting song delivered from on high has inspired may poets and writers, including our own John Bunyan who wrote 'Upon the Lark and the Fowler' in *A Book for Boys and Girls*. However, in centuries past the Skylark featured prominently on the menus of many a Bedfordshire countryman. An unknown poet, who in the eighteenth century wrote his 'Originals' on the history of Dunstable, quoted: 'These Larks are caught by labourers in the evenings and

212

mornings from Michaelmas to February with trammeling nets and are served up in great perfection as Lark Pie, at some of the inns in this town.' He goes on to say that Dunstable larks were packaged and sent to all parts of England as a delicacy. Steele-Elliott (1904) also confirms that large numbers were caught on Dunstable Downs, estimating an annual catch of up to 48,000 birds. In conversation with George Smith, one of the most successful bird-catchers in Luton, Steele-Elliott was informed that larks were captured in 'drag-nets; and in a good night two men could trap as many as 14 or 15 dozen. A 'clap-net' was used in the day time, when numbers trapped were far less. This method was used mainly in the autumn months. The majority of Dunstable Larks were then transported alive to the London markets.

More recently, Harding (1979) found the Skylark to be a widespread breeding species which was recorded in 367 (99%) of the county's 371 tetrads. The only parts of Bedfordshire where it was absent were three tetrads in the centre of Luton and one in Leighton Buzzard. It is most abundant on open farmland where it nests amongst ground cover, laying a clutch of three to four eggs in a depression in growing crops or grass. The nest is built of grasses and there are usually two or three broods. The Skylark population was probably at its lowest in the county during the mid 1950s to the mid 1960s when the combination of pesticide poisoning and the severe winter of 1962–3 seriously depleted numbers across much of England.

As an autumn passage migrant this species is most numerous when moving south-west through the county from September to November, with particularly heavy day-time movements noted along the downs at Luton and Dunstable. A passage through the Marston Vale on 26 October and 2 and 3 November 1952 of approximately 200 birds per hour is typical of the numbers migrating overhead during the October peak. The return spring passage from February to May is far less noticeable.

During the winter months the Skylark flocks with other small passerines on suitable fallow land, sometimes spending the entire winter in one area if food is plentiful. Hard weather forces birds further south-west as noted at Langford in February 1895 when 'immense numbers' passed overhead, and on 1 January 1979 when 'many thousands' were observed over Dunstable Downs. There have been many records of flocks up to 200 strong since 1946. The following list includes counts in excess of 200 during the post-war period:

1952 300 Stagsden, late November.
1976 600 Sewell, 25 January.
1977 200 Luton, 9 January; 350 Biggleswade, 31 January.
1978 800 Blunham, 20–1 December.
1981 300 Beadlow, 10 January; 300 Stanbridgeford, 11 January; 300 Radwell, 5 December; 250 Ickwell, 20 December; 550 Mogerhanger, 22 December; 2,300 Dunton, 22 December; 1,800 Sutton, 22 December.
1982 2,000 Thurleigh, 24 January.
1985 500 Everton, 18 January.
1986 1,000 Galley/Warden Hills and 750 Everton, December.

Shore Lark

Eremophila alpestris

A very rare vagrant.

The Shore Lark is a scarce winter visitor from Fenno-Scandia to parts of the East Anglian coastline, where numbers have declined in recent years. Inland it is rarely noted and there have been only two Bedfordshire records as follows:

> 1913 'In the last week of October 1913 a mature cock Shore Lark was caught on Dunstable Downs in Bedfordshire. The bird was trapped with a number of common Skylarks. No others of the species were observed. When I saw the bird it was doing well in a large cage, eating mostly canary seed. It seemed to be getting tame very quickly' (Rowan 1913–14).
>
> 1971 One at Houghton Regis ChP on 10 October.

Sand Martin

Riparia riparia

A common passage migrant and localised breeding species (**Map 54**).

In Bedfordshire the Sand Martin has had to rely mainly on the quarrying activities of man for the availability of vertical cliff faces, its preferred nesting site. It appears that formerly it was far more abundant as a breeding bird, despite there being less suitable habitat available. Steele-Elliott (1904) knew of a large colony of *c*.1,000 pairs in a railway cutting near Sandy station, and he speculated that the true figure could have been far higher.

Unfortunately there are no further breeding details of this species in the county until a 1961 survey by the BTO gave a total of 1,265 nests. The largest colony was at Heath and Reach with 375 nests, followed by smaller colonies of about 200 nests each at Shefford, Sandy, Leighton Buzzard, and Wyboston. Harding (1979) recorded the Sand Martin in 64 (17%) of the county's tetrads over the period 1968–77. The majority of records came from the Ouzel river valley sand pits around Leighton Linslade and the gravel extraction sites along the River Ouse, particularly at Harrold and Wyboston. Other scattered records away from the main river valleys came from quarrying activities along the Greensand Ridge and at several other areas in the county where localised earthworks were in operation. In the Marston Vale small colonies were found at Elstow and Kempston Hardwick, but generally speaking the clay pits are unsuitable for this species for breeding. The nest is at the end of a horizontal tunnel up to a metre in length where a clutch of four to five eggs is laid towards the end of May. There are normally two broods.

As noted by Harding, the Sand Martin suffered a dramatic decline in numbers, similar to the Whitethroat, when in the Sahel region of Africa during the 1968–9 winter, which probably accounted for the paucity of records over the study period. The recovery had been slow and erratic, and once again numbers declined in the summer of 1984, undoubtedly as a result of the continuing drought in the Sahel. In the early 1980s a colony of up to 250 pairs had become established at Radwell GP but was soon deserted as conditions became unsuitable. By the end of the decade small colonies of under 100 pairs each were recorded in the Ouzel valley at Grovebury Farm SP, Churchways SP, Leighton Buzzard Golf Course, and at Aspley Heath, Potton SP, and along the River Ouse at Bedford Embankment where nesting occurred in drainage pipes.

The Sand Martin is the first hirundine to arrive back in the county from its African wintering grounds and can often be seen flying low over our still waters from late March. The earliest record was at Blunham GP on 12 March 1978 with the majority of migrants passing through from mid April into May. Jackson (1980) in his study on hirundine migration 1948–78 found the mean arrival date to be 31 March which compares well with Steele-Elliott's data.

In the autumn this species is the first of the martin family to return south with migration well under way by August. The mean departure date is 30 September and the latest record was at Sandy on 27 October

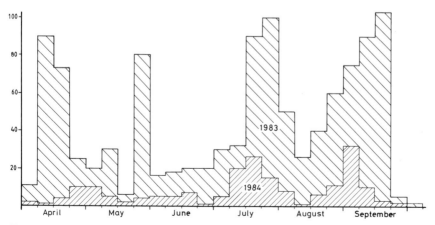

Figure 3.14 *Sand Martin: spring passage totals at Priory CP, 1983 and 1984, using ¼-month periods*

1961. Jackson demonstrates a distinct trend towards earlier departure which is inconsistent with other passerine trends (Williamson 1975).

Because of its gregarious nature the Sand Martin has been trapped and ringed in large numbers and particularly in the 1961 BTO enquiry. Wilkinson (1979) published a paper that discussed colony fidelity and inter-colonial movements as well as roost studies and migration analysis. There was evidence of interchange between colonies within the county and elsewhere in southern England, as well as an interesting record of a juvenile ringed at Harrold on 20 August 1978 which was caught at roost at Llangorse Lake, Powys on 2 August 1979. Even more exceptional was another juvenile, also ringed on 20 August 1978 at Harrold which was retrapped at a colony at Grude, Klepp, in Rogaland, Norway on 18 June 1979 having moved 832km north-north-east.

Swallow

Hirundo rustica

A widespread and abundant passage migrant and summer visitor (**Map 55**).

> This pretty bird, O! how she flies and sings,
> But could she do say if she had not wings?
> Her wings bespeak my faith her songs my peace,
> When I believe and sing my doubting cease.
>
> John Bunyan

The true harbinger of summer, the Swallow is as familiar today as it was to the poet John Bunyan in the seventeenth century and to the naturalist Steele-Elliott 200 years later. It breeds commonly throughout the Bedfordshire countryside nesting in outbuildings, sheds, and barns where it constructs a nest of mud and straw on a ledge or rafter. Harding (1979) recorded the Swallow in 332 (89%) of the county's tetrads over the 10-year study period 1968–77. This species breeds from mid May through until August with young occasionally seen in the nest in September, and exceptionally in October as was recorded at Westoning in 1954. Two or three broods of four to five young are raised in a typical breeding season.

The Swallow is a common and widespread spring passage migrant, moving through the county on a broad front. However it is particularly conspicuous when seen pausing to feed over the river valley mineral extraction pits where it can occur in large numbers. Although the first migrants usually arrive in early April the main arrival is not until later in the month and continues throughout May and into June. Jackson (1980) gives a mean arrival date of 5 April in his study period

216

1948–78, suggesting a slightly earlier arrival than at the turn of the century. The earliest county record was on 17 March 1978 at The Lodge, Sandy, followed by sightings on 20 March at Bromham in 1947 and Goldington in 1951.

Following the breeding season and prior to the return migration Swallows, together with other hirundines, form roosts in reed beds, willow scrub, or osiers. Notable assemblies have been 1,000 at Bedford SF in August 1955, 2,000 at Houghton Regis ChP on 13 September 1964, 4,000 at Radwell GP in September 1977 followed by 10,000 there in September 1980 and 1,000 in 1986, and 1,000 at Brogborough Lake in September 1986. At Radwell and Brogborough Hobbies have been noted preying on birds coming to roost.

The main autumn passage of this species occurs throughout September and into early October, with November sightings in many years, the latest being one at Blunham Lake on 30 November 1986. The Swallow spends the winter in Africa south of the Sahara with some birds travelling the full length of the continent to the Cape of Good Hope.

House Martin

Delichon urbica

A common passage migrant and summer visitor (**Map 56**).

Whereas the Swallow is a familiar and welcome visitor to the country-man the House Martin is equally familiar to the urban dweller where it commonly breeds in our town centres, industrial estates, and housing complexes. Harding (1979) found it in 252 (68%) of the county's tetrads with a notable absence of breeding records in the more open arable countryside of North Bedfordshire. This species has a protracted breeding season from late May until September, with second or third broods often noted in the nest during October. The nest is built of mud and grass and is typically sited under the eaves of a building where small colonies often develop.

As a spring migrant the House Martin can occur over the county's still waters from early April, but the main arrival is not until later on in the month or early May and in some years it is scarce until June. March dates are unusual for this species, with the earliest being on 14 March 1965 at Luton, with only four other late March sightings from 1946 to 1987.

Although an autumn passage through the county is noticeable during August, the majority of our breeding birds do not depart until September. The House Martin often forms pre-migratory roosts at this time of the year, often in company with other hirundines. Notable concentrations have occurred at Radwell GP in the 1970s and 1980s.

October sightings are not unusual for this species and there have been many November records throughout the post-war period. Jackson (1980) found a distinct trend towards later departures for the House Martin during the period 1948–78. The latest migrants recorded in the county were singles at East Hyde on 1 December 1976 and at Bedford on 8 December 1948. The House Martin spends the winter in Africa, south of the Sahara.

Tree Pipit

Anthus trivialis

A localised summer visitor and passage migrant (**Map 57**).

Both Davis (1855) and Steele-Elliott (1904) give the status of this species as common and an abundant summer migrant but it obviously showed a preference for particular localities. Mr J. King in Steele-Elliott notes that it was uncommon around Langford but common on Barton Hills and around Southill Park, Rowney, and Warden Warrens. Steele-Elliott records its arrival dates as 14 April 1877 and 8 April 1984 at Kempston, 14 April 1895 and 3 April 1896 at Elstow.

The Tree Pipit usually arrives in the county during the second week of April, but a bird on passage was noted at Blows Downs as early as 6 April 1980. Departure dates are more variable, sometimes the last being recorded in the first week of September, sometimes remaining until the end of the month. A record on 13 October 1987 was exceptional. During the late 1950s it was known to nest on Flitwick Moor and Galley Hill but few accurate records were kept at this time. Harding (1979) showed clearly that this species nests almost exclusively along the Greensand Ridge, regularly breeding at Stockgrove Park, Charle Wood, Wavendon Heath, Fox Covert, Chicksands Wood, Maulden Wood, and The Lodge, Sandy. A small colony exists on the Clay-with-Flints around Whipsnade and Studham with other records from Luton Hoo, Galley Hill, and Hexton. The survey indicated that 21–50 pairs were present in TL14 and more than 20 pairs in SP92. During the survey the Tree Pipit was recorded in 53 of the 371 tetrads. It was confirmed breeding in 14, thought probable in 25, and possible in 14.

During the 1980s the population remained relatively stable but was apparently under-recorded, with display noted at 11 sites in 1981 and 10 sites in 1984 including four pairs at The Lodge, Sandy. Breeding was also noted during the early 1980s at Willington Wood before the trees were felled for gravel extraction. In 1986 10 pairs were recorded along the Greensand Ridge and four on chalk whilst in the following year these numbers were 11 and two respectively, with 10 pairs present in the Aspley Heath complex.

Meadow Pipit

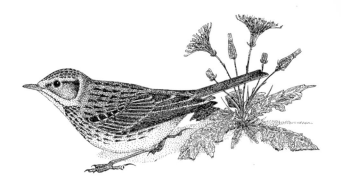

Anthus pratensis

A common passage migrant in spring and autumn, and winter visitor. Uncommon breeding bird (**Map 58**).

Davis (1855) records this species as being common but Steele-Elliott (1904) notes it as being better known in the county as a winter migrant than as a resident, 'appearing in numbers during the autumn and distributing themselves generally where suitable food can be found'. Towards the latter end of September small parties could be flushed from among the turnip crops whilst flooded meadow lands and sewage farms formed a great attraction to them. As a nesting species it was rather local, formerly nesting commonly around Bedford, breeding regularly in the Longholme meadows before they became public, Newnham, Rammemere Heath near Heath and Reach, The Firs near Leighton Buzzard, and Whipsnade.

The status of the Meadow Pipit appears to have changed during recent years. Steele-Elliott knew the species better as a winter visitor. Records of large numbers in the early 1950s indicate that this was still the case. About 100 were noted at Bedford SF during the winter of 1950 and *c*.50 in the following year. Although some large parties are still recorded during the winter months (for example 74 roosting at Sandy Lodge in December 1972), the species has perhaps become better known as a passage migrant during the spring and autumn. Spring passage may begin in early March and continue into the first half of April, with flocks particularly favouring the gravel-pit and chalk downland sites. This movement was particularly well illustrated in 1984 (Table 3.9).

TABLE 3.9   *Meadow Pipit spring passage records, 1984*

Date	Place	Number
22 March	Priory CP	60
26 March	Priory CP	110
28 March	Harrold GP	100
31 March	Priory CP	153
31 March	Whipsnade	132
1 April	Radwell GP	200
7 April	Priory CP	100
7 April	Blows Downs	150
10 April	Priory CP	150

The variety in plumage of the birds on spring passage is tantalising but a least a few have been consistent with *A. p. whistleri* from western

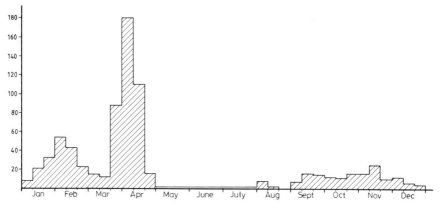

Figure 3.15 *Meadow Pipit: total numbers observed at Priory CP, 1983, using ¹/₃-month periods*

Scotland, having deep cinnamon-buff underparts and being darker on the back.

A southward movement also takes place during September and October: in 1981 300 moved south over Harrold GP on 3 October and 100 were present at Radwell GP on the following day.

The origins of the birds which winter in the county are not fully understood, but a bird ringed at East Hyde in January 1985 was recovered in Iceland in October of the following year. It is probable that birds from the Icelandic and Scandinavian populations replace local breeding birds which move south in the autumn and winter in Iberia and North Africa. A bird ringed at Bedford in June 1969 was recovered in December of the same year in Portugal.

Harding (1979) indicates clearly that the Meadow Pipit shows a marked preference for two main areas as defined by the surface geology. One area is the line of Oxford Clay which extends from Little Barford in the north-east to Salford in the west. Of the 80 or so tetrads to the north of this line this species was observed in only two and none was found to be breeding. The chalk areas in the south of the county form the second area. In 1969 it was estimated that 51–70 pairs occupied territory in TL02. During the survey this species was recorded in 83 tetrads, confirmed as breeding in 40, thought probable in 12, and possible in 31.

Water Pipit

Anthus spinoletta

Scarce passage migrant and winter visitor.

The Water Pipit breeds in the mountains of southern Europe and many move between August and September to the lowlands close to their breeding grounds. Some, however, migrate long distances to winter in Belgium and along the Atlantic and Channel coastlines of France and Portugal. A few of these have found their way to Bedfordshire.

The Water Pipit and Rock Pipit were recognised as separate species by the British Ornithologists' Union Records committee in 1986 (*Ibis* 128: 602–3).

The first recording of this species, and the earliest of the winter records, was at Wyboston on 1 October 1967 since when there have been 24 other records in 14 of the next 20 years with usually no more than one or two records in any year. Of the 13 records before 1975 10 were in the winter and three in the spring. During this period there was one other October record, four in November, and four in December. Nearly all of these records were of single birds which remained for only a day or two, but one at East Hyde SF on 16 December 1970 stayed until 16 March of the following year. One at Chalton SF on 28 February 1971 remained until 10 April and was joined by a second from 6 April. Later that year one at the same locality on 27 December was joined by a second on the following day, and one of these remained until 9 January 1972. Apart from the first record, all the above subsequent observations were of birds at the sewage farms of Chalton (8) and East Hyde (4). From 1975 onwards there was a complete reversal of this pattern with 11 of the 12 records being in the spring. This was probably due to the demise of the old-style sewage farms which provided suitable feeding during the winter. The influence of the mineral extraction pits also became significant. Of the 12 records, three were at sewage farms (Dunstable 2, East Hyde 1), six at gravel pits (Priory CP 3, Harrold 1, South Mills 1, Radwell 1), one at a clay pit (Stewartby), and two at Totternhoe. From 1975 onwards there have been two records in the second half of March, eight in April, one in May, and one in November.

Rock Pipit

Anthus petrosus

Scarce passage migrant and winter visitor.

There have been 21 records of the Rock Pipit in Bedfordshire, fairly evenly distributed between spring, with 11 records, and autumn with nine. The first county record was of one at Bedford SF on 3 April 1955. The Rock Pipit remained a very rare bird with only two other records up to 1970, at Stewartby on 4 October 1961 and at the same locality on 15 October 1964. Records were more frequent after 1970, being seen on 11 occasions in 17 years. In spring, birds have been observed between 16 March and 13 April and in autumn from 28 September to

13 November. There has been only one record outside this period, one at Blunham on 1 January 1980.

TABLE 3.10   *Seasonal distribution of Rock Pipits by habitat, 1955–87*

	Clay Pits	Gravel Pits	Sewage Farms
Winter	–	1	–
Spring	–	9	2
Autumn	3	1	5

Apart from three together at Priory CP on 27 March 1982, all of the 21 other records have been of single birds.

Unfortunately it has not been recorded whether any birds of the Scandinavian sub-species *A. s. littoralis* were involved.

Rock/Water Pipit

Anthus petrosus/spinoletta

1967   1 at Bedford SF, 9 November.
1972   1 north over Wyboston GP, 18 March.
        1 at Sandy SF, 24–5 March.
1973   1 at Dunstable SF, 22 April.
        1 at Dunstable SF, 26 October.
        1 at Sandy SF, 18 November.

Yellow Wagtail

Motacilla flava

Blue-headed Wagtail   *Motacilla flava flava*

Scarce but now fairly regular passage migrant, mainly in spring.

The first county record of this sub-species was of a male at Bedford SF on 18 April 1948. This, or another male, was seen with a presumed female near Cardington Mill on 8 May and again on 28 May. On 12 June F. C. Gribble made a detailed description of the female and proved it to be a Blue-headed wagtail. There was strong, but not

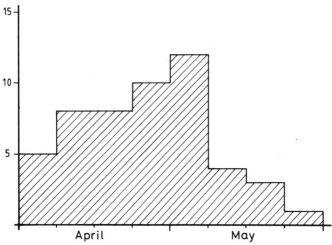

Figure 3.16 *Blue-headed Wagtail: numbers observed on spring passage at Priory CP, 1982–7, using European standard five-day periods, beginning 11–15 April*

conclusive, evidence to suggest that this pair bred and raised young. The adults were seen intermittently after this and the male was last recorded on 15 September.

Between 1948 and 1970 there was only one other record, a male at Bedford SF 11–14 April 1950, with further records in six of the 10 years 1970–9. After not being recorded in 1980 it has been observed in every year since then. In the period 1970–87 there were 30 April records and 20 in May. There have been three June records, one at Blunham GP 19–26 June 1971, one at Wrest Park on 10 June 1973, and one at South Mills NR 10–14 June 1987, and one August record, at Girtford on 20 August 1981. As with the British race nearly all records have been around the margins of gravel and clay-pit lakes, particularly those of Priory CP, South Mills, Harrold, Radwell, Blunham, Stewartby, and Brogborough with three early records from the sewage farms of Bedford, Biggleswade, and Sandy.

Yellow Wagtail   *Motacilla flava flavissima*

A common spring and autumn passage migrant. Local summer resident (**Map 59**).

Steele-Elliott (1904) noted this species as a fairly abundant summer migrant showing a liking for the company of cattle on the grasslands, where it fed upon the flies which were disturbed by them. The earliest dates of arrival given by him are 15 April 1877, 7 April 1894, both at Cardington, and 9 April 1895 at Langford. It generally nested amongst growing crops. About 200 were flushed by him from a roost at the junction of the New Cut (Bedford) and the River Ouse on 9 August 1892.

The earliest arrival date is a bird at Leagrave on 21 March 1978 but the main arrival usually takes place during the second half of April, with the bright yellow males arriving first. In some years large flocks gather during this period, particularly at sewage farms or on short-grass areas near to water. Before the increase in the gravel and clay pits during the 1960s and 1970s, the old style sewage farms provided the main habitats for birds on spring passage. In April of 1947 about 75 were observed at Bedford SF and 100 were present at the same locality in April of the following year. The modification of habitats by the reinstatement of land bordering the worked-out gravel and clay pits during the late 1970s and early 1980s created ideal feeding areas for birds on spring passage. Groups of 40+ on spring passage at gravel and clay-pit sites, 1979–87 are as follows:

1979   c.60 at Harrold GP, 7 May.
1982   100 at Harrold GP, 10 April.
       53 at Priory CP, 3 May.
1983   85 max. at Priory CP, 20 April.
1984   50 at Stewartby Lake, 15 April.
       50 at Radwell GP, 15 April.
       60 at Priory CP, 16 April.
1985   40 at South Mills NR, 27 April.
       78 at Priory CP, 27 April.
       40+ at Radwell GP, 28 April.
       40 at Stewartby Lake, 29 April.
1986   50 at Radwell GP, 23 April.
       57 at Priory CP, 3 May.
1987   62 at Stewartby Lake, 20 April.

Breeding is almost totally confined to river valleys and other damp habitats such as sewage works. Harding (1979) confirmed it as breed-

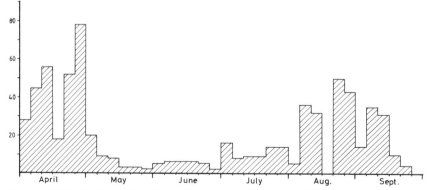

Figure 3.17   *Yellow Wagtail: total numbers observed at Priory CP, 1985, using European standard five-day periods*

ing in 44 tetrads, probable in 15, and possible in a further 25. A survey along the River Ouse in Bedfordshire in 1983 revealed 30 confirmed and 21 possible territories.

Return passage may begin as early as the end of July with parties gathering to feed, often at the same areas used on a spring passage. A party of 69 was present at Priory CP on 30 July 1984. Numbers increase during August, reaching a peak in early September. Two hundred were observed flying SW over Double Arches Quarry on 1 September 1963, c.100 were at Harrold GP on 14 September 1983 and c.100 were at the same locality on 16 September of the following year: 80–100 were at South Mills NR on 16 September 1987. Most birds have moved on by the end of September but occasionally one or two may remain into October. Apart from an injured bird which was present at Chalton SF on 7–18 December 1972, the latest date was of one at Bedford SF on 13 October 1951.

A bird ringed in the county on 14 June 1969 was recovered in Morocco 2,225km south on 12 April 1975.

Grey-headed Wagtail   *Motacilla flava thunbergi*

A male at Priory CP from 30 April to 14 May 1984 is the only county record.

Grey Wagtail

Motacilla cinerea

Scarce local breeding bird, regular autumn passage migrant, and uncommon winter visitor (**Map 60**).

Steele-Elliott (1904) gives the status of this species as being 'generally distributed and fairly abundant throughout the county' outside the breeding season. However as a breeding species he knew of only a few records, one from the Grand Junction Canal near Leighton Buzzard and two from Woburn Park. Prior (*Zoologist* 1878) mentions it being particularly common during August of that year with small parties of five or six being seen and in 1879 mentions parties 'of a score or more' roosting in the reed beds along the River Ouse. A. Covington frequently noticed this species feeding on the roofs and out of the spouts of houses in the centre of Bedford. Nesting was noted at Willington Locks in 1920 and 1921, at Tempsford in 1920, and at Castle Mills, Bedford about 1940. Since then it has nested in only 11 years involving at least 19 pairs. Nine of the breeding records have occurred at Luton Hoo with others at Biggleswade, Chalton SW, East Hyde,

Leighton Buzzard, Linslade, Shefford, and Tempsford. Other possible breeding sites have been Bromham Mill and Heath and Reach. Harding (1979) recorded it in 13 tetrads. Breeding was thought possible in six tetrads, probable in four, and was confirmed in three. Birds are recorded outside their breeding areas from late July onwards but these records probably involve dispersed breeding birds. A more significant increase takes place from the end of September and during October when birds from other parts of Britain or the continent may be involved. Outside the breeding season birds are widely scattered throughout the county and are observed at such places as sewage works, river banks, and mineral extraction pits, with the number of localities varying between 10 and 20 (in recent years 16–18) for any single year. Large numbers are rarely recorded and, apart from birds with young there are only two records of more than five: a party of 12 at Pictshill, Turvey on 23 August 1952 and seven at Luton SW on 13 February 1983.

White and Pied Wagtail

Motacilla alba

White Wagtail *Motacilla alba alba*

Regular spring and scarce autumn passage migrant.

The nominate race of the White Wagtail was not recognised during the time of Steele-Elliott and no record of its occurrence in the county

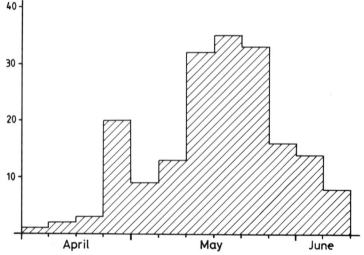

Figure 3.18 *White Wagtail: numbers observed on spring passage at Priory CP, 1982–7, using European standard five-day periods, beginning 11–15 April*

was published until 1942 when a male was present at Bedford SF on 8 April. The second record was in 1947 when two males were observed on spring passage at Bedford SF. Records were intermittent until 1960 after which it was recorded in every year.

Passage may start as early as mid March but normally the end of the month, reaching a peak during the second half of April. The vast majority of records are of single birds. There have been five records of four birds and only two of five. The largest party on spring passage was one of nine at Luton Hoo on 29 March 1985. Of the 186 records 1948–87, 26 were in March, 138 in April, and 22 in May.

Autumn passage takes place from the end of August but the problems with identification at this time of the year cause it to be under-recorded.

Pied Wagtail   *Motacilla alba yarrellii*

A common resident and passage migrant (**Map 61**).

Steele-Elliott (1904) recorded this species as nesting commonly throughout the county, particularly along its waterways, but deserting these summer haunts during the winter to feed at such favourite habitats as sewage farms where they gathered in large numbers. Also during the winter it was often observed roosting in 'considerable numbers' in the willows and reed beds along the River Ouse near Bedford, with Steele-Elliott noting 50–60 on 8 January 1892.

The Pied Wagtail is well distributed throughout the county and can be seen not only near to sewage works, rivers, and lakes but also on short-grass areas such as parks and playing fields, or in towns where insects are found along roads and on roofs. Harding (1979) showed that the Pied Wagtail is a common breeding species with breeding confirmed in 118 of the 371 tetrads (31%). Birds were recorded during the breeding season in a further 121 tetrads. As the county's population is very sedentary it is probable that these records also refer to breeding birds. It was less frequently recorded in large areas of intensive agriculture, particularly those in the north of the county.

During the winter months hard weather may reduce the availability of suitable feeding habitats. At this time feeding territories break down and numbers may be seen feeding together.

Outside the breeding season Pied Wagtails form large communal roosts utilising such sites as reed beds, greenhouses, or industrial buildings.

Roosts of more than 100 in recent years have been:

1952 200 flying to Luton Hoo from New Mill End on 14 December.
1955 120–50 at Stewartby Lake on 6 November.
1968 300 roosting under the roof of George Kent Ltd, Luton, during the winter.
     500+ roosting at Goldington Power Station, Bedford.
1972 Roost in greenhouses at Willington reached a peak of *c*.200 on 15 August.

1979	300–400 roosted at Harrold GP.
	400–500 roosted in glasshouses at Cotton End.
1980	250 at Harrold GP in October.
	230 at reed beds at Queens Park, Bedford on 16 November.
1981	150 at Harrold GP on 14 October.
	597 at Queens Park, Bedford on 16 November.
1982	522 at Queens Park, Bedford on 3 November.
1983	330 at Queens Park, Bedford on 30 November.

In spring there is a passage of Pied Wagtails through the county which may commence towards the end of March and continue through into mid or late April. This passage of birds returning to northern Britain from France and the Iberian peninsula is very variable and may be related to the severity of the preceding winter. It is followed in the autumn by a less obvious southerly movement as birds return to their wintering areas.

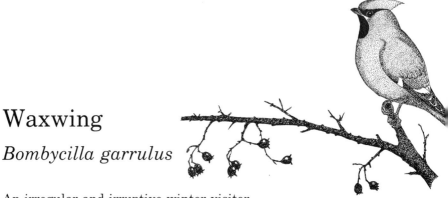

Waxwing

Bombycilla garrulus

An irregular and irruptive winter visitor.

A Waxwing in a Bedfordshire park or garden feeding on a berry-laden bush, is, for many birdwatchers, an event long to be cherished. Invasion years are few and far between and are inextricably linked to the crop of Rowan berries which are its staple diet during the winter. The Waxwing, of the nominate race *B. g. garrulus*, breeds in the taiga forests of Fenno-Scandia eastwards to west Siberia.

The irruptive nature of this species was noted by Steele-Elliott (1904) when he documented the invasion of 1882–3, commenting 'Waxwings were reported commonly about the county and one was shot at Biggleswade on 15 January 1883'. The earliest recorded Waxwing in Bedfordshire was noted in the *Zoologist* and referred to an adult male shot at Luton on 23 January 1847. Steele-Elliott commented that many instances of this species probably went unrecorded which is undoubtedly still the case today. He reported on a small 'Incursion of Waxwings' during the winter of 1913–14 at Biggleswade, Bedford, and Sharnbrook (*British Birds* 7: 319–21). Likewise a solitary record was noted between Markyate (Hertfordshire) and Dunstable on the late date of 15 April 1914 (*British Birds* 8: 49).

From 1946 the Waxwing has occurred in 14 years, with a notable 12-year absence 1975–87. Most records are from December to February with extreme dates at Sandy Lodge on 13 November 1965 and at Bedford on 3 April 1947. Due to this species' preference for berries the majority of occurrences have come from Bedford and Luton where many ornamental berry bushes are grown in gardens and parks. Generally it is found singly but in irruption years it can occur in small parties, the largest being a group of six at Luton on 23 February 1947. In total during the post-war study period approximately 80 individuals have been recorded, just over half of which have been noted in the two irruption winters of 1946–7 and 1965–6.

TABLE 3.11 *Waxwing records, 1947–87*

Date	Period of record	Sites	Total numbers
1947	11/1–3/4	7	30
1948	15/2	1	2
1949	16/2–27/3	2	3
1954	14/2	1	2
1956	3/1–16/2	2	4
1958	22/1–?/2	3	7
1960	26/12	1	1
1964	4/1–9/1	1	1
1965–6	13/11–31/3	7	14
1970	4/3	1	1
1970	?/11	3	4
1971	5/12–31/12	2	5
1975	7/1–12/1	1	1
1987	21/1–1/3	3	3

Dipper

Cinclus cinclus

A very rare vagrant.

There are only two records of this species in Bedfordshire. The first was reported to Steele-Elliott (1904) by Mr Cane, a Luton taxidermist, as having been obtained in Luton Hoo c.1870. In March 1900 a Mr W. J. Chalk reported seeing one along the River Ivel. There have been no modern sightings despite a number of records from other counties in the region of individuals of the nominate dark-bellied continental race *C. c. cinclus*.

Wren

Troglodytes troglodytes

A very common resident (**Map 62**).

The 'Jenny Wren' is one of Bedfordshire's most ubiquitous and abundant birds. It is commonest in woodland and mature gardens but is also present in a wide range of marginal habitats, providing some ground cover is available. Harding (1979) recorded its presence in all 371 of the county's tetrads with confirmed breeding in 202 tetrads, probable breeding in 129 tetrads, and possible breeding in a further 40 tetrads. Due to the highly sedentary nature of the Wren Harding considered that records referring to probable and possible breeding almost certainly related to breeding birds. It is an adaptable species, amply proven by the wide range of nesting sites used. Thick ivy is a favourite woodland and garden site, while hedgerow banks, walls, outhouses, and old birds' nests are all utilised. The male builds several well-concealed domed nests from which the female selects one in which to lay a clutch of up to 11 tiny white eggs. There are normally two broods during April to June. One of the most unusual nest sites chosen by this species was on the axle of a pole wagon at a timber yard in Bedford in 1950. The wagon had been used daily for journeys of up to 20 miles but the male continued to feed the female on her return. The nest was eventually resited nearby and the young fledged successfully.

Being a small insectivorous species the Wren suffers great mortality during prolonged cold weather such as in the winters of 1962–3, 1978–9, 1981–2, and 1985–6. This is illustrated by the results of a Common Bird Census plot at Old Warden (Figure 3.19) which recorded

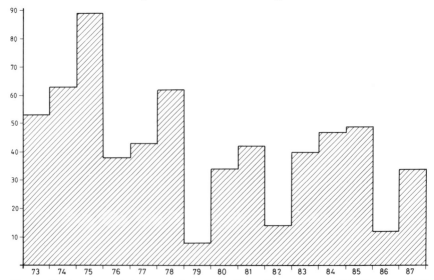

Figure 3.19 *Wren: total annual counts of breeding pairs at Old Warden CBC Plot, 1973–87*

a dramatic decline after the aforementioned winters followed by a rapid rise in subsequent years.

A study of ringing data for Bedfordshire's Wrens reveals that none have been recovered outside the county, confirming their sedentary nature.

Dunnock

Prunella modularis

A very common resident (**Map 63**).

Along with the previous species the Dunnock is one of the county's most common and familiar birds. It has been known by a variety of names, from Hedge Sparrow and Hedge Accentor to the delightful 'Shufflewing', a name derived from its shuffling feeding action.

The Dunnock is most at home in gardens and parks with plenty of bushes and shrubs. It also occurs in woodland, hedgerows, downland, and most other marginal habitats, providing some ground cover is available. In Steele-Elliott (1904) this species was classed as an abundant resident, a status similarly afforded to it when the Breeding Birds Survey was published (Harding 1979). During the 10-year study period for the Atlas it was recorded in all 371 of the county's tetrads with confirmed breeding in 210 tetrads, probable breeding in 123 tetrads, and possible breeding in a further 38. The nest is usually low down in thick cover such as bramble or hawthorn where two or three clutches of four to five eggs are laid. Breeding normally commences in April although in 1897 Steele-Elliott recorded a nest containing young as early as 27 March.

A study of ringing data has shown Bedfordshire's Dunnocks to be highly sedentary with only one recovery of an individual over 10km from its natal area. There is a small passage of birds of the browner continental race into eastern England during the autumn but none has been known to penetrate inland to Bedfordshire. Our birds all belong to the British race *P. m. occidentalis* which is also found in western France.

Steele-Elliott noted a number of colour aberrations, including albinos at Stondon in November 1885 and at Meppershall in February 1892. A leucistic bird was shot at Holme Farm, near Biggleswade, although no further data are given.

Robin

Erithacus rubecula

A very common resident (**Map 64**).

The status of the Robin has remained unchanged since Steele-Elliott (1904) described it as 'far too numerous and familiar to need any reference to its distribution.' It is perhaps most abundant around human settlements, in parks and gardens, where it is a popular visitor to bird tables during the winter months. The county's woodlands also hold significant populations particularly the more overgrown deciduous copses and spinnies.

Not surprisingly, Harding (1979) recorded it in all 371 of the tetrads surveyed with a very high (64%) confirmed breeding instance in 237 tetrads. The breeding period ranges from late March to the middle of June after which this species becomes very secretive for a month or so whilst in moult. Unusual nesting sites for the Robin are legendary and several of the more interesting ones were recorded by Steele-Elliott: in 1865 a pair nested between the horns of a stuffed goat's head that was positioned in an outhouse in Woburn Abbey, and at Southill Park a pair nested inside an old sack hanging from a beam in a wood yard which was swinging constantly to and fro in the wind. More normally the Robin nests low down in thick cover or amongst ivy, where a clutch of between four to six eggs is laid. There are two, sometimes three broods. Bedfordshire Robins belong to the race *E. r. melophilus* which is restricted to the British Isles and is mainly sedentary.

A study of ringing recoveries reveals only local post-breeding dispersal records, with no instances of the continental nominate race *E. r. rubecula* occurring. However in early December 1973 an influx of Robins was noted at Luton Hoo, along with c.50 at Eversholt Lake and c.20 at Chalton SF on 2 December. It is possible that these records could relate to the more migratory population from Fenno-Scandia and the Low Countries.

Nightingale

Luscinia megarhynchos

Formerly more common, now a scarce summer visitor (**Map 65**).

This supreme songster was in Steele-Elliott's (1904) day an abundant summer visitor which bred commonly in thickets, spinnies, and copses across the county. In larger plantations and woodlands (presumably where rotational cropping was practised) it was particularly numerous and pairs were even noted in thick hedgerows or garden shrubbery. Steele-Elliott summarises its then status in Bedfordshire: 'It is almost needless for me to mention any localities where these birds can be heard to advantage, but I might suggest an evening's walk through Elstow and then along the Ampthill Road, or in the vicinity of the small plantations around Biddenham, at Kempston or at Clapham, all being within a short walk of Bedford.' In the south of the county Davis (1874) classed the Nightingale as common in the Luton district.

Studies on the Nightingale during the breeding season in Britain by Ticehurst and Jourdain (1911–12) revealed it still to be regular and numerous in Bedfordshire while in the early 1940s Henry Key (1946) remarked: 'Almost every coppice held one or two pairs at Stagsden and between Everton and Sandy.' During the post-war period there was little quantifiable data on this species until the 10-year study period for the *Bedfordshire Bird Atlas* (Harding 1979). It was still considered to be reasonably widespread, with numbers fluctuating annually, typical of a trans-Saharan migrant. In 1952 the Nightingale was more abundant than usual in the thickets and woods of north Bedfordshire and along the Greensand Ridge. An unusual record was of one singing in Bedford town centre throughout June of 1951. In 1964 came the first indication of a general decline in numbers as records were received from only one locality, Hanger Wood.

Harding (1979) recorded the Nightingale in 64 (17%) of the county's tetrads, with a high instance of probable breeding in 49 tetrads referring mainly to singing males holding territory. Numbers fluctuated throughout the survey period from a maximum of 23–42 pairs in 1969 to a low of just four pairs in 1973. The Atlas results showed just how dependent this species is on damp woodland where thickets and herbaceous growth abound. This is particularly noticeable along the Greensand Ridge where there is an almost complete absence of records from Leighton Buzzard north-east to Ampthill, contrasting with good numbers from Maulden through to Potton. This is mainly due to an inlier of Oxford clay on that part of the Greensand outcrop which affords damp plantation areas in woods such as Maulden Woods, Wilstead Wood, Chicksands Wood, Warden Warren, Home Wood, Waterloo Thorns, and Potton Wood. Further concentrations were noted in the clay country at Marston Thrift, Wootton Wood, and the copses around Stagsden, where there is much blackthorn and hazel scrub. North of the River Ouse near Sharnbrook a healthy population was recorded in the deciduous woods of Odell Great Wood, Park Wood, Dungee Wood, Forty Acre Wood, Great Hayes Wood, West Wood, Worley Wood, and Melchbourne Park. In the south of the county a scattering of records was reported from the clay-with-flint copses in the Caddington, Slip End, Kensworth, Whipsnade, and Studham areas, but most notable at Dedmansey Wood. By the late 1980s the main population was still along the Greensand Ridge woodlands with lesser numbers in the north-west of the county and a complete absence from the now more mature clay-with-flint woods south of Luton. Almost nothing is known of the breeding biology of this species in the county due to its secretive nature, apart from the fact that it is most vocal from the end of April to late May. On 14 June 1986 an adult was seen carrying food at Old Warden.

Two national censuses of the Nightingale by the BTO in 1976 and 1980 revealed 13–30 and 39 singing males respectively in Bedfordshire. The increase in numbers was considered to be as a result of more thorough observer coverage. The earliest ever spring migrant was at Tebworth on 7 April 1987 with normal arrival dates during the second half of April and early May and a mean arrival date of 20 April. Sightings of migrants away from traditional sites are rare with the following of note: one at The Lodge, Sandy on 30 April 1974, one at Blows Downs on 4 May 1984, and five at Priory CP on 26 May 1985. The only autumn record during the post-war period was an immature at Harrold CP on 27 August 1984.

Bluethroat

Luscinia svecica

A very rare vagrant.

There has been only one occurrence of this classic east-coast drift migrant in Bedfordshire, at Mountfield Road, Luton on 28 May 1987 (*Beds Naturalist* 42: 47). This record coincided with a large spring influx along the east coast when approximately 100 individuals were reported (*British Birds* 80: 458).

Black Redstart

Phoenicurus ochruros

An annual spring migrant, which has bred, and a rare autumn passage migrant and winter visitor (**Map 66**).

Steele-Elliott (1904) knew of the Black Redstart as a rare winter visitor to the county, referring to four occurrences in and around Bedford which were known to him from the Bedford taxidermist Mr A. Covington. The Luton taxidermist Mr Cane reported three records in the south of the county from 1865 onwards. In 1931 a male was noted at Eaton Socon on 3 March (*British Birds* 25: 54).

A study of data in the modern county bird reports 1946–87 reveals presence in 24 years with annual records from 1969 leading to an increase in sightings in the 1980s, particularly during the spring. This apparent increase is probably due to greater observer activity rather than a genuine increase in numbers.

Evidence of breeding has been noted in 11 years, mainly from the industrial areas of Luton and always in close contact with human activity. Details are as follows:

1958   A male in Luton on 4 April and 5 May.

1963   A pair was present at Vauxhall Motors, Luton from 21 June to 13 August.

1964   A first-year male singing from a dog-food factory in St Leonards Street, Bedford from 16 June to 20 July. A pair at Vauxhall Motors, Luton between 21 June and 13 August, though breeding was not confirmed.

[1966]   Two probable sightings in central Luton in June.

1970   A female at The Lodge, Sandy on 7 May, 29 June, and 30 August.

1972   A female built a nest, laying five eggs, at Vauxhall car factory, Luton. The eggs were incubated for a month but failed to hatch and were found to be infertile.

1973   The first successful breeding record for the county when a pair hatched four to five young in a crane at the Vauxhall car factory, Luton. Two young eventually fledged on 16 June and the family remained in the area for a further two weeks. A singing male was reported in central Luton during July.

1974   A pair bred in a nest on the side of a stone shed at Vauxhall car factory, Luton. Two broods of three juveniles were successfully raised in April and June respectively.

1976   A pair summered at the above locality.

1980   A male was seen with food at the Trimoco Hire depot, Skimpot, Dunstable.

1982   A pair reared two broods at RAE Thurleigh in a nest situated

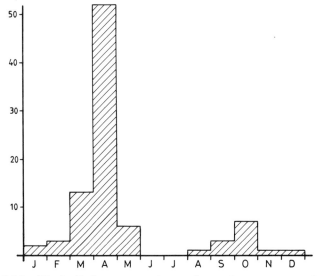

Figure 3.20 *Black Redstart: numbers observed on passage by months, 1946–87*

on a mobile refuelling trailer, which was occasionally moved up to 200 yards during incubation. All the young fell prey to a cat and the adults remained in the area until early October.

1986 A singing male at Vauxhall car factory on 12 May.

In recent years the Black Redstart has become a near regular spring passage migrant, in small numbers, particularly along the chalk downlands in the south of the county. The majority of sightings occur in early April when birds regularly appear at such well-watched localities as Blows Downs, Whipsnade Zoo, and Houghton Regis ChP. Outside the spring period this species is generally rare (Figure 3.20). A mid March to mid May breakdown of records has given the following results for 1946–87 using European standard five-day periods:

17–21 Mar.	22–6 Mar.	27–31 Mar.	1–5 Apr.	6–10 Apr.	11–15 Apr.
2	3	5	16	6	14

16–20 Apr.	21–5 Apr.	26–30 Apr.	1–5 May	6–10 May	11–14 May
12	6	9	4	3	1

Redstart

Phoenicurus phoenicurus

A regular passage migrant and rare summer visitor (**Map 67**).

The male Redstart observed in bright nuptial plumage is one of the county's most handsome summer visitors. Breeding numbers have evidently been declining since Davis (1855) described it as common in the Luton area during the early part of the last century. Steele-Elliott (1904) spoke of this species as having declined, although he still considered it to be a fairly abundant breeding bird throughout the county. In his correspondence with local taxidermists and bird collectors some idea of its distribution can be appreciated when compared to today. Often referred to as the 'Firetail', the Redstart bred commonly at Woburn Park, where it nested not only in holes in trees but also along the Park wall and in the deer-sheds. At Turvey it was found nesting in old stonework and at Bedford pairs used to nest regularly in pollarded willows along the River Ouse. The Redstart was recorded at Flitwick and Leighton Buzzard, where it was common, and around Tingrith where it nested in boxes placed in the grounds owned by Col. Barclay. Steele-Elliott personally found the Redstart at Ampthill, Bromham, Old Warden, and Southill, and similar districts where mature timber existed.

The decline in numbers continued and H. A. S. Key (1946) described the Redstart as being 'restricted to a few breeding pairs scattered along the Greensand Ridge'. From 1946 to 1987 it continued to breed locally, with the majority of records coming from the western end of the Ridge. Woburn is the centre of the complex where a small population still regularly breeds in the old pines at Charle Wood, and Old and New Wavendon Heaths. Sporadic breeding has occurred at Lowes Wood, Aspley Wood, and in the scattered oak woods in Woburn Park itself. To the south of Woburn near Heath and Reach occasional breeding has been reported from Stockgrove CP, Shire Oak, and Kings Wood, and similarly at the Millbrook complex. In the woods around Old Warden numbers have declined since the 1940s to such a degree that only one or two pairs bred annually in this area until the late 1960s at Palmers Wood, Warden Warren, Keepers Warren, Rowney Warren, Shuttleworth, and Southill Park, and it now no longer regularly nests, the last confirmed breeding being in 1969 at Southill Park. It is still possible that one or two pairs may linger on, as much of the prime habitat is private, keepered land and therefore inaccessible to the birdwatcher. Redstarts also bred regularly at Sandy Warren until the mid 1970s but have subsequently declined and presence has been sporadically noted in the breeding season at nearby Potton Wood.

Elsewhere in Bedfordshire, away from the centre of the county, nesting has occurred at Whipsnade in 1950; Luton Hoo in 1953, 1959 and 1973; Stagsden in 1956; and at Sharnbrook in 1977. Birds arrive on the breeding grounds by late April and normally raise two broods from mid May onwards. The nest is located in an old tree stump or hole where a clutch of five to seven eggs is laid. Once the breeding cycle is complete Redstarts are seldom seen in their natal woodlands after late July.

As a spring migrant it is regularly recorded on passage during April in small numbers, particularly along the chalk escarpment in the south of the county. Intensive fieldwork at Blows Downs during the 1980s (Dazley 1990) has shown mid April to be the period when

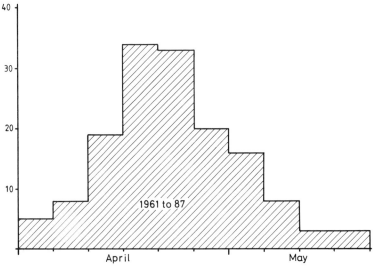

Figure 3.21 *Redstart: numbers observed on spring passage, 1961–87, using European standard five-day periods*

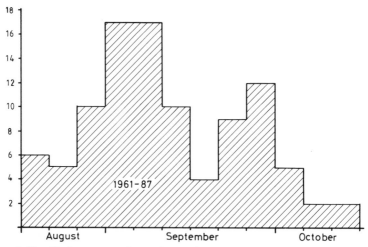

Figure 3.22 *Redstart: numbers observed on autumn passage, 1961–87, using European standard five-day periods, beginning 19–23 August*

passage is strongest. Sometimes up to five individuals can be seen daily filtering through the hawthorn scrub. The earliest migrants in Bedfordshire were two at Houghton Regis ChP on 23 March 1986 with the only other March record being a single at Thorn on 25 March 1956. Spring passage soon declines towards the end of April with limited numbers recorded by the latter part of May.

The autumn migration is typically more protracted and complex, and less understood. Significantly, daily autumn counts at Blows Downs are not maintained. The 1961–87 data reveals a more widespread distribution with a peak in early September and again later in the month. There are 10 October records, the latest being one which was caught and ringed at Odell Woods on 28 October 1979. Redstarts winter in a wide band of savannah habitat south of the Sahara desert, westwards towards the Gold Coast.

Whinchat

Saxicola rubetra

A regular passage migrant which formerly bred (**Map 68**).

The history of the Whinchat as a breeding species in Bedfordshire has been one of rapid decline, to a point where it now no longer breeds with us. In Steele-Elliott (1904) it was a common summer visitor breeding regularly in hay meadows, downland, rough grassland, and along railway embankments and cuttings. It seems as though the breeding status of this species remained unchanged until about the 1960s as from 1946 to 1967 it was recorded annually. The chalk downs around Luton and Dunstable were regular haunts along with the

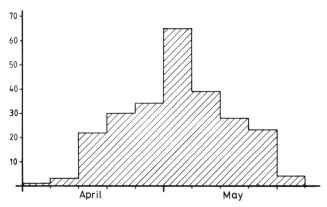

Figure 3.23 *Whinchat: numbers observed on spring passage, 1961–87, using European standard five-day periods, beginning 5–10 April*

peripheral grassy areas at the clay pits such as Stewartby and Coronation pits. Nesting was also regularly recorded at Bedford SF and Biggleswade Common during the 1950s. In 1967 the Whinchat was not recorded as breeding anywhere in the county, with only sporadic nesting until 1975 when a pair bred on the downs east of Luton. During fieldwork for the *Bedfordshire Bird Atlas* (Harding 1979) it was recorded in 14 tetrads (4%), with confirmed breeding in five tetrads and possible breeding in another nine. Subsequently it has not been recorded breeding, apart from possibly on Dunstable Downs in 1981 when a pair held territory during May. The loss of this species as a breeding bird in Bedfordshire correlates with a decline across much of south-east England during the post-war period, the reasons for which are not fully understood.

As a passage migrant however the Whinchat remains a familiar sight, with birds arriving in the county mainly from late April. A peak is reached in early May but passage continues throughout the

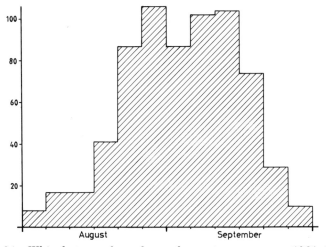

Figure 3.24 *Whinchat: numbers observed on autumn passage, 1961–87, using European standard five-day periods*

month, with sometimes one or two sightings into June. The Blows Downs migration watchpoint typically records a small spring passage annually, but elsewhere on the downs birds are regularly noted from Whipsnade through to the Pegsdon Hills. Elsewhere in the county during the spring, it is more thinly spread with a scattering of records from the river valleys and clay pits. The earliest ever migrant was at Potsgrove on 10 April 1987.

The Whinchat is far more numerous and widespread during the autumn and most are still recorded along the downland ridge, as well as at Dunstable and Bedford SWs and the county's mineral lakes. Returning birds begin to filter through the county from July, although a group of *c*.18 at Bedford SW in mid July 1981 was exceptional. Small parties of up to 10 are quite common from mid August to mid September as passage reaches a peak. October records are by no means rare until mid month and the latest bird seen was one at Shillington on 22 October 1987. This species winters in savannah scrubland in tropical Africa, south of the Sahara.

Stonechat

Saxicola torquata

An irregular passage migrant and occasional winter visitor (**Map 69**).

Steele-Elliott (1904) classified the 'Furzenchat' as an occasional breeding species, although formerly he considered it to be more common. In the 1870s it was recorded as nesting at Southill and Rowney Warren, and a pair was also noted near Henlow. Other localities mentioned where breeding occurred were Woburn, Leighton Buzzard, Bedford, and between Southill and Shefford.

In 1946 the Stonechat bred in the Flitwick area, and was present in the spring and summer at Barton Hills and Roxton. Severe winters cause a high degree of mortality to this species and following the very cold winter of 1947 there were no further confirmed records of nesting in the county until 1977, when a pair reared five young at Houghton Regis ChP. Juveniles were again raised at the latter site in 1978 (Harding 1979). Apart from suspected breeding at Eversholt in 1964 and Eaton Bray in 1971, there have been no subsequent confirmed breeding records, despite increased observer activity throughout the 1980s.

As a dispersive migrant and winter visitor to Bedfordshire the Stonechat varies in number considerably from year to year, depending upon its breeding successes mainly along the coastal areas on the western seaboard and heathlands of southern England. A study of data from 1946 to 1987 highlights this widely fluctuating pattern and reveals two distinct peaks. Following a series of relatively mild winters during the 1950s numbers increased to a peak over the

September–April period of 1959–60 and 1960–1. Up to 30 individuals were recorded in each period with wintering noted at Bedford SF, Barkers Lane GP, Stewartby Lake, Willington GP, and Wyboston Lake. Most records refer to single birds or pairs, although four wintered at Stewartby Lake in January 1961. There then followed a 10-year period after the harsh 1962–3 winter when the Stonechat was generally scarce and even absent in 1965. However in 1974–7 it was again present in good numbers during the autumn and winter at a wide range of localities; predominantly in the Marston Vale clay pits, along the Ouse valley, and at Dunstable and Bedford SWs. Numbers have continued to fluctuate throughout the 1980s.

As a spring migrant this species is much scarcer, with only a limited passage noted from March to the end of April, relating to wintering birds returning to their natal areas.

Wheatear

Oenanthe oenanthe

A common spring and autumn passage migrant and occasional breeder (**Map 70**).

Considering the habitat requirements for this species it seems likely that it has never been a common breeding bird in Bedfordshire. Formerly, when the chalk downlands were more widely sheep-grazed it nested more regularly, as mentioned by Steele-Elliott (1904) when a Mr Crossman found four nests on the downs at Whipsnade in May 1898. However numbers are limited even where breeding conditions are suitable. Elsewhere in the county the Wheatear used to breed in old stone walls at Sharnbrook, Stevington, Newnham Ruins, Cox's Pit, and on Crawley Heath.

A study of data from 1946 has shown breeding to have become more sporadic. In 1949 two pairs bred at RAE Thurleigh, followed by five pairs in 1950 that raised several juveniles. It seems likely that breeding occurred at this location until at least 1957 when possible nesting was mentioned in the county bird report. Breeding was considered likely, but not proven, at Barton Springs and Warden Hills in 1964, at Willington in 1968, and Streatley in 1969. Harding (1979) recorded it in 10 tetrads, with confirmed breeding at Sharpenhoe Clappers and Barton Hills, and in 1975 at Houghton Regis ChP where a pair reared three juveniles. Confirmed breeding was recorded at Warden Hills in 1979 and 1981, and again at Houghton Regis ChP in 1984. The most recent nesting locality for this species, and one which shows potential for the future, was in the Marston Vale at Rookery ClP in 1987, where a pair was noted with juveniles. Also in 1987 a juvenile noted at Bromham in July was considered to have been bred locally.

As a spring passage migrant the Wheatear is widely recorded across the county, often in small parties, and sometimes in groups of 10–20. The earliest records are one at Dunstable SW on 5 February 1967 and four at Barton Hills on 22 February 1981, both sites, significantly, in the south of the county. An ongoing study of Wheatear migration at Blows Downs, 1985–90 (Dazley 1990) on a daily basis from mid March

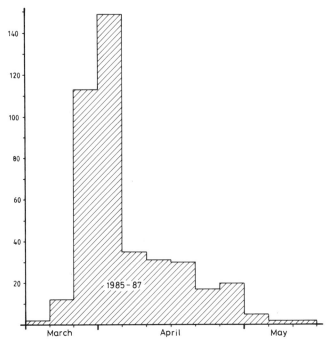

Figure 3.25 *Wheatear: numbers observed on spring passage at Blows Downs, 1985–7, using European standard five-day periods*

to mid May has shown a strong two-week peak at the end of March and beginning of April, followed by a rapid decline until the end of April when there is a second wave of birds, boosted by arrivals of the Greenland Race *O. o. leucorrhoa*. After mid May it is generally scarce with only the occasional straggler until the month end. This arrival pattern is reflected across the county, although nowhere else seems to receive the high numbers that are recorded on Blows Downs, where counts of over 20 birds have been:

1985 30 March, 28; 1 April, 27; 3 April, 20.
1986 3 April, 20.
1987 5 April, 20–30.

During the autumn, passage commences in late July and may last until the end of October with a slight peak from mid August to mid September. It is far less numerous at this time of year, although the distribution pattern is still as widespread. At Blows Downs the return migration of this species has been little studied, although it does not seem to reach the intensity of the spring passage. The latest Bedfordshire record was one at Flitwick on 1 November 1987.

242

Ring Ouzel

Turdus torquatus

A regular spring passage migrant.

Steele-Elliott (1904) considered the Ring Ouzel to be a regular migrant through the county, which was more usually recorded in the autumn than the spring, the reverse of which is true today. He documented many autumn records in the late nineteenth century, most of which had been shot, and several spring sightings. One reported by Mr A. F. Crossman on 18 January 1891 is the only winter record of Ring Ouzel in Bedfordshire, although the locality was not given. The Bedford taxidermist Mr A. Covington stated that this species was extremely shy and generally seen in groups of four or five. He considered the juveniles on autumn passage 'fat and good eating' and once received a pied specimen from Kempston.

Ring Ouzel data from 1946 has shown it to have been sporadically recorded until the mid 1960s, after which it has occurred annually. The earliest spring record was at Girtford on 28 February 1981 with the latest at Billington on 27 May 1983 where a party of four were noted. The main arrival is in early April followed by a peak in mid month which gradually declines by early May. The majority of records come from the chalk downland region in the south of the county and

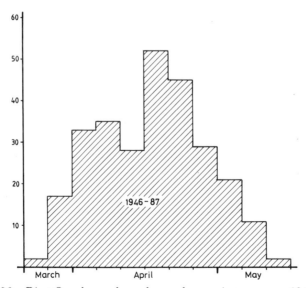

Figure 3.26   *Ring Ouzel: numbers observed on spring passage, 1946–87, using European standard five-day periods*

quite often involve small groups of up to five birds. Studies of spring migration at Blows Downs throughout the 1980s (Dazley 1990) have firmly established the Ring Ouzel as a regular passage migrant to Bedfordshire. Observations on a daily basis from 1985 highlight the scale of the passage. A group of seven on 28 March 1987 was the highest number ever recorded.

In the autumn it is far scarcer, with only 11 records in 1946–87; the earliest being one on 11 September 1977 at South Beds Golf Course, Luton and the latest at Bedford SF on 3 November 1963.

Blackbird

Turdus merula

An abundant resident and autumn passage migrant (**Map 71**).

The Blackbird is a common and widespread bird throughout Bedfordshire, exploiting a wide range of habitats from town gardens and woodland to hedgerows in the more agricultural districts. An assessment of its status from Steele-Elliott (1904) to the present suggests that this species has never been anything but numerous. Because the Blackbird is so familiar there is little reference to it in the county bird reports with only Harding (1979) giving any quantifiable data. Not surprisingly the Blackbird was recorded in all 371 of the county's tetrads with confirmed breeding in 307 tetrads, probable breeding in 43 tetrads and possible breeding in a further 21 tetrads. The only studies of population dynamics carried out are at Old Warden and The Lodge, Sandy, where Common Birds Census surveys have been monitoring breeding pairs since the early 1970s. Both localities have, in common with national trends, fluctuated from a peak in the mid 1970s to a slightly lower level during the 1980s.

The breeding season is normally from March to June, when two or three broods of between four to five eggs are laid. Exceptionally early nesting dates were recorded at Chiltern Green on 31 December 1954 when a nest was found completed, and on 15 January 1972 at Mowsbury Park, Bedford, when a single egg was found in a nest, followed by a clutch of three on 16th. The nest is usually situated in natural cover or in outbuildings, but can also be on the ground as recorded at Putnoe Wood and Stagsden in 1954, or at high level as at Kempston Park in 1955, 25 feet up an elm tree.

There is little relevant ringing data concerning the Blackbird in our county except for the record of one ringed at Whipsnade Zoo on 21 May 1937 which was recovered at Ennistymon, Co. Clare, Ireland on 7 January 1939 (*British Birds* 32: 332). In neighbouring Hertfordshire, ringing has revealed that many passage and wintering Blackbirds originate from Fenno-Scandia and the Low Countries (Gladwyn and Sage 1986), and it can be reasonably assumed that Bedfordshire's immigrant Blackbirds are of similar origin. Late autumn concentrations are regularly noted at Blows Downs, with a maximum of 500 on 25 October 1964; at Priory CP 88 were noted on 5 November 1983 and 62 on 23 November 1985.

Fieldfare

Turdus pilaris

A common passage migrant and winter visitor.

The harsh chuckling flight call of this handsome northern thrush is a familiar sound throughout Bedfordshire during the winter months. Early in its stay with us, it can be found stripping hedgerow berries, particularly hawthorn, but as these are quickly exhausted large flocks assemble on open country to feed, particularly along the river valleys. During severe weather this species will even resort to feeding in gardens, as noted by Steele-Elliott (1904) in the harsh winter of 1895, who referred to the Fieldfare by its local name of 'Felt' or 'Felfer'.

Studies of data from the post-war period reveal a peak autumn passage towards the end of October and into early November, although there are many September dates of lesser numbers. Of six August records, the earliest one was at Kempston on 9 August 1984 followed by one at Wyboston on 14 August 1966. Being a highly vocal migrant, the Fieldfare is easy to observe in late autumn as it passes westwards through the county. Notable observation points are the chalk downlands and the Marston Vale where sometimes many thousands can be seen on active migration. The following large-scale autumn movements are of note: 4,000 south-west over Bedford SF on 6 November 1960; 3,000 over Barton on 6 November 1966; 7,000 west over Bedford on 25 October 1974; and 1,000 over Priory CP on 2 November 1986. There are many records of loose migrating flocks of up to 500 strong during this period but unfortunately none of the counts are coordinated and quantifiable.

Due to the Fieldfare's nervous nature and its continuous quest for food, wintering birds may vary greatly in number throughout the season. Severe weather induces further movements westward during which time it can become almost absent. Mild wet weather attracts birds to feed on stubble, pastureland, airfields, playing fields, and parkland where flocks several hundreds strong are common. Exceptional gatherings were 2,000–3,000 at Bedford SF on 12 December 1954; 500+ at Barton Hill Farm on 9 January 1977; 810 at The Lodge, Sandy on 22 January 1984; and 700 at Everton on 9 March 1985. Other localities which regularly attract large wintering flocks of Fieldfares, along with other thrushes, are the ley meadows around Tottenhoe and Eaton Bray, flood meadows at Priory CP, Radwell, and Harrold, parkland at Luton Hoo, Woburn Abbey, and Wrest Park, and the airfields at Cranfield, Tempsford, Thurleigh, Cardington, and Luton.

Fieldfares roost communally in scrub or woodland at this time of year but numbers are poorly documented in Bedfordshire. The following counts are of note: 2,000 at Brickhill Woods on 29 December 1962 and 1,000 at Blows Downs on 23 November 1980. The return passage north-eastwards to Fenno-Scandia peaks in late March to early April with stragglers often noted during May. There are two June occurrences relating presumably to late spring migrants, at Wyboston on 12 June 1966 and at The Lodge, Sandy on 17 June 1978.

In 1976 and 1977 Fieldfares were recorded at Old Warden on the Greensand Ridge during the breeding season. On one occasion, in June 1976, a bird was seen carrying food, indicating probable breeding nearby with further sightings into July. In 1979 at the same site a bird held territory throughout late April, and on 5 May 1986 an agitated male was present but was not subsequently recorded.

Song Thrush

Turdus philomelos

A common resident and passage migrant (**Map 72**).

Steele-Elliott (1904) found the Song Thrush nesting abundantly across the county and considered it to be one of our commonest birds. Indeed it was still a very familiar species when fieldwork for the *Bedfordshire Bird Atlas* commenced in 1968. Harding (1979) recorded it in all 371 tetrads with a high instance of confirmed breeding in 294 (79%) tetrads. Song Thrushes nest low down in bushes, brambles, or similar thick cover and will even breed in sheds and outbuildings close to human habitation. Two to three clutches of three to five eggs are laid from April to May and in urban areas there is a high degree of predation of fledglings by domestic cats.

Although the Song Thrush is still a common bird in the county, numbers have steadily declined since the early 1970s. Two regularly monitored Common Birds Census plots at Old Warden and The Lodge, Sandy correlate with the national trend. At Old Warden an average of 40 pairs bred on a mixed farmland plot in the early 1970s compared to a mid 1980s average of 10 pairs and at The Lodge, Sandy numbers have dropped similarly. Reasons for this apparent decline are unclear and probably relate to a number of factors including climatic fluctuations and changing farming practices as referred to by O'Connor and Shrubb (1986).

Studies elsewhere in Britain have found that some British Song Thrushes migrate into France and the Iberian Peninsula during late autumn (Lack 1986), during which period birds on passage have been recorded at Blows Downs. Another movement occurs from north-east Europe in the autumn with migrants passing through the British

Isles. A Song Thrush ringed on 25 October 1982 at Rottumerplaat (Frisian Islands), Netherlands was recovered at Langford on 1 February 1984.

Redwing
Turdus iliacus

An abundant spring and autumn passage migrant and common winter visitor.

In general the Redwing arrives slightly earlier during the autumn than the Fieldfare, with which it is often associated as a winter visitor. It is mainly a nocturnal migrant and can be easily tracked across the county by means of its distinctive 'see-ip' contact call. The first migrants usually pass overhead during late September, with a peak from mid October to mid November. Studies by Reay (1959) of Redwings migrating over Bedford from 11 October to 14 November 1960 revealed peak passage dates on 12 October and 8 November with birds moving in a southerly direction. In 1972 a 'huge mid-October' passage was recorded westwards over Sandy and Bedford when *c*.2,125 and *c*.4,500 were counted respectively on 12 and 15 October. More recently a well-recorded early autumn movement was documented on 25 September 1984 which involved, predominantly, flocks of less than 200 birds. Sightings were reported from 10 localities across the county, with a near continuous day and night passage over Dunstable and Blows Downs. The highest count was at Priory CP where 700 were logged moving south-west in 90 minutes; but clearly many thousands of Redwings were on the move across Bedfordshire that day.

As with the Fieldfare, Redwings are continually restless when with us and are subject to further cold-weather movements during the winter months. When the hips and hawthorn berries have been picked clean they seek out worms and other invertebrates from wet meadows, pastureland, airfields, and parklands and will readily come into gardens and orchards to feed on rotting fruit. Flocks of up to 500 can be seen regularly at this time of the year and numbers vary annually depending on weather conditions. Records of large winter flocks are irregularly noted in the bird reports from 1946, but the following are worthy of mention: 1,000 on 2 February and 2,000 on 12 December at Bedford SF in 1948; 1,500 at Felmersham on 17 March 1972; and at Sewell a flock of 4,000 on 30 December 1976 which had reduced to 2,500 on 2 January 1977. Roost counts are similarly irregularly recorded in Bedfordshire but include: 1,500 at Brickhill Woods on 29

December 1962; 1,000+ at Charle Wood on 10 February 1978; 2,000 at Harrold GP on 2 December; 3,500 at Shillington on 9 December 1979; and 2,000 at Blows Downs in November 1980.

The spring passage is less dramatic than in the autumn and by the end of April most have returned to breed in the northern European birch forests. Occasionally during this period the Redwing is met with in song, as at Bromham on 16 March 1953, Bedford on 18 March 1955, Clapham on 12 April 1971, and on the Pegsdon Hills on 16 April 1978. There are only four May records, at Sandy Lodge on 8 May 1973, Priory CP on 11 May 1984, Kensworth on 2 May 1985, and at The Lodge, Sandy where one was present from 11 May to 15 June 1976.

Ringing results from other counties in the region have shown that the majority of our Redwings originate from Fenno-Scandia and northern Russia and are of the race *T. i. iliacus*. However, a male ringed at Waterloo Thorns, Everton on 12 October 1987 was of the Icelandic race *T. i. coburni*.

Mistle Thrush

Turdus viscivorus

A widely distributed resident (**Map 73**).

This species was known to Steele-Elliott (1904) by its local name of 'Screaming Thrush' or 'Screamer.' He considered it to be common throughout the county, a status similarly afforded it today, although in some more intensively farmed districts, particularly in north Bedfordshire, it is absent.

The Mistle Thrush is one of our earliest breeding birds with pairs well established by late February in preparation for egg-laying in March and April. At this time of year it frequents woodland, orchards, parkland, large gardens, and areas of scattered timber, providing nearby pasture of uncultivated land is available on which to feed. Harding (1979) recorded breeding in 232 (63%) of the county's tetrads, with confirmed breeding in 114 tetrads, probable breeding in 33 tetrads and possible breeding in a further 85. In early spring the nest is almost as conspicuous as the prominently singing male, and is normally situated in the fork of a tree, often at considerable height. There are usually two clutches of four to six eggs, and as soon as breeding is finished by late May or early June family parties desert their natal areas.

During the summer and autumn months post-breeding flocks are highly mobile, exploiting freshly mown hay meadows and grazing land. Many move to the county's parklands such as Luton Hoo, Woburn Park, Wrest Park, and Whipsnade Zoo, where gatherings of up to 50 are quite regular. However a count of *c*.60 feeding on rowan berries near Shire Oak, Heath and Reach on 1 September 1973 was exceptional.

From December onwards the post-breeding flocks tend to disperse and the Mistle Thrush becomes far more elusive. It is well known that adults will vehemently defend a winter berry or fruit supply, and Snow (1969) postulated that many first-winter birds may partially migrate southwards into France if they fail to establish such a winter territory.

Grasshopper Warbler

Locustella naevia

A regular but localised summer visitor (**Map 74**).

The breeding population of this species has fluctuated over the past 100 years in relation to habitat changes in England and climatic variations in its wintering quarters south of the Sahara. In Bedfordshire it is a localised yet widespread summer migrant breeding in dry open scrubland on the downs, young conifer plantations and rough ground along the river valleys, and around the clay pits. Whatever habitat is utilised, bramble patches or low thickets of hawthorn and dog rose are always in evidence, from which the Grasshopper Warbler emits a high-pitched song known as 'reeling'. The nest is situated amongst a tangle of ground cover and there are normally two broods.

Steele-Elliott (1904) mentioned Sheerhatch Wood as a stronghold for this species and it was also reported in woodland at Stagsden and Bromham. The osier beds and water meadows along the Ouse valley were used for breeding. In the Ivel valley at Langford, in 1891, a Mr King found a nest containing several young in an osier bed. This particular wetland habitat has since all but disappeared from the county. Nesting also occurred at Harlington, Thurleigh, Oakley, Flitwick, Pegsdon, and in the Woburn area.

A study of post-war breeding data records a population increase during the 1960s, correlating with an increase in coniferous plantations, particularly along the Greensand Ridge. This boom coincided with the inception of fieldwork for the *Bedfordshire Bird Atlas* (Harding 1979), revealing some high concentrations. In 1968 25–40 pairs were estimated to have been present in the 10km square TL14, predominantly at the Old Warden complex, Rowney Warren, and Home Wood, followed by an increase in 1969 to 51–70 pairs. A further 25–35 pairs were recorded in TL06 during 1969 and breeding records were received from every 10km square in the county. Over the 10-year study period for the Atlas breeding was recorded in 86 (23%) tetrads with the majority of records (65 of them) in the probable breeding category. During the 1970s and 1980s annual numbers have steadily declined to 29–30 singing males mainly from the Greensand woodlands at Aspley Heath, Charle Wood, Maulden Wood, Wilstead Wood, Old Warden, Home Wood, and Potton Wood. 1981 was a record year when 44–6 singing males were recorded from 18 localities.

As a migrant species the Grasshopper Warbler arrives from mid April with a peak during early May, steadily declining towards the month end. It is then that it occurs outside its normal breeding habitat. There have been two early arrival dates; one at Dunstable SW on 2 April 1977 and one at Flitwick Moor on 7 April 1961. As a returning passage migrant it is silent and unobtrusive and there are few records, the latest being at Chicksands Wood on 25 August 1986.

Sedge Warbler

Acrocephalus schoenobaenus

A locally numerous summer visitor and common passage migrant Map 75).

The 'Reed Sparrow' as it was sometimes referred to in the nineteenth century, used to be common everywhere in Bedfordshire, prior to changes in land use during the present century. However, it is still commonly found along the river valleys and around the margins of mineral excavations where it can be locally abundant. Lesser numbers occur along farmland ditches and drains, and there are thriving populations at the county's three main sewage treatment works at Bedford, Chalton, and Dunstable, where patches of lush, aquatic herbage, consisting mainly of willowherb, sedge, and nettle flourish. Occasionally it is found in drier areas, an adaptation which seems to be increasing in recent years. The nest is usually built close to the ground amongst thick herbaceous growth from where one or two broods are reared. Steele-Elliott (1904) recorded a nest at Tempsford which was situated eight feet above ground atop a hedgerow.

Harding (1979) recorded presence in 135 (36%) of the county's 371 tetrads with confirmed breeding in 58 tetrads, probable breeding in 46 tetrads, and possible breeding in a further 31 tetrads. There was a noticeable lack of records from the drier areas in the north and south of the county, and a loose correlation with distributions along the Ouse and Ivel river valleys. An indication of population levels was attained in 1983 when a survey of riparian birds was carried out along three main watercourses. Along the Bedfordshire section of the River Ouse 230 confirmed breeding territories were counted, with 32 along the Ivel and 12 along the Ouzel. At Priory CP counts of singing males have recorded 44 in 1982 (Spring Passage), 17 in 1983, 22 in 1984, and 26 in 1985, 1986, and 1987.

As a spring migrant the Sedge Warbler is widely recorded from mid April into May, when it can occur in atypical surroundings such as town gardens. There is a light spring passage through Blows Downs most years. The earliest county record was at South Mills NR on 4 April 1985. By late August most birds have deserted their breeding grounds, as passage migrants continue to pass through the county until late September. There are five October records, the latest being at Barkers Lane GP on 8 October 1966; although Steele-Elliott refers to one being shot near Langford in December.

The Sedge Warbler winters south of the Sahara in the tropical region of Africa and southern Africa. The only foreign ringing recovery relating to Bedfordshire was one ringed at Bedford on 10 July 1971 and recovered in Morocco on 11 April 1972. Another record of interest was a bird ringed at Harrold GP on 15 August 1981 which was recaptured on Fair Isle on 28 May 1982.

Marsh Warbler

Acrocephalus palustris

A very rare vagrant.

The rapid decline of the Marsh Warbler during the 1980s has brought it to the verge of extinction as a breeding species at its former stronghold in the English West Midlands. As a summer visitor it spends only a short period in England, from June to August, enough time to rear just one brood. It winters in east Africa.

Formerly this species was more widespread across the lowlands of central England and it was from the latter part of the nineteenth century that Steele-Elliott (1904) draws reference to a correspondence with a Mr C. F. Woods: 'About 1868, when living at Woburn I had a nest of six eggs brought to me from Crawley Moor. From the references made at the time I have little doubt of the correctness in their identification. I think also I have seen the bird in other localities around Woburn.'

The only record this century comes from Mr George T. Atchison: 'On July 1st 1917 I found a nest with eggs built two yards on the Huntingdon side of the Hunts–Beds border. The nest was in a bed of small osiers, very much overgrown with a mass of nettles, hops, bineweed, etc. Mr W. Farren of Cambridge, has been kind enough to confirm the accuracy of identification' (*British Birds* 11: 66).

251

Reed Warbler

Acrocephalus scirpaceus

A localised summer visitor and common passage migrant (**Map 76**).

Known simply as 'Reed-bird' or 'Reed-Wren' this species was considered to be a common summer migrant by Steele-Elliott (1904), who recorded it plentifully along all our main watercourses and parkland lakes. Few species are so dependent on one plant for breeding as the Reed Warbler and consequently it is rarely seen away from phragmites beds, except on migration. The general 'tidying up' of the countryside, and in particular the canalisation of our waterways, in recent years has seen a steady decline in numbers: indeed if it were not for quarrying activities which allow phragmites to flourish the Reed Warbler would be a scarce breeding bird in Bedfordshire.

Harding (1979) recorded breeding in 58 (16%) of the county's tetrads with a clear distribution pattern along the Ouse and Ivel rivers. The main colonies along the Ouse are where gravel has been extracted and the pits have become exhausted, allowing marginal wetland habitats to prosper. At Harrold CP some 30 pairs nest most years with lesser numbers at Priory CP, Willington GP, and Wyboston Lakes. In 1983 a survey along the River Ouse recorded 112 singing males mainly in small colonies of under five pairs scattered along the river in small patches of reed. Small populations also exist along the River Ivel, notably at Girtford and Langford, and along the River Ouzel around Leighton Buzzard. In the Marston Vale small colonies have become established in reed beds at Brogborough Lake and Coronation ClP with peripheral breeding at Stewartby Lake, Rookery ClP, and Chimney Corner ClP. In the south of the county there are three isolated colonies of up to 20 pairs each, at Luton Hoo, Battlesden Lake, and Houghton Regis ChP. Southill Lake regularly holds a small colony and sporadic breeding has been reported from Toddington Manor, Flitwick Moor, Pavenham, Felmersham NR, Stanbridgeford, and sewage treatment works at Bedford, Chalton, and Dunstable.

The Reed Warbler constructs its intricate nest in May in phragmites beds, wrapped around reed stems, in which it lays a clutch of three to five eggs. Many pairs are double-brooded and the first brood is a favourite host for the parasitic Cuckoo. Occasionally nests are recorded away from reed beds, as at Great Barford in 1955 when nests were found in osiers and even in a nearby wheat field. In 1986 two pairs were found nesting in a hawthorn hedge at Grovebury Farm SP 100 metres from water.

The earliest spring migrant was at Houghton Regis ChP on 7 April 1960, although the majority of birds do not arrive until early May. Studies at Blows Downs (Dazley 1990) during the 1980s have revealed two passage migrants in song during May.

The return passage is a protracted affair with a steady movement from August through September and into early October. The latest recorded sighting was of one at Priory CP on 20 October 1987. The

Reed Warbler winters in tropical Africa south of the Sahara and there are two foreign ringing recoveries of Bedfordshire birds *en route* to their winter quarters. One ringed at Bedford on 20 August 1967 was recovered on *c*.15 October 1967 in the Algarve, Portugal and one at Girtford on 10 August 1985 was recovered at Etang Des Noes, France on 1 September 1985.

Subalpine Warbler

Sylvia cantillans

A very rare vagrant.

This Mediterranean scrub warbler has only occurred in Bedfordshire once, a male at Bison Hill on 7 May 1986. This record falls in the peak spring arrival period for this vagrant to Britain (Dymond *et al.* 1989), and is one of the few inland records.

Lesser Whitethroat

Sylvia curruca

A widespread summer visitor and common autumn passage migrant (**Map 77**).

The true status of this shy, retiring warbler is difficult to assess, due to the paucity and irregularity of records over the years. Davis (1874) regarded it as common around Luton, an area of the county from which it is regularly noted today, and Steele-Elliott (1904) regarded it as 'equally distributed over the county'. Harding (1979) reaffirmed this status by plotting it in 166 (45%) of the county's tetrads. The Lesser Whitethroat is a bird of marginal habitats, such as scrubland found around many of our mineral quarries and along the chalklands. It occurs in mature hedgegrows and thickets of hawthorn and black-thorn but will not tolerate scant hedgerow cover on intensive farm-land. Plantations in the early stages of growth are utilised along with gorse-covered land along the Greensand Ridge, particularly at Heath and Reach, Maulden, and Sandy. Studies on Lesser Whitethroats by Wilkinson (1962) at Biddenham 1960–1 revealed nest-building to take place in mid May, followed by egg-laying with the young hatching in early June. The young deserted the nest about 10 days later and ranged over the natal site until late July. The nest site at Biddenham was situated in a hawthorn in a large garden bordered by farmland.

Lesser Whitethroats arrive in Bedfordshire in late April to mid May with the earliest being one at Odell Plantation on 12 April 1980. Spring migrants are more often than not heard in song, a dry tuneless rattle. On return passage from late July to September there is a notable increase in sightings in late August as migration reaches a peak. Observations at Blows Downs during this period in 1983 revealed 17 birds in one small fall of migrants. It is not unusual during August and September for birds to occur in town gardens. Most migrants have moved through by late September and the only October sighting was at Brickhill, Bedford on 18 October 1975.

There is one foreign ringing recovery of a Bedfordshire bird that had been ringed at Harrold GP on 17 May 1980 and was recovered at Krenovice, Czechoslovakia on 28 April 1981. English Lesser Whitethroats winter in north-east Africa.

Whitethroat

Sylvia communis

A common and widespread summer visitor and passage migrant (**Map 78**).

Steele-Elliott (1904) regarded the Whitethroat as our commonest warbler and due to its familiarity with the countryman it was known by a variety of local names such as Haybird, Nettle-creeper, and Cutthroat. It is a typical 'scrub' warbler being found in farmland hedgerows, woodland glades and borders, scrubland, and large bushy parks and gardens. The nest is built low down in dense cover and a clutch of four to five eggs is laid from late May onwards. There are usually two broods.

During the winter of 1968–9 Whitethroat numbers were severely depleted as a result of a prolonged drought in their wintering quarters in the Sahel region of Africa. The summer of 1969 saw only a quarter of the normal population return, the like of which has not been seen with any other common Bedfordshire migrant. The crash occurred during fieldwork for the *Bedfordshire Bird Atlas* (Harding 1979), which probably accounted for the less than complete distribution on the tetrad map. However, because of a partial recovery during the latter part of the 10-year survey it was eventually recorded in 265 (71%) of the county's 371 tetrads. Numbers have continued to increase through the 1980s but it is still not as plentiful as before 1969.

The Whitethroat's scratchy song betrays its presence on spring migration as the first birds begin to arrive in mid April. Passage continues well into May with a peak early on in the month. The earliest record was at Stockgrove CP on 4 April 1981. Autumn passage is from early August to mid September with the latest record being at South Mills NR on 10 October 1987. This species winters in Africa south of the Sahara.

Garden Warbler

Sylvia borin

A common summer visitor and autumn migrant (**Map 79**).

Steele-Elliott (1904) refers to this species as being common throughout the county with a population status similar to the Blackcap. However he goes on to emphasise the difficulties he had in separating the two species by song alone, a problem which still exists today. In general the Garden Warbler prefers woodland with a thick understorey of scrub and will even tolerate downland hawthorn scrub, where there are few standard trees. Young coniferous plantations are a favourite haunt as are large gardens and rough uncultivated land providing there is a tangle of briars, nettles, and brambles.

Harding (1979) recorded the Garden Warbler in 159 (43%) of the county's 371 tetrads and considered it be less common than the Blackcap. Three distinctive distribution bands were noted on the tetrad maps. The first, in the south of the county, was associated with the chalk downland and clay-with-flint copses, with a second band relating to the Greensand Ridge woodlands; a smaller concentration was noted in the deciduous woods in the north around Odell, Souldrop, and Melchbourne. The Garden Warbler nests low down in shrubs or bramble from where a clutch of four to five eggs are laid. They are laid in late May or early June and there is generally only one brood.

Although the earliest spring migrant was on 12 April 1972 at Luton, the main arrival is from late April to early May and lasts until the end of the month. Return passage commences in late July and peaks in September, when an increase in passage birds had been noted recently at South Mills NR and Blows Downs. It is normally silent on autumn migration, therefore one singing at Biggleswade on 18 August 1945 was of interest. There are fewer than 10 October records, the latest being on 7 October 1985 at Priory CP. This species winters in central and southern Africa.

Blackcap

Sylvia atricapilla

An abundant summer visitor and passage migrant, increasingly wintering in small numbers (**Map 80**).

The status of this species as a common and widespread summer migrant seems to have changed little since Steele-Elliott's (1904) day. It is the most arboreal of the Sylvia warblers preferring broad-leaf and plantation woodland with ground cover to more open scrubland habitats. The Blackcap is equally abundant in different types of woodland, such as a dry mature deciduous type at Stockgrove CP to the damper Maulden Woods and the carr-type birch and alder wood at Flitwick Moor. It occurs in town parkland, large gardens, and most of the county's smaller copses and spinnies. Harding (1979) recorded it in 255 tetrads showing a widespread distribution pattern across the county. The nest is built from May onwards in a thicket, with a clutch of three to six eggs laid towards the end of the month. There are often two broods. An early instance of breeding was recorded at Hardwick Spinney, Stagsden in 1952 when a nest containing one egg was found on 20 April, with four young fledging by 16 May.

Due to this species' increasing habit of overwintering with us, it is difficult to determine which are genuine early spring migrants. In general, however, it is not uncommon for passage birds to occur from mid March, but the main movement is from mid April to mid May, as confirmed by studies on spring migration at Blows Downs (Dazley 1990). Return passage commences in late July and lasts until September with a peak in August when birds are often encountered in urban settings, sometimes in song.

The Blackcap winters in south-east Europe and north Africa, particularly in the Iberian Peninsula. Bedfordshire's only foreign ringing recovery concerns a bird ringed at Cranfield on 15 September 1982 that was recovered at Villa Martin, Cadiz in Spain on 20 November 1982, having moved 1,736km south-south-west.

Overwintering by this species is a recent phenomenon in response to generally milder winters. It often relies on food put out on bird tables and in defence of this can become highly territorial and aggressive to other species. Ivy berries also form a staple part of its diet at this time of year. The first record of overwintering in the county was at Oakley in February 1955 followed by one at Leighton Buzzard on 1 March 1959 and one at Bedford in February 1972. Subsequently Blackcaps have been noted from December to February in every year from 1974 except 1978, and during the 1980s records have come from up to seven different localities.

Wood Warbler

Phylloscopus sibilatrix

A local summer visitor and rare passage migrant (**Map 81**).

The earliest historical record of the Wood Warbler was in 1847–8 when Professor Newton corresponding with Steele-Elliott (1904) stated that 'the Wood Wren was rather plentiful in the plantations of oak and larch at The Hazells, near Everton', although Steele-Elliott considered it to be rather uncommon and very local in its distribution across the county as a whole. He knew it to breed at nine woodlands, mainly on the Greensand Ridge, around the Woburn and Southill estates, and further south at Luton Hoo. The woods adjoining Ampthill Park and Aspley woods are also mentioned, both being sites where this species still occurs. Hine (1934) corroborates breeding at Southill and nearby Warden and Rowney Warren, referring to it as a regular nester.

Between 1946 and 1987 the localised status of the Wood Warbler has changed very little in Bedfordshire, though in only six years was it unrecorded. From 1961 it has occurred annually, albeit erratically in numbers, with a high of eight pairs in 1967 contrasting with solitary sightings during the early 1970s. Harding (1979) recorded it in 14 tetrads, five pairs being the maximum in 1974, but in three years it failed to breed at all. This population fluctuation is no doubt due to the Wood Warbler being on the eastern edge of its British range in Bedfordshire, coupled with the hazards of being a sub-Saharan migrant.

Of the 21 Greensand woodlands in which this species has been recorded, only Charle Wood, Aspley Heath, The Lodge, Sandy, and Maulden Wood are regularly used, with sporadic appearances at Stockgrove CP, Ampthill Park Wood, and in the clay-with-flint woods around Luton Hoo and Studham. At Charle Wood it is found in mature conifers with scattered sweet chestnut and oak, allowing a sparse undergrowth of bracken and brambles to form. Around Aspley Heath the pine plantations are more uniform but have been invaded by silver birch forming a close upper canopy and an understorey almost devoid of ground cover except for bracken and occasional clumps of bilberry. Undoubtedly some Wood Warblers are overlooked each year, despite the distinctive song, but it seems unlikely that more than 10 pairs are present in any one year, with one to five pairs about the average.

Spring migrants have been recorded from seven scattered localities away from known breeding woods between 21 April and 11 May. In 1983 a small influx occurred consisting of three birds at Bedford on 23 April (one stayed until 28 April), three singing males at a Luton cemetery on 1 May, one at Luton Hoo on 2 May, and another at Blunham on 11 May. The earliest spring record was at Kingshoe Wood on 12 April 1952. Departure for the wintering grounds, to forests and savannah south of the Sahara, commences in late July, with two at The Lodge, Sandy on 2 September 1982 the latest recorded.

Chiffchaff

Phylloscopus collybita

A widespread summer visitor and common passage migrant (**Map 82**).

The Chiffchaff is a common summer migrant to Bedfordshire, breeding in all types of woodland providing there is an ample upper canopy of standards and some ground cover in which to nest. The domed nest is situated amongst undergrowth where a clutch of five to six eggs is laid. There are often two broods.

Common Birds Census data suggest a general decline in numbers during the 1970s which could account for the gaps in distribution in Harding (1979), who recorded it in 254 (68%) of the county's tetrads, with a noticeable concentration of records from the Greensand Ridge woodlands. The Chiffchaff's distinctive double-note song enables it to be instantly recognised on spring migration. Passage birds can often be heard from early March but the main movement does not occur until late March/early April and can be quite dynamic, followed by a sudden drop off from mid April. The autumn passage takes place throughout September and prevails into the first half of October. It is widespread and less dynamic than in the spring, and birds are often heard emitting a half-hearted version of the spring song.

As with the Blackcap, this species has taken to overwintering in recent years with the first such record noted at Barkers Lane GP on 26 December 1966. Subsequently, wintering birds have been recorded every year to 1987, except for three years in the 1970s. In 1986 birds were observed at a record eight localities, widely scattered across the county but with a preference for wetland sites. The Priory CP/Bedford SW area consistently harbours one or two wintering birds along with The Lodge, Sandy, Stewartby Lake, and the sewage treatment works at Dunstable and Chalton. An individual at Stewartby Lake on 6 December 1987 showed characteristics of the northern race, *P. c. tristis*. The majority of British Chiffchaffs winter around the Mediterranean Basin, the Iberian Peninsula, and into north Africa.

Willow Warbler

Phylloscopus trochilus

An abundant summer visitor and passage migrant (**Map 83**).

The Willow Warbler is the most widespread and abundant member of the warbler tribe, occurring as it does in a wide variety of woodland and marginal habitats: indeed there are few county woodlands that do not resound to its sweet, lilting song during the summer months. Apparently its status today is much the same as in the Victorian period as both Steele-Elliott (1904) and Davis (1855) refer to it as being a very common species, which was known locally as the Willow Wren, Banking Bottle, or Oven Bird, the latter two names relating to the shape of its nest.

Harding (1979) recorded this species in 304 (82%) of the county's tetrads, mapping a widespread distribution, and in some areas recording high densities of singing males. Fieldwork carried out by Halton over the years 1979–83 (Nau *et al.* 1987) at Dunstable Downs showed the Willow Warbler to be the most abundant breeding bird with an average of 144 pairs per year. Of the 31 breeding species recorded during the study period the Willow Warbler accounted for 28% of the total number of breeding birds, almost double that of its nearest competitor, the Yellowhammer. Common Birds Census data from two woodland plots at Old Warden and The Lodge, Sandy suggest numbers were at an all-time high in the mid 1980s, with 36 pairs and 42 pairs breeding in 1985 and 1986 respectively. The domed nest is built on or near the ground amongst grass or rough herbage in which a clutch of six to seven eggs is laid. The breeding cycle begins in May and normally involves only one brood, but some second broods do occur.

The Willow Warbler is a very common spring passage migrant, occurring as it does from early April to late May. Studies at Blows Downs (Dazley 1990) during the 1980s have shown a peak passage around mid April. On occasions, when weather conditions are correct, small falls occur as happened on 17 April 1984, when there were 50 at Priory CP, 32 at Stewartby Lake, and 20 at Brogborough Lake, followed by 32 on Blows Downs on 20 April. The earliest spring record was one at Bedford on 17 March 1952. During the autumn large numbers pass through the county on a broad front during August and September. Between 1946 and 1987 there were three records in early October and one exceptionally late bird at Blunham on 10 November 1984. Steele-Elliott (1904) recorded one at Newham on 27 December 1878.

British Willow Warblers belong to the nominate race *P. t. trochilus* which winters in Africa south of the Sahara. There is one foreign ringing recovery, a bird ringed in Bedfordshire at Harrold GP on 4 July 1979 which was retrapped at Setubal in southern Portugal on 21 October of the same year.

Goldcrest

Regulus regulus

A widespread resident and common autumn passage migrant (**Map 84**).

The tiny Goldcrest is one of Bedfordshire's most inconspicuous birds, preferring to stay in the thick cover of coniferous trees for much of the year. Its thin, high-pitched tinkling song is commonly heard throughout the county's evergreen woodlands, particularly along the Greensand Ridge, but also in deciduous timber where thickets of ivy abound. Harding (1979) highlighted its preference for pine woods, with a wide band of records running through the middle of the county south-west to north-east. Other concentrations were noted in the deciduous woods in north Bedfordshire and on the clay-with-flint copses in the south. Across the county as a whole it was recorded breeding in 143 (39%) tetrads during the study period 1968–77. The nest is a delicate structure, normally suspended in thick cover at the end of a conifer branch. The clutch size varies from seven to ten eggs and there are two broods.

The Goldcrest is susceptible to a high mortality rate during harsh winter weather, at which time of year it tends to join other small passerines, forming roving flocks, throughout the county's woodlands and scrubland.

Migration through the county is poorly documented, although during the spring at Blows Downs it is erratically recorded from mid March to mid April. In the autumn from September to November large numbers move through the county on a broad front and can occur at unlikely localities such as town parks and gardens. This late autumn movement was noted by the Bedford taxidermist Mr A. Covington in the late nineteenth century when he recorded 'considerable numbers' about Bedford, some being picked up exhausted. He also recorded as many as 42 Goldcrests being brought into his shop one day, the majority killed by children with catapults.

Firecrest

Regulus ignicapillus

A rare breeding species and increasing spring passage migrant.

Steele-Elliott (1904) knew of only two records of this species in the county, both of which were received by the Bedford taxidermist Mr A. Covington. The first was a male killed at Ampthill about 1873, followed by a female, also from Ampthill, for which no date was given. On 1 April 1916 the Duchess of Bedford (1915–16) described in some detail the sighting of a male Firecrest that she observed from a purpose-built bird hide at Woburn Park.

Analysis of records in the county bird reports 1946–87 has shown a marked increase in records in recent years, with a single sighting in 1969 followed by a series of records from 1972 to 1976 which correlated with the establishment of a breeding population in the coniferous woodlands of neighbouring Buckinghamshire (Batten 1971) and elsewhere in southern England (Batten 1973). It was during the latter colonisation period that Bedfordshire had its first probable breeding record in the pine woods of the Greensand Ridge on the county boundary with Buckinghamshire. Breeding season records are as follows:

1972   A singing male at Aspley Heath on 14 May, followed by a second on 7 June, with probable fledged young with one pair on 25 June. All birds had dispersed by mid July.

1974   A pair at Aspley Heath during the breeding season, outcome unknown (Harding 1979).

1975   A singing male at Warren Wood on 8–9 June.

1976 A singing male at Houghton Hall, Houghton Regis on 12–15 June.
1983 A male singing at Old Warden on 8 May.
1984 A male at The Lodge, Sandy on 1 May was joined about three weeks later by a female. A nest was built in a Douglas fir close to the main building of the RSPB headquarters from which at least three juveniles fledged on 16 July, with the last sighting on 19th. This was Bedfordshire's first confirmed breeding record.
Two at Aspley Heath on 15 May.
1985 A pair was suspected of breeding at Ampthill Park Wood from 17 April to 2 July. A male at The Lodge, Sandy on 4–13 June, with a male at Old Warden on 25 May.

England's breeding population of Firecrests is migratory and is increasingly recorded in the county on spring migration, especially at Blows Down (Dazley 1990). All spring migrants for the period 1947–87 are listed below:

1973 A female at Tebworth on 1 and 6 April.
1975 One at Dunstable Downs on 8 March.
1981 A male at Little Brickhill Copse and a pair at Rushmere Park on 28 March.
1982 One at Shortmead House, Biggleswade 12–13 April.
1984 A single at Blows Downs 11–12 April.
1986 A female on Blows Down 18–19 April and one at The Lodge, Sandy on 4 May.
1987 A male at Aspley Heath on 26 April.

There is only one autumn record, at Houghton Regis on 13 October 1969, and a single winter sighting from Flitwick Moor on 9 February 1987.

Spotted Flycatcher

Musciapa striata

A locally common summer visitor (**Map 85**).

The Spotted Flycatcher is one of our latest arriving summer migrants from its winter quarters in tropical and southern Africa. It was known locally as the Common Flycatcher or Wall Bird, a name derived from its breeding habits. Steele-Elliott (1904) considered it to be common and widespread throughout the county during the nineteenth century and remarked upon its affinity to human habitation, quoting one nest in Lurke Street, Bedford, positioned in the fork of a wall-trained grape vine, which was used annually for nineteen years.

This species continues to be a familiar woodland migrant in Bedfordshire today but is probably not as numerous as in Steele-Elliott's time.

Harding (1979) found it relatively widely distributed, with breeding records in 248 (67%) of the county's tetrads. However, there were some noticeable gaps in the tetrad map, particularly in the Marston Vale, and the intensively farmed areas in the north-east of the county. Spotted Flycatchers are dependent upon flying insects for food and therefore air pollution from the Stewartby brick works could account for its absence in this sector of the county. National Common Birds Census data record a general decline in numbers from the early 1970s and more noticeably from 1982, which has also been reflected on Bedfordshire's census plots. The reasons for this decline may be attributed partly to a change in habitat in its African wintering grounds. Breeding commences from late May when a clutch of four to five eggs are laid in a nest positioned typically amongst ivy on a tree trunk, or on a wall. There are normally two broods.

The earliest spring record of the Spotted Flycatcher was at Hanger Wood on 11 April 1965, which was exceptionally early, as the main arrival period is not normally until the second half of May or early June. Few sites in the county have reported a spring passage of this species.

Autumn passage is similarly unobtrusive although September movements have been recorded at Blows Downs and South Mills NR. A fall of 30 was of note at Luton Hoo on 12 September 1971. Between 1946 and 1986 there have been only seven October records, the latest at Biddenham on 6 October 1964.

Red-breasted Flycatcher

Ficedula parva

A very rare vagrant.

The strength of this species appearing on the Bedfordshire List rests on an account by David Seth-Smith (1931–2) in which he reports on a detailed sighting of a male and probably two females at Whipsnade Park Zoo on 30 April 1931. The sighting was by keepers Billet and MacDonald, both of whom were keen and competent ornithologists. E. A. Billet later went on to study the breeding birds of the Park in some detail (Huxley 1936–7). Spring records of Red-breasted Flycatchers in England are very rare indeed and nearly always relate to eastern coastal counties. The Bedfordshire record then is clearly unprecedented, being so far inland, but did occur in the peak spring migrational period and at a now confirmed passage migration area, the chalk downland escarpment.

Witherby *et al.* (1938–41) refers to this record when describing the distribution of the Red-breasted Flycatcher in the British Isles.

Pied Flycatcher

Ficedula hypoleuca

An annual spring and autumn passage migrant with one confirmed breeding record.

The Pied Flycatcher is a familiar breeding bird in the oak woods of western Britain, but is absent from the English eastern counties. Sawford (1984) refers to a clutch of five eggs taken near Sandy on 20 June 1896 by F. Saunders, as the only confirmed breeding occurrence of this species in Bedfordshire. In Steele-Elliott (1897–1901) Mr C. F. Woods refers to annual nesting at Woburn Park in the late nineteenth century; however, Steele-Elliott fails to include the account in his 1904 writings, suggesting he doubted the authenticity of the record. Possible breeding was also reported from Pepperstock in the south of the county, in the same period. The only recent summering record was in 1953 when a pair possibly bred in a Bedford orchard (*Beds Naturalist* 8: 39–40).

A study of the data in the county bird reports from 1951 to 1987 reveals a slight shift in the migratory pattern of this species with an increase in spring sightings during the 1980s. Spring birds have occurred at a wide range of localities across the county although there is a slight bias towards the southern chalk downland sites at Whipsnade Park Zoo, Blows Downs, and Kidney Wood. Migration occurs from mid April to mid May with the earliest record at Sandy Lodge on 16 April 1971 and the latest at Whipsnade Park Zoo on 30 May 1953.

At Sandy Lodge from 1965 to 1978 there was an exceptional series of autumn records in every year except 1967 and 1968, which account for the majority of the county's autumn records. In 1972 three birds were present 2–20 September. Subsequently the Pied Flycatcher has become much scarcer during the 1980s. Extreme autumn migration dates were at Sandy Lodge on 8 August 1975, and at Sutton Fen on 21 October 1978. There is one other October record, at Totternhoe on 1 October 1983.

Totals of Pied Flycatchers in Bedfordshire in autumn 1951–87, using European standard day periods:

Aug. 4–8	Aug. 9–14	Aug. 14–18	Aug. 19–23	Aug. 24–28	Aug. 29–2 Sep.
1	1	4	6	11	8

Sep. 3–7	Sep. 8–12	Sep. 13–17	Sep. 18–22	Sep. 23–27	Sep. 28–2 Oct.
8	11	8	8	3	3

Bearded Tit

Panurus biarmicus

An irruptive autumn and winter visitor.

This handsome member of the Timaliidae (babbler) family is a familiar sight and sound in the reed beds of East Anglia. It is an irruptive species, moving away from its natal area in late autumn, and has occurred in Bedfordshire at a number of our mineral excavation sites, particularly those with a reed bed or a patch of willow scrub. Steele-Elliott (1904) documented an early nineteenth-century record of two or three specimens which were shot along the River Ouse, and of a male shot at Great Barford in the winter of 1867. Davis (1855) refers to this species as being rare in the Luton area, without giving any specific details.

There were no further records of the Bearded Tit in the county until 1965, since when it has occurred in 12 years up to 1987. This increase in records correlates with the expansion of its breeding range throughout south-east England (O'Sullivan 1976) from where most of our records originate, or possibly even from further afield as shown by the recovery of a Dutch ringed bird in Hertfordshire in 1965 (Gladwyn

and Sage 1986). It normally occurs in small parties from October to March, although there has been one April record, in 1973. Bedfordshire records from 1965 are as follows:

1965 Two at Bedford SF from 21 November to 11 January 1966.
1972 Up to three at Dunstable SF from 26 November to 17 February 1973.
1973 Two at Wyboston Lake on 19 April and two at Sandy GP on 17 October 1973.
1977 Seven at Harrold GP on 6 November decreasing to four by 13th.
1979 Four near Icknield School, Luton on 20 October with one on 26 January.
1980 Two at Houghton Regis ChP on 3 December stayed until 8 February 1981.
1982 One at Stewartby Lake on 8 January and two at The Lodge, Sandy on 30 October.
1983 A group of 10 at Brogborough Lake from 11 February to 3 March.
1984 Two at Harrold GP on 2 November.
1987 Two at Stewartby Lake on 27 October.

Long-tailed Tit

Aegithalos caudatus

A common resident (**Map 86**).

This species was known to Steele-Elliott (1904) by the delightful local names of Long-Tom and Pudding Bag. Its status has remained unchanged, being fairly common across the majority of the county, with the exception of the sprawling urban complexes of Luton and Bedford. It is also absent from the more intensively farmed areas of north Bedfordshire.

The Long-tailed Tit is a bird of woodland edge, copses, spinnies, and scrubland and as a result was recorded by Harding (1979) in such habitats in 192 tetrads (52%). The majority of records came from the Greensand Ridge woodlands and the deciduous woods in north-west Bedfordshire, with further concentrations in the clay-with-flint copses in the south of the county.

The domed nest, usually built in a thorn bush, is an avian work of art and is constructed of mosses, wool, cobwebs, and hair and lined with feathers. Steele-Elliott referred to a nest dissected by the Bedford taxidermist Mr A. Covington, which contained 2,050 feathers as well as wool and other materials. There is normally one clutch of 8–12 eggs laid during May.

The post-breeding period produces roving flocks of up to 30 which can increase further during the winter as several family groups remain together. Although very under-recorded, a count of 38 at Bison Hill during December 1986 was of note, along with 40 at Tiddenfoot SP on 26 November 1987. It is at this time of year that small parties can occur in our town parks and gardens.

Marsh Tit

Parus palustris

A fairly common resident (**Map 87**).

This highly vocal black-capped tit is very difficult to distinguish from the closely related Willow Tit by plumage details alone. Fortunately it does have a distinctive call and song enabling a positive identification in the majority of cases.

The Marsh Tit is thinly but widely distributed across the county's deciduous copses and woods but is largely absent from the more sterile coniferous plantations. In the damp birch and alder carr of Flitwick Moor it is as numerous as anywhere in the county. It appears to have a particular affinity for birch woodland as at Kidney Wood, Luton, where flocks of up to 10 have been reported during the 1980s.

Harding (1979) recorded this species in 122 (33%) of the county's tetrads, with the majority of records from the Greensand Ridge woodlands and a cluster of records from the clay-with-flint copses around Luton. The Marsh Tit nests in natural tree holes and occasionally nesting boxes, where a clutch of 5–10 eggs are laid during April or May. There is usually only one brood. Following the breeding season it flocks together with other members of the tit family and spends the winter roving local woodlands in search of food. It is at this time of year that it may occur in rural parks and gardens and may even come to food put out at bird feeders.

Willow Tit

Parus montanus

A scarce resident (**Map 88**).

The Willow Tit was not recognised nationally as a distinct species until 1897 and was therefore unknown to Steele-Elliott in the Victorian era. Problems with identification still persist today, especially outside the breeding season when it is generally more silent. Although this species must have occurred in Bedfordshire for many years, it was not until 1937 that the first sighting was recorded at Luton Hoo (Meiklejohn 1937–8). Snow (1948) also noted it at Putnoe Wood in 1948. As observers became aware of the differences between the two 'black-capped' tits more records followed from Flitwick Moor in 1956, Luton Hoo in 1957, and several other localities mainly along the Greensand Ridge.

Harding (1979) recorded it in 107 (29%) of the county's tetrads. Its distribution followed closely that of the Marsh Tit and as Harding stated, 'it is to be hoped that there were not many errors in the correct identification of both species.' The 107 tetrad records for the Willow Tit compared with 122 for the Marsh Tit is higher than the national average in favour of the Willow Tit.

This species has a preference for damp woodlands such as at Flitwick Moor and Maulden Woods, and also occurs along our river valleys where it favours overgrown willow scrub and sallows surrounding the older more established lakes. It is a hole nester, but is different from other members of the tit family in that it excavates its own cavity, usually in a rotting stump of willow, birch, or elder. There is one clutch of eight to nine eggs, usually laid in late April or early May. Post-breeding birds gather together with other small passerines from late summer onwards to form roving flocks throughout the natal woodlands. A study of ringing data has revealed the Willow Tit to be a very sedentary species. One record of a bird ringed as a juvenile on 20 July 1980 at Harrold GP showed remarkable longevity, it being retrapped at Turvey on 10 April 1984.

Coal Tit

Parus ater

A locally abundant resident (**Map 89**).

The Coal Tit is one of the few species to have benefited from the recent planting of non-native coniferous plantations in many parts of England, including Bedfordshire. Although it occurs in all woodland types it is most numerous in an acid wood environment, particularly where there are scattered stands of more mature timber such as at Stockgrove CP, Ampthill Park Wood, and The Lodge, Sandy. This species also occurs in town parks and gardens where it is a frequent visitor to garden bird feeders.

Harding (1979) recorded the Coal Tit in 139 (37%) of the county's tetrads with the majority of records from the three main woodland types: the clay woods in the north, the Greensand Ridge, and the clay-with-flint copses around Luton. The general paucity of records in some parts of Bedfordshire is attributable to a lack of woodland habitat, and is most noticeable in the Marston Vale in the 10km squares SP94 and TL04. National Common Birds Census data show the Coal Tit population to be at an all-time high in Britain, due to post-war afforestation, and Bedfordshire's woodland plots also reflect the national trend.

The Coal Tit is a hole nester but will also breed low down in banks or in the base of abandoned tree nests. It nests in April or May when a large clutch of up to 11 eggs is laid. In common with other members of the tit family, post-breeding family parties often combine with other small passerines to form roving winter flocks. Bedfordshire's Coal Tits are highly sedentary and belong to the race *P. a. britannicus* which is unique to Britain. There is one exceptional record of longevity for this species relating to an adult ringed at Bedford on 7 February 1975 and recovered at Peterborough, Cambridgeshire on 3 December 1983, having lived for at least 10 years.

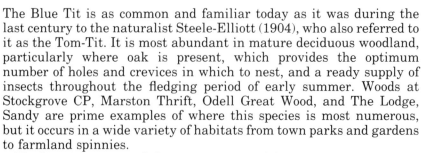

Blue Tit

Parus caeruleus

A very common resident (**Map 90**).

The Blue Tit is as common and familiar today as it was during the last century to the naturalist Steele-Elliott (1904), who also referred to it as the Tom-Tit. It is most abundant in mature deciduous woodland, particularly where oak is present, which provides the optimum number of holes and crevices in which to nest, and a ready supply of insects throughout the fledging period of early summer. Woods at Stockgrove CP, Marston Thrift, Odell Great Wood, and The Lodge, Sandy are prime examples of where this species is most numerous, but it occurs in a wide variety of habitats from town parks and gardens to farmland spinnies.

Harding (1979) recorded it in 354 (98%) of the county's tetrads, and speculated that further surveying in the blank tetrads would probably have resulted in evidence of breeding in all squares. The Blue Tit nests in a variety of man-made structures including letter-boxes and purpose built nest-boxes, but naturally nests in tree holes or crevices where it lays a large single clutch of up to 14 eggs. A detailed study of a pair breeding in a nest-box was made at Bedford in 1962 (Kitchener 1963a).

Outside the breeding season this species forms the basis of roving tit flocks and it can occur some distance from its natal woodland. It is a regular visitor to garden bird feeders across the county during the winter months but is equally at home foraging a farmland hedgerow or a river valley reed bed.

Analysis of ringing data has shown the Blue Tit to be mainly sedentary in Bedfordshire; although a juvenile ringed at Odell Great Wood on 21 June 1980 and controlled at Cheltenham, Gloucestershire on 13 December had moved 108km.

Great Tit

Parus major

A common resident (**Map 91**).

This most handsome member of the Paridae family is commonly distributed throughout Bedfordshire's woodlands, parks, and larger gardens, and can also be found wherever there is scattered timber or scrubland. As with the previous species it is most abundant in semi-natural deciduous woodland, although it is never as numerous as that species. On a well-studied Common Birds Census plot at Old Warden it is outnumbered about 3:1 by the Blue Tit.

As expected Harding (1979) discovered evidence of breeding in a high proportion of the county's tetrads, 315 (85%). However, there were two noticeable gaps on the tetrad map. He suggested that there was no apparent reason for this as suitable habitat exists in the TL06 10-km square; but in the Marston Vale section of TL04 this is not the case, there being sparse tree cover in what is a heavily quarried part of Bedfordshire.

The Great Tit is naturally a tree-hole nester but will utilise nest-boxes and other man-made structures. One of the more unusual was a pair that nested in the top section of a beehive at Burdleys Manor, Stagsden in 1951 (*Beds Naturalist* 6: 29). A large clutch of up to 11 eggs is laid in late April or May, and the fledging period coincides with the emergence of many woodland insects, particularly caterpillars. There is usually only one brood.

Outside the breeding season the Great Tit roams the countryside and urban gardens in small groups, often in company with other members of the tit family, although generally it is less gregarious than the Blue Tit. A study of ringing data has shown the furthest this species has moved from its natal woodland is 117km north-north-east and relates to a juvenile which was ringed at Odell Wood on 16 June 1985, controlled at Gibraltar Point, Lincolnshire on 29 March 1986.

Nuthatch

Sitta europaea

A locally common resident (**Map 92**).

Harding (1979) recorded the Nuthatch in 67 (18%) of the county's tetrads and found it to have a restricted range with concentrations in roughly three areas along the Greensand Ridge. In the Heath and Reach and Woburn areas it is most abundant where the woodland is mature, as at Stockgrove CP and Charle Wood, and in the more open parkland on the estate where there are many ancient oaks. It is common in the woods and parks around Flitwick, Ampthill, and Maulden where it regularly visits garden bird feeders.

The third concentration is at the north-eastern end of the Greensand Ridge around Old Warden, Ickwell, and Sandy. It is noticeably absent from the boulder clay woods in the north-west of the county, but does occur in the woods and parks in and around Luton, including Wardown Park in the centre of Luton. The Nuthatch could be termed numerous only in parkland habitat typically found on the country estates at Luton Hoo, Southill, Wrest Park, and Woburn.

This species usually nests in tree holes but will also utilise purpose-built nest-boxes, where it reduces the size of the entrance hole with mud. A single clutch of up to 11 eggs is laid normally in late April or May. Common Birds Census data for the county indicate a slight increase in breeding birds during the 1980s.

Treecreeper

Certhia familiaris

A common resident (**Map 93**).

The Treecreeper is a well-established but unobtrusive species present in the majority of Bedfordshire woodlands, including our coniferous plantations. Harding (1979) recorded its presence in 169 (46%) tetrads with a noticeable correlation with the three main woodland types: the boulder clay woods around Odell, the Greensand acid woods, and the clay-with-flint copses in the south. As with the previous species, the Treecreeper is most abundant in ancient woodland and mature parkland where large deciduous trees provide the optimum feeding conditions.

This species usually nests behind loose bark or amongst thick ivy stems where a clutch of five to six eggs is laid during April or May. It is sometimes double-brooded. Outside the breeding season the Treecreeper is often encountered in roving tit flocks when it can be found foraging in farmland hedgerows and scrubland.

Golden Oriole

Oriolus oriolus

A very rare summer visitor.

This widespread summer visitor to continental Europe now has a regular small breeding population in the East Anglian poplar plantations. Bedfordshire has similar woodlands north of the Greensand Ridge and could possibly attract this colourful and highly vocal species.

Steele-Elliott (1904) suspected it occurred more regularly than it was actually recorded and notes the many instances of birds in Northamptonshire given by Lord Lilford (1895). Records were received from the latter part of the nineteenth century from Luton Hoo, Ravensden, Tingrith Manor, and possibly Woburn Park. There have been several records since 1946 as follows:

[1967] A possible male heard at Maulden Woods on 9 April.
1973 A male heard singing for 35 minutes at Sandy Lodge on 21 May.
1977 A male in song at Sutton Fen on 22 May and 11 and 27 July was in suitable breeding habitat, although breeding was not suspected. A male heard near Sandy Lodge on 7 June.
1982 A male seen and heard at Wyboston Lakes on 8 June.
1985 A male at Bedford on 10 April.
[1987] A possible male singing in a north Bedfordshire woodland on 5 May.

Red-backed Shrike

Lanius collurio

Formerly a regular summer migrant, now a very rare vagrant (**Map 94**).

271

The Butcher Bird, as it was more generally termed, was in the nineteenth century a widespread breeding species in Bedfordshire and according to Steele-Elliott (1904) 'was probably commoner now with us than in former years'. He writes of it as being regularly encountered near Bedford when on bird-nesting forays as a schoolboy, and later on observed it more or less commonly in other parts of the county, particularly along the chalk downlands where it was most abundant. A Mr A. H. Hoar referred to this species as 'fairly abundant' around Leighton Buzzard and Mr J. King of Southill, writing about 1880, noted it as common in that area and mentioned taking several clutches of seven eggs. At Turvey it was not so common but breeding was recorded from Flitwick. Davis (1855) and Smith (1904) both mention this shrike in the Luton and Dunstable areas respectively and Hine (1934) refers to a full-grown Linnet being impaled on a long thorn of a shrike's larder at Pegsdon Hills. The diaries of George North, an egg-collector from Bedford, give further insight into how common this species once was, when in 1902 and 1903 he collected clutches of between three and six eggs from Barton, Sharpenhoe, Bromham, and Goldington.

The subsequent decline of the Red-backed Shrike nationally has been well documented (Ash 1970 and Bibby 1973), and has been the subject of much ornithological debate. Reasons put forward for this decline have been many and varied but it seems as though a general range contraction has been occurring in Britain for over 100 years (Sharrock 1976). Certainly in Bedfordshire its final demise has been carefully documented.

Until 1959 it was recorded breeding annually in limited numbers in the south of the county, mainly along the chalk escarpment. An average of five pairs per year was noted, typically from sites such as Dunstable Downs, Blows Downs, Winsdon Hill, Bradgers Hill, Stopsley, Warden and Galley Hills, East Hyde, Sharpenhoe, Pegsdon Hills, and Barton Hills. In 1955 a pair fledged young at Cutenhoe Road, Luton followed by suspected breeding at Whitehill Avenue, Luton in 1956. Both nest sites were in urban settings. At Blows Downs in 1956 a maximum of five pairs bred with a further five pairs scattered around the Luton and Dunstable area. Elsewhere in the county between 1946 and 1959 breeding was noted at Coopers Hill, Wilstead, Arlesey ChP, and Whipsnade. From 1960 breeding was intermittent until 1971 when the final pair bred in the chalklands at Pegsdon Hills, on the border with Hertfordshire. Unexpectedly the last breeding record in the county came in 1975 from the Blue Lagoon, Arlesey.

It is worth documenting the final years of the Red-backed Shrike as a breeding species in Bedfordshire:

1960   A pair present at Someries allotment, Luton.
1961   One pair bred at Skimpot, Blows Downs raising one or two young. Another pair at Pegsdon Hills on the Hertfordshire border.
1962   A pair at Someries, Luton raised two young. One pair seen with four juveniles on the county boundary at Hexton. The last recorded breeding at Blows Downs when a pair raised three young.

1963 No breeding records.
1964 A male with young at Hexton on the Herts/Beds border. A pair on Barton Hills, with a female noted at Sharpenhoe Clappers.
1965 Two pairs bred at Pegsdon Hills raising at least three juveniles.
1966 Two pairs raised five to six young at Pegsdon Hills. One pair at Galley Hill.
1967 Two pairs again bred successfully at Pegsdon Hills. A pair raised at least one young at Sharpenhoe Clappers.
1968 Two pairs bred at Pegsdon Hills raising five juveniles.
1969 Males at Pegsdon Hills and Barton Hills, but no females. A female at Keepers Warren.
1970 A male at Pegsdon Hills in May.
1971 A pair raised two young at the traditional Pegsdon Hills site for the final time. Single males noted at Galley Hill and Charle Wood in June.
1972 An unmated male at Pegsdon Hills in June.
1973 No breeding records.
1974 No breeding records.
1975 Final breeding in the county at the Blue Lagoon, Arlesey when a pair raised three juveniles.

Single males continued to appear, at Sundon on 19 June 1977, Houghton Regis ChP on 10–11 June 1978, Potton Road, Biggleswade where a dead bird was found on 17 June 1979, and near Chicksands Woods on 22 June 1979. As this species exhibits a high degree of site fidelity subsequent annual checks were made of traditional sites, but without success.

According to past data the Red-backed Shrike used to arrive on its breeding grounds towards the end of May or early June and had departed by early August once it had raised a single brood. The nest was usually built low down in a thicket, mainly of hawthorn or bramble, but nests in blackthorn and holly bushes have been recorded. The single clutch of three to six eggs was laid in June with the young on the wing about a month later. George North noted 16 June as the date when most clutches were generally laid and he recorded taking a clutch of white eggs, which was considered to be unusual.

As a passage migrant there were few records. Listed below are birds from the final decade:

1972 One at Sandy Lodge on 16 August.
1973 An adult between Husborne Crawley and Brogborough on 16 August.
1974 Two on Blows Downs on 18 May.
1979 One near Eggington on 7 October was the last as well as the latest ever county record.

It seems unlikely that the Red-backed Shrike, once a common summer visitor to the county, will ever recolonise its chalk downland haunts, sadly relegating it to the list of birds lost to Bedfordshire.

Lesser Grey Shrike

Lanius minor

A very rare vagrant.

Steele-Elliott (1904) records a probable sighting of this nationally rare species at Woburn in the first week of September 1894. The information came via Lord Lilford from the Duchess of Bedford: Lord Lilford considered the record worthy of mention but 'with a mark of interrogation'.

There is one other record of a corpse, found along the River Ouse on 25 January 1907 (Gardner 1907–8).

Great Grey Shrike

Lanius excubitor

An irregular winter visitor which has become more frequent in recent years.

This species' habit of perching prominently in open country, whilst on the lookout for prey, must have contributed to its decline during the Victorian era, judging from the catalogue of destruction recorded by Steele-Elliott (1904). Using information gathered from the county's taxidermists and bird-catchers, he quoted approximately 30 specimens which they had received, spanning the second half of the nineteenth century. Not surprisingly Steele-Elliott speaks of the Great Grey Shrike as an irregular winter visitor which by the turn of the century was becoming more scarce.

Data from 1946 reveals little change in status: it remains an irregular winter visitor, although it has become more frequently recorded from 1970. Overall it has occurred in 27 years in the 42-year study period, and from 1966 has only been absent in 1976–8 and in 1987. A monthly breakdown of sightings (Figure 3.27) shows the earliest date to be one at Old Warden Tunnel on 22 September 1974 and the latest on 10 April at Odell Great Wood and Wyboston in 1971 and 1975 respectively. The main wintering period is from October to March with a peak in December and January.

Records of Great Grey Shrikes have been received from all corners of the county with the majority of sightings along the river valleys, the Greensand Ridge, and the chalk downlands. Quite often individuals

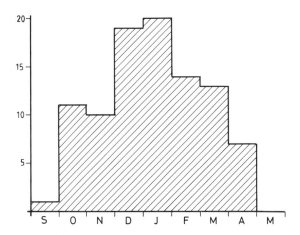

Figure 3.27   *Great Grey Shrike: total monthly counts, 1946–87*

remain throughout the winter months and show a high degree of site fidelity, some returning in subsequent years. Notable long-staying birds include: one at Bedford SF from 1 January to 19 March 1949, one at Luton from 26 December 1952 to 1 February 1953, one at Dunstable SW from 25 December 1971 to 18 March 1972, one in the Biggleswade/Sandy area from 3 November 1974 to 2 April 1975, one at Stanbridgeford from 30 November 1980 to 22 March 1981, one in the Blunham/Girtford area from 1 November 1981 to 3 February 1982, one at Priory CP from 17 November 1983 to 4 April 1984, one at Biggleswade Common from 3 January to 5 March 1985, and a single in the Ivel valley between Girtford and Blunham between 7 January and 31 March 1986.

It is difficult to assess accurately the exact number of Great Grey Shrikes that have occurred in the county from 1946 to 1987 but it is probably about 60 individuals, several of which may have returned over two or three winters, further confusing the true total. Birds wintering in eastern England originate mainly from Scandinavia and consist of the northern race *L. e. excubitor* which also winters else-where in Europe.

Woodchat Shrike

Lanius senator

A very rare vagrant.

This annual vagrant to southern England from the South-Western Palearctic region has occurred in Bedfordshire on one occasion, between Goldington power station and Barkers Lane GP from 17 July to 29 August 1972 (*British Birds* 66: 351).

Jay

Garrulus glandarius

A common resident (**Map 95**).

During the nineteenth century this species was locally known as the Jaypie. According to Steele-Elliott (1904) it was very common in large blocks of woodland, particularly where game-rearing was not practised, which included many of the woods in the north of the county, including the Crown land plantations around Stagsden. In Hanger Wood Steele-Elliott found four or five Jays' nests in an hour, proportionately estimating 20–30 pairs across the wood as a whole. Even in areas that were heavily keepered he considered it 'capable of withstanding all the devices used for its total extermination.'

Today it is still a familiar member of the county avifauna, being most numerous along the Greensand Ridge woodlands, where it often visits garden bird tables in the winter. The deciduous woods in the clay country in north Bedfordshire are still favoured, along with the clay-with-flint copses on the chalk scarp slope, south of Luton and Dunstable.

Harding (1979) recorded the Jay in 147 (40%) of the county's 371 tetrads with confirmed breeding in 39 tetrads, probable breeding in 33 tetrads, and possible breeding in a further 75. Due to the sedentary nature of this species Harding considered that the records of possible breeding in most cases referred to breeding pairs. The single clutch of five to six eggs is usually laid during May in a well-concealed nest situated in the lower canopy of a tree or in thick undergrowth. Incubation is for 15–16 days and the young fledge after approximately three weeks.

An exceptionally late fledgling was found, barely able to fly, at Rowney Warren on 14 November 1965. A post-breeding flock of 17 at Whipsnade Zoo on 6 October 1981 was of note as were up to 29 at The Lodge, Sandy in the late summer of 1986.

As described by John and Roskell (1985) unprecedented numbers of Jays occurred in Britain, probably from the continent, during late September and October 1983. In Bedfordshire, flocks of eight and 10 were noted at Whipsnade Zoo in late September followed by 12 at Luton Hoo on 12 October. A party of 18 flew over arable land near Fancott on 18 October and 13 were seen together at Whipsnade. A four-fold increase was recorded in the Aspley Heath/Woburn area in early October, and elsewhere in the county Jays appeared at localities where they are seldom encountered. It is quite probable that some of these birds were of the continental race *G. g. glandarius*, as well as our essentially sedentary endemic subspecies *G. g. rufitergum* which also disperses in search of food.

Magpie

Pica pica

A very common resident (**Map 96**).

Strikingly marked, garrulous and ubiquitous, it seems hard to believe that the Magpie was ever anything other than a common Bedfordshire bird. However this was not always the case. In the Victorian era it was widely persecuted in game-rearing districts and consequently Steele-Elliott (1904) afforded it the status of only locally common in such areas where gamekeeping was absent. It is assumed that its status remained the same until after the Second World War when a general increase was noted across the county: indeed in 1950 it was termed as abundant in many districts.

Subsequent years have seen the Magpie adapt to an urban and suburban environment as well as benefiting from increasing scrubland on the chalk downlands, an area where it is today probably most abundant.

Harding (1979) recorded it in 188 (51%) tetrads, with confirmed breeding in 74 tetrads, probable breeding in 22 tetrads, and possible breeding in 92. There was a preponderance of records in the southern half of the county, particularly in the 10km squares SP92, TL01, and TL02. A favourite nest site is in the top half of a hawthorn thicket, which affords good protection for its domed nest built of sticks and lined with mud and roots. The single clutch of five to seven eggs is laid in April, followed by a 17–21 day incubation period and a further 22–7 days before fledging occurs.

The Magpie is largely sedentary throughout the county but during the winter it may move locally, often visiting feeding sites in town gardens where it can become quite bold. At Dunstable Downs a large gathering of up to 150 individuals frequent a nearby pig farm to feed, winter roosting collectively in the adjacent downland scrub. Large numbers of Magpies can also be found on the waste disposal tips at Brogborough, Elstow, and Sundon during the winter months and it is commonly seen scavenging along the county's highways, picking clean road casualties.

Crows

Corvidae

The so called 'Black Crows' – Jackdaw, Rook, and Carrion/Hooded Crow – have long been a familiar part of the Bedfordshire scene despite constant efforts to eliminate them. During the sixteenth and seventeenth centuries an account was maintained by parish officials concerning the destruction of vermin throughout the county in which crows feature heavily (Steele-Elliott 1936). During this period the use of crow-nets was obligatory under Tudor Acts but was considered ineffective in keeping numbers under control. Consequently considerable sums of money were spent in some parishes employing field-keepers to use shot and powder. Wages varied from 10s 6d a month to annual payments of £1 2s 6d, and in the parishes of Milton Bryan and Oakley youths or older men were widely employed.

In general the 'Rook' was then referred to as the 'Crow', the term 'Rook' being used to describe young birds which were shot by local farmers to make the highly esteemed Rook Pie. Jackdaws were also known as 'Choughs', to add to the confusion, but were still subject to the crow-scarers' attention. A song often heard in Bedfordshire during that era was typical of the songs of the crow-scarer heard throughout England:

Away, birds, away!
I'll pick up my clappers
And knock you down back'ards,
So, away, birds, away!

Away, birds, away!
I'll pick up a stone
And break your backbone
So, away, birds, away!

Away, birds, away!
I'll pick up another

And kill your young brother
So away, birds, away!

The fortunes of the crow family plummeted during the game-preserving age of the Victorians and probably remained at a low level until the two World Wars when gamekeeping generally was less effective. During the post-war years numbers increased again as ideal feeding conditions became available at refuse tips at Brogborough, Elstow, and Sundon. Few studies have been carried out, but it is considered that many thousands of 'black crows' haunt these areas, mainly during the winter months.

Jackdaw

Corvus monedula

A locally common resident (**Map 97**).

During the early part of the last century, when there was a greater acreage of pastureland in Bedfordshire, the Jackdaw would have been a very familiar species. According to Steele-Elliott (1904) it formerly nested in many of the county's church towers, although he could only remember it breeding in the tower of Elstow Church.

As in Steele-Elliott's day parkland remains the Jackdaw's preferred habitat, where the combination of open grassland and mature timber afford ideal feeding and nesting conditions. Consequently it is most numerous at Woburn Park, Luton Hoo, Wrest Park, and Southill Park with smaller colonies scattered elsewhere along the Greensand Ridge. Away from these localities it is found in much smaller numbers, sometimes being represented by only one or two pairs in close canopy woodland where there are sufficient old deciduous trees. Harding (1979) found there to be a thriving population in the woods around Odell and along the Ouse valley, but there is evidence to suggest that numbers have declined since. Certainly in the south of the county in the clay-with-flint woodlands around Caddington and Kensworth it is not as numerous today as it once was. Harding noted the Jackdaw was present in 267 (72%) of the county's tetrads with confirmed breeding in 100 tetrads, probable breeding in 29, and possible breeding in a further 138. A typical Bedfordshire nest site is in a hole or the cleft of an old parkland oak or chestnut where a single clutch of four to six eggs is laid in a nest of twigs lined with hair or wool. The eggs are usually laid towards the end of April and following a 17–18 day incubation period the young fledge after a further 28–30 days.

Outside the breeding season this species tends to flock together with other members of the crow family where it can be found in good numbers at the county's landfill sites. The largest number ever recorded in the county was at Luton Hoo on 5 September 1977 when

279

approximately 3,000 birds were present. Other large counts were 1,000 at Knocking Hoe and 600 at Lower Stondon on 3 September 1979, 100 at Everton on 29 March 1980, 1,000 flying west to roost over Heath and Reach on 7 February 1982, 500 at Little Barford on 8 January 1983, and 350 near Shefford on 18 August 1987. There is a tendency for this species to feed and roost communally with Rooks.

Although there is no positive evidence to suggest that birds of the Fenno-Scandian race *C. m. monedula* have occurred in Bedfordshire, one was recorded in neighbouring Hertfordshire at Radlett on 10 March 1940 (*British Birds* 41: 174). Bedfordshire's Jackdaws belong to the Western European race *C. m. spermologus* which breeds as far south as Morocco.

Rook

Corvus frugilegus

A common resident and probable autumn and winter visitor (**Map 98**).

The Rook has always been a familiar part of the Bedfordshire country-side, and was even more so during the last century when Steele-Elliott (1904) described it as 'common in all parts of the county.' Along with the previous species it has declined in recent years due mainly to changing farming practices resulting in lower acreages of grazing land, a factor which is vital in the Rook's ecology. It has also had to adapt to the loss of its preferred nesting tree, the elm, due to disease during the 1970s. In 1943–6 the BTO carried out a national Rook census, during which Bedfordshire's rookeries were counted in 1945. In 1975 a further survey was implemented enabling a comparative assessment to be made (Figure 3.28), with some reservations due to county boundary changes in 1964. The results were discussed in a paper by Livett (1976) in which he found the average number of nests per rookery had fallen from 32 in 1945 to 22 in 1975. Corroborating this decline was the fact that during the 1945 census six rookeries contained more than 200 nests, but by 1975 none reached this figure. In 1945 the largest rookery in Bedfordshire was at Chalgrave where a total of 598 nests was counted (today the colony numbers c.100 nests) and in 1975 the largest count was 190 nests at Luton Hoo. The overall statistics from 1945 and 1975 registered a general countrywide decline and highlighted a noticeable decrease along the Greensand Ridge. Livett postulated that the planting of conifers, resulting in unsuitable habitat, was the probable cause for decline.

Further data on breeding Rooks was gathered for Harding (1979), during which evidence of breeding was recorded in 241 tetrads (65%). Confirmed breeding was recorded in 140 tetrads, with probable breeding in a further 90 tetrads. Formerly the elm was the main nesting

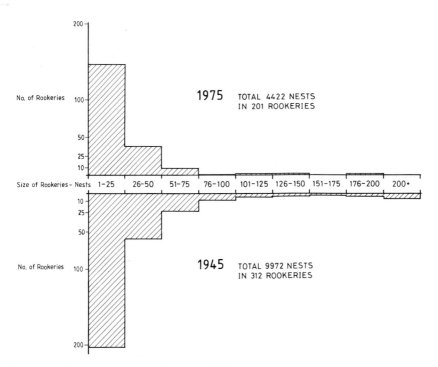

Figure 3.28   *Rookeries in 1945 and 1975*

tree but today rookeries are found predominantly in oak, ash, sycamore, beech, and horse chestnut. A recent adaptation has been the
utilisation of the poplar windbreaks around the Bedford clay pits,
most noticeable at Stewartby, where rookeries tend to be strung out
in a loose line rather than bunched tightly together. Steele-Elliott
(1904) commented upon a letter to the *Field* in 1898 concerning a
colony of 30 nests at Milton Bryan which were unusually sited in a
row of pollard willows, several of which were only a few feet from the
ground. He also recorded rookeries in holly and Scots pine. In 1949 a
colony became established at St Peter's Green, Bedford but was displaced in 1953, after which the Rooks moved to elms near the Bunyan
statue. This colony was one of several in the urban areas of Bedford
(Key 1953). Rooks are early breeders, with nest building or repair
work to their stick-built nests often noted in January and February.
The single clutch of three to five eggs is laid towards the end of March
with the young fledging in late May or early June.

Between 1940 and 1951 the Bedford School Natural History Society
carried out studies of Rook roosts in the northern half of the county
(*Beds Naturalist* 5: 27–8). At the Second Bedfordshire Ornithological
Conference on 18 November 1950, a lecture on 'Roosting and Awaken-
ing' summarised these movements, mainly from observations at a
roost wood at Pavenham. Although the studies were more concerned
with flight times and routes to and from roosts and feeding grounds,
it was noted that the numbers of Rooks attending roosts increased
during October. This could be attributed to birds from the Low Countries moving west for the winter as suggested by the following foreign
ringing records: one ringed as a nestling at Giethorn, Overijssel, Hol-

land on 8 May 1949 was recovered at Ampthill on 11 May 1950 and another ringed at the same locality on 10 May 1949 was found dead at Toddington on 2 March 1950. Unfortunately there is little quantifiable data on the wintering Rook population in the county bird reports; although 1,000+ at Sundon Refuse Tip on 13 December 1981 and 1,500 at roost near Little Barford on 8 January 1983 are both of note. There is also a substantial number of Rooks throughout the winter period at Brogborough and Elstow landfill sites, where they gather to feed with Jackdaws and other members of the corvid family. In south Bedfordshire, counts of up to 1,000 Rooks have been seen passing over Dunstable in the winters of 1981–7, to and from feeding grounds in the Markyate area of Hertfordshire.

Carrion Crow

Corvus corone corone

A very common resident (**Map 99**).

Along with several other members of the corvid family this species has returned from the verge of extinction to become an abundant and familiar Bedfordshire bird. It was hunted during the Victorian era for game preservation, and when Steele-Elliott (1904) undertook 'a very liberal census' in 1899, he adjudged the county total to be no more than 20 pairs distributed across 13 localities mainly in north and central Bedfordshire. Mr A. Covington, a Bedford taxidermist, also commented 'My favourite of all birds is surely enough fast verging upon its doom.' Davis (1855) referred to it as uncommon in the Luton area during the early part of the century. Steele-Elliott considered it to be more widely distributed up until the 1850s.

Today the Carrion Crow is so common it rarely merits attention in the annual county bird reports; indeed the only reference regarding breeding numbers was in the early 1950s when it was considered to breed abundantly in the north of the county. Fieldwork for Harding (1979) revealed evidence of breeding in 303 (82%) of the county's 371 tetrads. Confirmed breeding was recorded in 118 tetrads, followed by probable breeding in 23 tetrads, with possible breeding in a further 162 tetrads. Harding considered the high degree of possible breeding a consequence of efficient gamekeeping in the 10km squares TL06, TL13, and TL14. During the breeding season the Carrion Crow can be encountered in a wide range of habitats but is most numerous on open farmland north and south of the Greensand Ridge where it nests in hedgerow trees, small spinneys, or on woodland edge. Pylons are also utilised as nesting platforms for its untidy nest built of sticks and foliage, lined with hair or wool. The single clutch of four to five eggs is laid in April with the young fledging approximately eight weeks later. In recent years breeding has occurred in town parks at Luton and Dunstable.

Outside the breeding season loose flocks are noted at Brogborough, Elstow, and Sundon landfill sites where numbers may reach several hundred strong. Some of these birds may be from other parts of eastern England or the near continent, although much research is needed to ascertain their true origin. A large assembly of Carrion Crows has wintered at Dunstable Downs Pig Farm for many years along with Magpies, and at Dunstable SF on 16 March 1969 about 250 were present. The only other statistics for this species were 42 shot at Stagsden in the winter of 1952–3 and c.40 counted at Bedford SF on 6 April 1963.

During the 1980s a small number of Carrion Crows in the Eaton Bray, Totternhoe, and Dunstable districts have been noted with varying degrees of white in the wing, forming in some individuals a broad wing bar. This is common in young birds and widespread.

Hooded Crow

Corvus corone cornix

Formerly a regular winter visitor, now very rare.

In the nineteenth century this race of the Carrion Crow, known locally as the Royston or Dunstable Crow, was a common winter visitor to most parts of the county, particularly along the Ouse and Ivel river valleys (Steele-Elliott 1904) and on the southern chalk downlands (Davis 1855 and Smith 1904). Steele-Elliott found the sewage farm at Newnham to be a favourite haunt along with Fenlake and Goldington.

From 1946 until modernisation in the early 1970s both Bedford and Dunstable SFs regularly attracted small numbers to feed during the winter months. In fact from 1946 to 1956 Hooded Crows were recorded annually at these sites, but then only intermittently until the final sighting at Dunstable SW on 22 January 1971. Elsewhere in the county it was noted every year, mainly singly, until 1979 from a wide scattering of sites. Only at Brogborough Tip and Whipsnade Zoo was it recorded in consecutive years. The last two sightings were at Whipsnade on 13 April 1983 and at Brogborough Lake on 15 January 1985. During the period 1946–87 the majority of records occurred from November to April with December to February the peak months. First and last dates were at Thorn on 15 October 1972 and at Flitwick Moor on 1 May 1950.

Bedfordshire's Hooded Crows originated from the formerly highly migratory Scandinavian population, which seems to have recently adjusted to improved feeding conditions in their home range by using refuse tips. This has resulted in fewer birds needing to migrate across the North Sea into eastern England in search of food and probably explains the recent paucity of records throughout the 1980s (Perrins 1987).

Raven
Corvus corax

Formerly a resident breeder until the mid nineteenth century. Now extinct.

Davis (1855) refers to this species as being common around Luton in the early part of the nineteenth century, and Steele-Elliott (1904) stated 'Until the middle of the 19th century the Raven must have been fairly well known as a resident bird within the county'.

He mentioned a pair that bred at Haynes Park until 1849 and of a pair regularly breeding at Silsoe Park whose young were robbed by some of the servants and sold in London. Mr J. King in correspondence with Steele-Elliott remembered a pair nesting at Southill Park until at least 1844, and Mr A. Covington, a Bedford taxidermist, mentioned the Raven breeding at Bolnhurst, Keysoe Wood, and Thurleigh before 1840.

The final recorded breeding site of this species in Bedfordshire came from Mr C. F. Woods who worked at Woburn Park 1848–71, during which time a pair nested for some years in a large beech tree. Mr Woods considered it unlikely that they ever raised a brood due to persistent persecution, and consequently the largest passerine on the county list passed into history.

There has been one modern record, at Everton, when one flew over moving north-east on 25 September 1978. Due to the highly sedentary nature of the Raven the likelihood of an escaped bird cannot be ruled out.

Starling
Sturnus vulgaris

An abundant resident, passage migrant, and winter visitor (**Map 100**).

Cheeky, garrulous, and ubiquitous, the Starling is one of Bedfordshire's most familiar birds. It was described by Steele-Elliot (1904) as 'an exceedingly numerous resident', a status that could be similarly afforded it today. Harding (1979) recorded evidence of breeding in 370 (100%) of the county's 371 tetrads within a diverse habitat range from woodland, towns, parks, garden, farmland, and quarries. The nest is nearly always built in a hole, be it in a tree, building or quarry cliff, and sometimes in the foundation of a larger bird's nest. At Bromham in 1899 Steele-Elliott found this species utilising a Magpie's nest. In a note in the *Zoologist* 1877, Mr C. M. Prior gave details of Starlings taking possession of Sand Martin holes, although the locality was not

specified. The breeding season starts in April when a clutch of four to six eggs are laid and the young are usually fledged by mid June. Most pairs are single brooded.

As an autumn passage migrant and winter visitor the Starling is often recorded in huge flocks, or 'murmurations', as birds stream across the county from eastern Europe and the Soviet Union. On 18 October 1893 Mr A. F. Crossman sent word to Steele-Elliott of 'a tremendous migration of birds that passed over Bedford town, consisting principally of Starlings, their excrement being particularly noticeable about the streets the following morning'. More recently in 1950 after easterly gales several thousands were noted over Bedford SF on 1–8 October and on 22nd. Other large movements recorded were 25,000 at Houghton Regis on 25 December 1962 and 100,000+ at Carlton on 20 November 1981.

A study of ringing data reveals many of Bedfordshire's migrants to have originated from the Low Countries. There are two records of birds ringed in Bedfordshire being recovered on the continent: one as expected in the Netherlands, but the second record relates to a bird ringed at Luton on 3 February 1956 that was recovered at an unspecified locality in Sweden on 23 July 1956.

At roost the Starling is particularly noticeable as it assembles in loose, noisy pre-roost groups, before departing to the main roost. A summer roost at Crown Farm, Turvey on 2 May 1912 comprising 20,000 birds was found to contain predominantly males (*British Birds* 23: 273). H. A. S. Key (1956) described the behaviour of this species at roost in north Bedfordshire during 1956.

Further roost studies were carried out in south Bedfordshire by W. G. Harper (1960) in 1957–9 using radar, in which methods of dispersal to and from roosting and feeding areas were investigated.

The following large roosts have been recorded:

1950   A roost at Eversholt contained several thousand birds.

1951	250,000 at Elstow.
1953	Many thousands at Stanford on 15 March.
1955	4,000–5,000 near Everton on 17 September.
1958	A considerable roost at Flitwick Plantation.
1980	50,000+ at Carlton in mid March.
1982	50,000–75,000 at Leighton Buzzard in January and February.
1986	10,000 at Winsdon Hill, Luton during both winter periods.

Rose-coloured Starling

Sturnus roseus

A very rare vagrant.

The Rose-coloured Starling is an annually occurring vagrant to Britain from south-western Europe and is a notable irruptive migrant. It is also widely kept by aviculturalists, a factor which must be considered when interpreting records. Bedfordshire records are as follows:

1875	A juvenile killed at Barton-in-the-Clay in August 1855 (Steele-Elliott 1904).
1913	An adult male picked up dead in October at Thurleigh (*Zoologist* 118 and *British Birds* 9: 29).
1978	An adult at Caddington from *c*.12–23 November (*British Birds* 73: 526).
1985	An adult male near Henlow Airfield on 22–4 May (*British Birds* 79: 577).

House Sparrow

Passer domesticus

An abundant resident (**Map 101**).

The status of this species has never been recorded as anything but common or abundant. At least as far back as the seventeenth century this species was considered a pest and parish officials made payments for its destruction. The earliest references found by Steele-Elliott (1936) were in the Churchwarden's Accounts for Harlington and Kempston, both in 1685, with payments being made six years later at Milton Bryan and at Houghton Regis in 1714. Payments were still being made at Sandy in 1861, at Willington in 1872, and Tingrith in

1873. Prices ranged from 1d to 6d a dozen but Cranfield payed as much as one shilling. Payments were also made for eggs, the records of Clifton in 1744 and Ravensden in 1757 being the earliest to mention this. Steele-Elliott, who made a thorough search of these parish accounts, calculated that although the records were very incomplete, payments were made for several million sparrows and tens of thousands of eggs. When the parish officers ceased payment, private sparrow clubs were set up in rural areas to keep the population in check and prevent damage to corn. By the end of the century these clubs were far less numerous but a report in the *Bedfordshire Times and Independent* on 12 July 1912 mentions that the Bletsoe Sparrow Club destroyed 1,083 adults, 360 young, and 698 eggs in 1911. Sparrows not only damaged crops but caused serious damage to thatched roofs by nesting in them. In certain parts of the county this habit resulted in its name of 'Theck Sparrow' or 'Thatch Sparrow'.

Although the House Sparrow is still abundant, particularly around human habitation, it seems that numbers have declined in rural areas. This may have been caused by the advances made in farming practice resulting in fewer weedy areas, fewer traditional stackyards and the increased practice of keeping animals in clean indoor conditions. The increase in the number of people providing food at bird tables has probably resulted in an increased urban population.

A study in 1986 of predation by domestic cats in Felmersham (Churcher and Lawton, *J. Zoology* 212: 439–55), showed that at least 30% of House Sparrow deaths in the village were due to domestic cats.

Flocks of several hundreds are regularly seen, particularly in stubble fields after harvesting, and large roosts can form in winter. Harding (1979) showed that this species was observed in all 371 tetrads and was proved breeding in 310 (84%).

Although the House Sparrow is so common in the county there is room for much further study.

Tree Sparrow

Passer montanus

An uncommon local resident (**Map 102**).

During the nineteenth century this species was an abundant resident, favouring areas less associated with man's presence.

During this century flocks of several hundreds collected in winter at a variety of habitats, but sewage works and open fields were the more favoured sites. Bedford SW regularly held large flocks with 500–600 in December 1957 building up to 1,000 by January of 1958 and 800 there in January 1967. In January 1970 750 feeding on stubble at Bidwell on 4 January had increased to 900 two weeks later. The BNHS report for 1971 reported that they were 'remarkably widespread and common' in the county with 800 being reported from Bedford SW in February and March. A flock of 500 was recorded at Dunstable SW in December 1976, 300 at the same site the following January, 200 at Harrold in December 1977, 300 at Maulden in February 1978, and 210 at Northill in January 1982.

During the early 1980s it became apparent that this species was declining. By 1984 only two pairs bred at Sandy where in 1975 the breeding population was 85 pairs. A similar state of affairs was recorded at Old Warden where only two pairs bred in 1984 after the breeding population reached 21 pairs in 1975. At Maulden Wood at this time the numbers of breeding Tree Sparrows was described as 'prolific'. A nest-box survey carried out there in 1975 by BNHS in four small sample areas occupying in total approximately 3% of the wooded area, revealed 55 pairs which laid a total of 504 eggs, of which 251 young fledged. The majority of the pairs produced two broods and 15 pairs produced three broods. The decline in the breeding population was also reflected by the size and number of wintering flocks, with 50 at South Mills in February being the largest recorded in 1985. Breeding was reported from only two locations in the following year but this did not represent an accurate picture. A more intensive effort in 1987 showed that the species was widely but thinly distributed throughout the agricultural areas of the county, nesting sparsely in old farm buildings, barns, and dead elms. This decline has been noted throughout England since 1978, particularly in the east and south, but the reasons are not known. It has been suggested that the reduction of nesting sites caused by the removal of old farm buildings, modernisation of existing ones, and felling of old trees may be a contributory factor in the decline of this species, but other species which use similar sites have not declined. The removal of dead elms has also been given as a cause, but only 6% of tree sites in the BTO nest record cards were in elms. The widespread use of herbicides in weed control seems to be a more likely cause as other farmland seed-eaters have also shown a decline over a similar period (Marchant et al. 1990).

Chaffinch

Fringilla coelebs

A very common resident, passage migrant, and winter visitor (**Map 103**).

The Chaffinch has been described as a common species since the time of Davis (1855). It has remained a common breeding resident, found in all types of woodland, copses, hedgerows, parks, and gardens in the county. During the Breeding Bird Survey of 1968–77 (Harding 1979), it was recorded in 345 of the county's 371 tetrads and was proved breeding in 147 (39%) of them. Breeding was probable in 145 (39%) and thought possible in 53 (14%). In 1984 35 pairs bred at The Lodge, Sandy with 24 pairs in the following year. However in 1985 40 pairs bred at Old Warden, the highest total since recording began in 1973.

Large flocks may appear during the winter when our resident birds are augmented by birds from Fenno-Scandia and the Low Countries. 'Several hundreds' were recorded at Bedford SF in 1950 with 500 there in December 1957. There have been several flocks of more than 250 since then: 500 near Cranfield on 16 March 1969, 250 at Houghton Conquest on March 23 1969, 300 in beeches at Markham Hills, Streatley in February 1977, 500 at Odell Wood in January 1980, and 300 in the Deacon Hill area in November 1987.

An adult ringed in Bedford on 20 January 1968 was recovered in Antwerp, Belgium on 4 November 1974 and a female found at Sandy on 3 February 1968 had been ringed as a juvenile near Antwerp on 8 October 1967.

Brambling

Fringilla montifringilla

A regular winter visitor in varying numbers.

Recorded by Davis (1855) as being common in winter. Steele-Elliott (1904) was aware of the relationship between the numbers of this species and the severity of the winter, writing that it visited us in limited numbers in mild winters but was very plentiful after prolonged periods of sharp frosts. It was recorded in good numbers from Woburn and Southill Parks as well as Chicksands Priory.

Although visiting us every winter from Norway, Sweden, and Finland, the numbers which do so vary greatly. In some years they are quite scarce while in other years they are common and widely distributed. Birds usually begin to arrive in October but the earliest was one at Sandy on 27 September 1966. However it is not until November or December that the main arrival takes place and in many years it may be January or February before the larger flocks are reported.

They are particularly fond of beechmast but where this is not available they can often be found feeding with other finches in a variety of habitats such as open fields, hedgerows, and sewage works. By mid April most have departed but there have been a few recorded towards the end of the month. Two males were singing at The Lodge, Sandy on 2 May 1973 and the latest was recorded at the same locality on 9 May 1980. An interesting record is of one at The Lodge, Sandy on 22 June 1978.

Although widespread in recent times flocks have usually been of 50 or less. Flocks of 150 were recorded at Bedford SF from January to March 1950, December 1953, and January 1954, with 100 there in January and February 1958. They roost communally, usually with Chaffinches, and it is at their roosting sites that some of the larger flocks have been recorded. A roost at Pegsdon Hills in January 1954 numbered 200 and one at The Lodge, Sandy held 200 in early April 1966. On 7 April of the following year 600 roosted at the latter site. Other large flocks have included 400 at Bedford SW on 21 January 1967, 500 at Flitwick on 2 February 1974, and 500 near Millbrook on the same day.

The winter distribution in Europe varies greatly as individual Bramblings are not faithful to any particular wintering area and may spend each winter in totally different places in their search for beechmast. This is well illustrated by a bird ringed at Bedford on 20 January 1968 which was recovered at Treviso, Italy, on about 15 December 1971, 1141km south-east.

Serin

Serinus serinus

A very rare vagrant.

A first-year female killed by a cat in Biggleswade on 20 February 1984 was the first county record (*Beds Naturalist* 39: 30).

Greenfinch

Carduelis chloris

A common resident (**Map 104**).

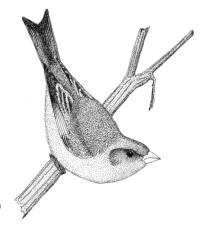

The Greenfinch has always been recorded as being common or very common in the county (Davis 1874, Steele-Elliott 1904). Harding (1979) recorded it as breeding in 44% of the county's 371 tetrads with probable breeding in a further 42%. There were signs of a decline in the breeding populations in some areas during the mid 1980s. In a survey area of 200 acres at Old Warden, only six pairs bred in 1984 and 1985, showing a reduction from 26 pairs in 1975. At The Lodge, Sandy 11 pairs bred in 1984 but this was reduced to six pairs in the following year.

Large flocks may gather during the winter and in the early 1950s many were noted around Bedford SF. A roost of 1,000 was recorded at The Lodge, Sandy in the winters of 1965–6 and 1966–7. In December of 1974 1,500 were recorded at the same locality and in November 1976 1,500 were present at Pegsdon Hills.

Of 121 recoveries of birds ringed in the county 58 were within 10km of where they were ringed, 55 within 100km, and eight more than 100km. Sixty-one of these were recovered south of the county, showing a south to south-westerly bias and only two were recovered any significant distance to the north. Of 88 recoveries of birds ringed outside the county, 81 were ringed in the south of England between October and April. These indicate a south to south-westerly movement of some birds out of the county during the autumn and a return movement in spring.

Goldfinch

Carduelis carduelis

A fairly common resident and passage migrant (**Map 105**).

Recorded by Davis (1855) as being common in the Luton area, Steele-Elliott (1904) informs us that before the passing of the Wild Birds Protection Acts of 1880 and 1881 this one-time common species was rapidly approaching extermination due to the activities of bird-catchers. After the passing of these Acts and with the additional protection provided by the Amendment Act of 1894 he reported that its numbers seemed to be gradually increasing. Towards the end of the nineteenth century it was generally distributed in suitable habitats.

It is commonly met with during the summer months in parks, farm-land, waste ground, scrub, gardens, orchards, and the margins of woodland, anywhere where there is a plentiful supply of weeds. In areas where agriculture is more developed and weeds kept under close control it is less common.

Harding (1979) proved breeding in 134 of the county's 371 tetrads (36%) with breeding thought probable in a further 96. Fewer records of breeding were received from the areas of boulder clay in the northern half of the county.

There have been recent signs of a decline in the breeding population. In 1984 and 1985 none bred at The Lodge, Sandy where several pairs had bred annually in previous years and in 1987 only three pairs bred at the Old Warden CBC site where 17 bred in 1975.

After the breeding season flocks begin to form and feed on areas where there is a plentiful supply of weed seeds. This is related to the type of summer with larger gatherings after hot dry summers. Flocks may be observed as early as the end of June but are more frequent during August and September. The size of flocks is quite small with few of more than 50. Parties of more than 100 are only seen occasion-ally, which is a little surprising when neighbouring Hertfordshire has flocks of 200–300 in most years (Gladwin and Sage 1986). The largest number ever recorded in Bedfordshire was a flock of 400 at Pegsdon Hills on 21 September 1969. Apart from this there have been only four instances of more than 100 in autumn: 150 near Dunstable Downs on 18 October 1953, 100 at Bedford SW on 22 September 1969, 100 at Harrold GP on 4 October 1981, and a flock which attained a maximum of 140 at Priory CP on 22 August 1983.

A large proportion of Goldfinches, probably about 80%, leave in autumn to winter in Belgium, France, and Spain but small numbers may be seen throughout the county where there is a suitable supply of food. Occasionally fairly large roosts form as in 1973 at The Lodge, Sandy when monthly maxima were 150 in January, 200 in February, and 150 in March. In the following December 100 roosted at the same site and 150 roosted at Flitwick Moor at the end of January 1977.

Return passage in spring is usually on a smaller scale than the autumn passage but 100 were observed in late April 1986 at The Lodge, Sandy.

A bird ringed at Bedford on 9 September 1967 was recovered on 8 November 1969 at Oost-Vlaanderen, Belgium, 301km east-south-east.

Siskin

Carduelis spinus

A regular but local winter visitor in varying numbers.

Davis (1874) knew this bird as a rare visitor in late autumn but the status given by Steele-Elliott (1904) is that of 'an irregular winter migrant, varying considerably in the numbers that visit us'. This accurately describes its status today. Steele-Elliott knew of it occurring in good numbers during some years at Flitwick Moor, Shefford, Clifton, Oakley, Bromham Park, and Fenlake. As is usual, most of the records mentioned are of birds feeding on alders. This species was noted as being numerous in the winter of 1878–9, and again in 1898–9.

There is an interesting record of this species breeding in the county in 1879 at Wavendon Rectory (*Zoologist* 1880, 257). Steele-Elliott obtained further information from the editor of this journal. The Revd Henry Gurney, on visiting one of his cottages in the spring of 1880, found a Siskin in a cage. He was told that it was taken from a nest during June of the previous year. The boy who found them told him of two nests, both with young, one in the fork of a maple tree and the other in a hornbeam. Four young were taken from the first nest and sold. Three young were reared from the second nest but it is not known whether the second nest was made by the original pair after the first young were taken or whether a second pair was involved.

Numbers are very variable, being abundant in some years and scarce in others. Poor years were 1958 (one record of three birds), 1977 (five records at four sites), and 1979 (five records at three sites). Most flocks contain less than 25 birds but flocks of 50–80 are seen in good years. There have been only 15 records of 100 or more as follows:

1949   100 at Southill Park 23–6 January.
1956   120 at Flitwick Moor on 12 February.
1963   100 at Bedford SW on 19 January.
1971   100 at Eversholt Lake.
1974   300 at Campton.
1980   100+ at Flitwick Moor on 24 February.
1981   100 at Campton Plantation on 28 January.
        125 at Eversholt Lake on 13 December.
1982   150 at Flitwick Moor on 24 January.
1983   120 at Eversholt Lake on 11 December.
1985   100+ at Harrold GP on 24 November.
        100 at Leagrove Marsh on 19 December.
        100 at Eversholt Lake 29 December.
1986   200 at Eversholt Lake 22 January.
        160 at Flitwick Moor on 1 February.

The majority of records are of birds feeding on alders with a few on birch or spilled corn. The first published garden record is of one in a Luton garden in March 1972 and the following winter there were a further four reports of birds feeding from red mesh bags of peanuts. Since then feeding in gardens has become a frequent occurrence in good years.

Siskins usually arrive from mid October with most departing by the end of March. Apart from records of summering birds, the earliest record is one on 14 September at The Lodge, Sandy, and the latest at the same locality on 8 May 1980. There have been several records of summering birds in the county in addition to the breeding record mentioned by Steele-Elliott. A male summered at The Lodge, Sandy in 1968 and again the following year when a bird also remained at Rowney Warren. There is also a record of a male in June and a female in July 1969 in conifers on Galley Hill. A pair was recorded at New Wavendon Heath on 26 June 1972 but there was no evidence of breeding. However a pair almost certainly bred at The Lodge, Sandy in 1983 when three juveniles were seen together with a male.

Linnet

Carduelis cannabina

A common resident and passage migrant (**Map 106**).

Steele-Elliott (1904) knew the Linnet as a common resident during the nineteenth century but was also aware that it took part in migratory movements. At these times it was caught in great numbers on Dunstable Downs, Steele-Elliott citing an instance of 20 dozens being taken by one pair of nets in one morning's work at this locality. The largest number of mixed finches, mainly Linnets, taken by two men working two pairs of nets was more than 50 dozen. A decline in this species during the nineteenth century was attributed to this cause until it was made illegal.

In present times, flocks of 100–200 have been seen regularly, particularly from August through to late April, but although large flocks can occur in winter this is due to birds from wide areas congregating and, as a result, they can be almost totally absent in some areas. Those flocks that are seen during the winter can be quite large, sometimes as many as 500, but 1,000 were seen at Woodside on 27 November 1955 and the same number roosted at The Lodge, Sandy during the winters of 1965–6 and 1966–7. There appears to be some movement from higher to lower ground particularly in severe winters (Lack 1986). Small numbers pass through the county during April from their south-west wintering areas in France and Spain, but during late summer and autumn larger numbers are observed. A flock of 4,000 at Rammamere Heath on the Beds/Bucks border on 11 August 1962 is the largest recorded in the county. A party of 2,000 occurred at Houghton Regis ChP on 24 September 1976 and 700 at Dunstable SW on 30 September had increased to 1,500 by 3 October in the same year.

Breeding is widespread throughout the county but is more common in the south and east and less common in the more highly developed agricultural areas, possibly reflecting the greater use of herbicides and the consequent reduction in the availability of weed seeds. Harding (1979) recorded it during the breeding season in 345 of the county's 371 tetrads, with breeding proved in 153 and probable in 121.

Twite

Carduelis flavirostris

A rare passage migrant and winter visitor.

Davis (1855) gave the status of the 'Mountain Linnet' as being seen 'occasionally in autumn' around Luton, but in the 1874 edition it was amended to 'small flocks in autumn and winter'. Steele-Elliott (1904) knew of it as a winter migrant 'occurring more particularly during the autumn'. A few were taken by birdcatchers amongst flocks of Linnets on the Warden and Dunstable Hills. A male and a female taken on Dunstable Hills on 17 October 1894 by Mr G. Smith were given to Steele-Elliott. Mr John Armour, another birdcatcher, took one or more every year from the neighbourhood of Shefford.

Since 1946 the Twite has been recorded in 13 years as follows:

1947   A male at Clifton on 26 January.
1949   'Several' at Flitwick on 7 December.
1953   One at Whipsnade on 2 September.
1954   One at Dunstable SF on 26 August.
1958   A dead female at Great Barford on 25 February.
1961   10 at Stanford GP on 19 November.
1965   One at Luton Airport on 13 November.
1970   Two at Stanford GP on 27 November.
1976   The Lodge, Sandy:
      60 on 6 February.
      45 on 7 February.
      48 on 8 February.
      30 on 9 February.
      30 on 16 February.
      67 on 18 February.
      22 near Sutton on 19 December.
1977   Five at Girtford GP on 16 April had decreased to three by 18 April and one on 29 April.
      One at Sandy GP on 25 March.
      One at The Lodge, Sandy on 4 November.
1980   One at Blunham on 10 November.
1984   Two near Houghton Park Farm, Ampthill on 2 January.
1986   Five at South Mills NR on 31 January.

It is probable that this species is overlooked as many of the above records have been of birds associating with parties of Linnets or in other mixed finch flocks.

Redpoll
Carduelis flammea

The Mealy Redpoll (*C. f. flammea*) and the Lesser Redpoll (*C. f. cabaret*) both occur in the county and are described separately (**Map 107**).

Mealy Redpoll   *Carduelis flammea flammea*

An uncommon winter visitor.

Davis (1855) described the Mealy Redpoll as 'occasional' around the Luton area but did not give any particular instances of its occurrence. Steele-Elliott (1904), although believing that it probably visited the county 'during some winters of undue severity', cites only one instance. This was reported to him by a reliable birdcatcher who, in 1894, caught two 'Stoney Redpolls' along with Lesser Redpolls in the alders which grew along the River Ivel between Chicksands and Stamford.

Since 1946 there have been only 11 records. Two were trapped at Rowney Warren and two were seen at Putnoe, Bedford, both during the first winter period of 1946. Two were at The Lodge, Sandy on 25 December 1972 with six there on 21 January 1973, and four on 24 March which had decreased to one by 10 April. A flock of 100 Lesser Redpolls at Girtford GP on 12 March 1976 contained 15 Mealy Redpolls. Two were seen at Bedford SW on 24 December 1980 and one was at Priory CP on 23 March 1981. Three arrived in a flock of 35 Bramblings at Priory CP, Bedford on 18 January 1986, and one or two roosted with Lesser Redpolls at The Lodge, Sandy during the first winter period of the same year.

The 1976 record may indicate that the Mealy Redpoll has been overlooked and so under-recorded when present in large flocks of Lesser Redpoll.

Lesser Redpoll   *Carduelis flammea cabaret*

A fairly common resident and common winter visitor.

The Lesser Redpoll was well known as a winter visitor to the county during the eighteenth century particularly in areas of alder and, to a lesser extent, larch, birch, and willow. It was caught in good numbers along the banks of the River Ivel where, in the autumn of 1894, 54 were caught in just a few hours. It was a scarce breeding bird but by the end of the century there were obvious signs of it expanding its range within the county. Steele-Elliott (1904) knew of only one instance of it nesting before 1894, at Clifton about 1870, but 10 years later knew of its breeding at about 12 sites.

During this century, although regularly recorded during the winter, particularly from Flitwick Moor, there are no published records of more than 40 until 1962 when a party of 150 was seen at Southill Lake in December. Since then numbers in excess of 100 have been recorded in most winters, usually along the valleys of the River Ouse and the River Ivel as well as along the Greensand Ridge. Flocks of more than 200 include 250 at Stockgrove Park, Luton in January 1974, 200 at Eversholt Lake in January 1975, 245 at Warden Wood and 200 at Warden Warren in January 1976; 200 at The Lodge, Sandy in February 1976 had increased to 350 by the end of March and this site held 300 during the first winter period of 1986.

Breeding probably continued at a low level until the early 1960s but there are no published records of breeding between 1904 and 1963, after which its breeding range rapidly expanded. In this year it was thought to have probably bred at Southill Park, Rowney Warren, and Heath and Reach. By 1965 it was recorded as breeding in small numbers in many localities in the southern part of the county and three years later the county's breeding population was put at 50–70 pairs. In 1969 it was recorded during the breeding season from at least 30 localities, being most numerous along the Greensand Ridge with an estimated 100–150 pairs in TL14, 25 in SP92, and 16–20 in TL02. The first breeding in a suburban area took place on the outskirts of Bedford and further urban colonisation continued in the following year. Harding (1979) showed that most breeding records were distributed along the Greensand Ridge, the valleys of the River Ouse and River Ivel, and on the chalk downlands. Breeding was confirmed in 47 tetrads, thought probable in 63, and possible in 44.

A decline in the breeding population occurred from 1979 with breeding noted from only five sites during the following five years. None bred at The Lodge, Sandy in 1985 for the first time on record and the one pair that bred in the CBC census site at Old Warden was the lowest since recording began there in 1973.

Two-barred Crossbill

Loxia leucoptera

A very rare vagrant.

Steele-Elliott (1904) records that a flock was found in one of the fir plantations at Ampthill on 3 January 1890 by three Bedford schoolboys. Five were secured by the use of catapults but one of these escaped. H. W. Finlinson considered that there were perhaps 20 of them. An influx of this species took place in the autumn of 1889 and birds were recorded in several other counties.

Crossbill

Loxia curvirostra

An irregular visitor, occasionally breeding (**Map 108**).

Davis (1855, 1874) knew of this species occurring in small flocks in the Luton area during the winter and Steele-Elliott (1904) considered that, by the end of the century, it could be considered of regular winter occurrence. Of the early records three were killed at Aspley in April 1864 and about 20 visited a fir plantation at Clapham Park in November 1866; but in the fir plantations of Ampthill, Woburn, Southill, Rowney Warren, and Sandy, Steele-Elliott considered that their occurrence was far too numerous for him to give details. Although there was a strong suspicion that it bred in the county there was no proof. Display was noted by Steele-Elliott at Southill Warren in April 1899 and Mr Crossman noted similar behaviour at Flitwick and Ampthill, again in April 1899.

A flock of 50+ was seen between Everton and Sandy on 1 August 1909 (*British Birds* 3: 190–1) and in the same year flocks totalling 26 on 24 December at Woburn peaked at 47 by 18 February the following year with about 12 remaining until 19 March (*British Birds* 3: 373). In the same year 12 were seen in Great Hayes Wood and what must be the largest number seen in the county this century occurred at Great Wavendon Wood on 28 March when 'probably not less than several hundred' were seen in small flocks, and about the same number was seen on the following day at Southill and Rowney Warren (*British Birds* 3: 403).

Between mid September and mid October 1927 20–30 were present at Whipsnade Zoo (*British Birds* 20: 176) and in 1928 'a considerable party' was seen at the same locality on July 19 (*British Birds* 23: 69).

Between 1946 and 1987 the Crossbill has been recorded in every year except 1954, 1955, 1961, and 1968. Most observations have been made at sites along the Greensand but although most have occurred in winter there seems to be no regular pattern, with large flocks being seen in all months between the beginning of April and the end of August. The main sites have been The Lodge at Sandy, Maulden Woods, Whipsnade, Woburn, and Aspley Guise. Others include Aspley Heath, Rowney Warren, Warden Warren, and Southill as well as many others. Numbers have usually involved parties of 15 or less but 22 were recorded at Sandy on 22 October 1962, 25 at The Lodge, Sandy on 20 October 1966, 30 at Maulden on 30 October 1966, 24 at The Lodge, Sandy on 3 August 1972, 37 at The Lodge, Sandy on 24 March 1973, 20+ at Maulden Woods on 1 January 1980, 25 in Ampthill Park on 27 April 1980, 20 at The Lodge, Sandy on 29 June 1983, 42 there on 10 May 1984, and 40+ there in early June 1985.

Although breeding was suspected by Steele-Elliott he was never able to confirm it. The first breeding was recorded by the Duchess of Bedford at Woburn Woods on March 14 1913 when she observed a bird sitting tightly on a nest (1912–13). Since then a pair bred at

Aspley Guise in 1957 and again in the same area in 1960. In 1964 a
pair bred in Rowney Warren. Three nests were located at The Lodge,
Sandy in 1967 and possibly as many as six pairs may have bred in
the Maulden/Clophill area in the same year. Juveniles were seen at
Sandy in 1973 and 1977 and a party of 25 at Ampthill Park in April
1980 included juveniles. A pair with six juveniles was seen at The
Lodge, Sandy in July 1983. There seems to be no correlation between
the county's breeding population and years following eruptions.

Bullfinch

Pyrrhula pyrrhula

A common resident (**Map 109**).

Noted by Davis (1855) as being common around Luton, the Bullfinch
gained an evil reputation during the nineteenth century due to its
fondness for the buds of fruit trees. More people depended upon their
own fruit trees at this time and thus it was persecuted by both pro-
fessional and amateur gardeners. Despite this it was a common bird
throughout the county (Steele-Elliott 1904).

It is a resident species inhabiting hedgerows, larger gardens, parks,
and the fringes of woodlands but is less common where agriculture is
intensive. In spring it feeds on the buds of shrubs and trees causing
severe damage to fruit trees. However, there is little commercial fruit-
growing in the county and people depend far less on the fruit which
they grow for themselves. Most parties are of less than six birds, more
usually two or three, but larger flocks have been seen in winter with
one of 20 at The Lodge, Sandy on 22 December 1984 and one of 19 at
Priory CP on 15 November 1986.

Harding (1979) showed that breeding took place in 138 of the county's 371 tetrads, was thought probable in 85, and possible in a further
95.

Hawfinch

Coccothraustes coccothraustes

A local resident in small numbers (**Map 110**).

The Hawfinch was more plentiful during the middle of the nineteenth century than it is nowadays, although it was reported by Davis (1855) as being scarce around Luton, but an increase probably took place around 1880. Mr Covington, the Bedford taxidermist, in writing to Steele-Elliott (1904) mentions that it was a 'somewhat rare bird' around 1870, 'appearing at uncertain intervals.' He says that 'two or three specimens brought in to be set up in one winter would be considered unusual'. After a very sharp frost in about 1880 large numbers appeared and many were picked up dead in gardens in Bedford. Mr Covington had upwards of 80 brought in to him, about 10 males to every female. They were also fairly common around Langford, Steele-Elliott himself counting 10 in March 1894 with over 30 reported to him from the same locality in March 1895. Steele-Elliott knew of the Hawfinch breeding at Southill Park, Bromham Park, Chicksands Priory, Great Barford, and Woburn and thought that it undoubtedly also bred at Flitwick, Ampthill, Luton Hoo, Silsoe, and Turvey.

Although the Hawfinch has been recorded at many sites since 1946 it has remained rather elusive. Most records, particularly those in the breeding season, have been along the Greensand Ridge and have included Ampthill Park, Bedford Park, Bedford SF, Bush Wood, Caddington, Coopers Hill, East Hyde, Flitwick, Galley Hill, Heath and Reach, Kidney Wood, Lower Stondon, Luton Hoo, Markham Hills, Maulden Wood, Millbrook, Milton House, New Mill End, Noon Hill, Odell Woods, Old Warden, Potton Woods, Sandy, Sheerhatch Wood, Shuttleworth, Southill Park, Studham, Warden Warren, Whipsnade, Woburn, and Wrest Park.

Although birds have been recorded intermittently over the last 40 years at several sites during the breeding season breeding has been difficult to prove. Pairs bred at Flitwick in 1955 and Whipsnade Zoo in 1957 and family parties were seen at Bidwell and The Lodge, Sandy in 1965. A pair bred at Sheerhatch Wood in 1968 and in 1969 at least four breeding pairs were found in TL14 at Keepers Warren, Southill Park (two pairs), and near Upper Caldicote. In 1978, 1984, and 1986 pairs were proved breeding at Eversholt, Bush Wood, and Old Warden respectively.

Lapland Bunting

Calcarius lapponicus

A very rare vagrant.

Only one record in 1966, when one was heard and seen in flight at Brickhill, Bedford, on 15 October. It was seen on the ground feeding with House Sparrows and Chaffinches on 22 October (*Beds Naturalist* 20: 33).

Snow Bunting

Plectrophenax nivalis

A rare winter visitor.

Given by Davis (1855) as a rare winter visitor its status is very much the same today. In the 1874 edition he gave one example of it being shot near Harpenden, but no date is given. Steele-Elliott (1904) recorded that after several years of absence this species could become fairly abundant, but was restricted to the southern part of the county, particularly around the chalk hills of Barton, Luton, and Dunstable. Mr G. Smith, an experienced birdcatcher in these areas, informed Steele-Elliott that it generally arrived in December after prolonged periods of exceptionally severe weather. Under such conditions he had known droves of more than 100 to occur. He cited the winters of 1893–4 and 1894–5 as being particularly good with some very fine specimens being caught. However, to birdcatchers from other parts of the county it was an unknown species. Mr A. Covington, the Bedford taxidermist, saw three together with two Stonechats at Cardington Cross in March 1897 and two at Putnoe in February 1899. Steele-Elliott (1904) himself had seen four specimens, one taken at Clapham Park and another at Willington about 1870. One was shot at Clapham in January 1894 and an undated specimen came from Biddenham.

In recent times it has remained a rare and infrequent visitor with seven definite and two possible records as follows:

1970   One male at Bidwell on 4 January.
         One male at Milton Ernest on 22–3 January.
1972   One at Harrold GP on 10 December.
1976   One female or immature at Dunstable SW on 25 December.
1977   One at Stopsley, Luton, on 24 October.
1978   One male, possibly two, at Sewell Railway Cutting on 12 February.
1980   One at Barkers Lane GP (Priory CP) on 8 November.
1987   One male on Blows Downs on 8–12 January.

Yellowhammer

Emberiza citrinella

A common resident (**Map 111**).

This distinctive bunting has always been recorded as common in the county (Davis 1855, 1874; Steele-Elliott 1904; Harding 1979). In the nineteenth century the scribbling pattern on the eggs caused it to be called the 'Writing Lark' although it was more generally known as the Yellow-Hammer, Yellow Ammer, or Yellow Bunting.

Harding (1979) showed that it was present throughout the county with the exception of densely populated areas and was proved to have bred in 157 of the county's 371 tetrads (42%) with probable breeding being reported from a further 161 (43%). In areas of intensive agriculture and where hedgerows have been removed Harding reports that large umbellifers were used as song posts. There was some indication, however, that this species was more sparsely distributed in these areas.

Flocks may form from autumn onwards but more usually occur from late December into February. Most contain less than 50 birds but 500 observed at Goldington in January 1968 was the largest flock ever recorded in the county. Other large flocks include 120 at Dunstable SF in February 1962, 140 at Copt Hall, Luton in January 1974, 300 on Pegsdon Hills in January 1976, 400 at Dunstable in February 1976, 400 near Bromham in December 1982, 150 at Priory CP in January 1984, 160 at Priory CP in January 1985, 150 in the same locality in February 1986, and 250 at Butterfield Green near Luton in February 1987. A flock of 100 at Dunstable SW in mid March 1984 is the only large flock recorded in this month.

Cirl Bunting

Emberiza cirlus

A former rare resident.

Davis (1855, 1874) records the Cirl Bunting as being rare or rarely seen around Luton. Steele-Elliott (1904) at the time of his writing had not seen this species in the county. Even during the second half of the nineteenth century it was obviously on the edge of its range in Bedfordshire. Saunders (1889) knew of only five records from East Anglia and considered it an accidental in neighbouring Northamptonshire. He mentions it as being fairly common, though very local, on the chalk hills of Bedfordshire. Steele-Elliott disagreed with him and considered it as rare there. Mr Cane, a Luton taxidermist, had only three pass through his hands in 40 years whereas Mr J. S. Wright of Clifton, also a taxidermist, could not recall having seen a specimen at all. Mr G. Smith, a birdcatcher who lived at Limbury, near Luton, had only taken two specimens in 20 years, both of them locally. In December 1869 Mr A. L. Jessop secured 10 males from a flock of 30 and one female from a party of six at Clapham Park and further enquires by him suggested that this species bred there in the previous year. These birds were passed on to Mr A. Covington, the Bedford taxidermist, who also received a male which had been killed at Oakley in January 1870 and two more from Bromham the following winter.

One was observed between Clapham and Oakley in 1889 and the head keeper at Woburn had one in his possession which was killed from a small party in the Park. The only confirmed breeding record at that time was of a pair at Cardington on 25 May 1896.

Since that time there have been only three published records; three at Bedford SF on 17 January 1946, a male at Whipsnade Zoo on 31 August 1946, and a male seen near the Icknield Way on 3 June 1947.

Reed Bunting

Emberiza schoeniclus

A common resident (**Map 112**).

Steele-Elliott (1904) was acquainted with the Reed Bunting, particularly during the breeding season, as being a fairly common bird in the county closely associated with wetland habitats such as the margins of rivers, streams, pools, and marshy areas as well as ballast holes. It was particularly abundant on Flitwick Moor. Sometimes called the Black-headed Bunting, Water Sparrow, or Reed Sparrow at that time, he was aware that in winter they frequently moved to stubble fields and roadside hedges, often in small parties. Davis (1855) records it as being common around the Luton area.

It is still numerous in similar habitats although a decline took place during the 1960s. Around that time it showed a tendency to spread to drier habitats, being present during the summer on Galley Hill and in Chicksands Wood with breeding taking place on Warden Hills at this time. Harding (1979) showed that it was found during the breeding season in 263 of the county's 371 tetrads (71%). Breeding was proved in 102 tetrads and thought probable in a further 102. A river survey in 1983 found 94 confirmed breeding pairs with another 46 possible along the River Ouse, four confirmed and two possible along the River Ouzel, and nine confirmed and one possible along the River Ivel.

During the winter months the Reed Bunting often moves into stubble fields and rough weedy patches to feed, but during the early 1970s it was increasingly observed in gardens during severe weather. This habit continued into the 1980s, but in recent years it has been noticed that this species is occurring in urban areas in mild winters. Many Reed Buntings form communal roosts during the winter. Most roosting flocks have been of less than 40 birds but the roost at Harrold GP held 200 in October 1980, 250 in mid September 1981, and 300 in early January 1983. There is some evidence to suggest that small spring and autumn movements take place through neighbouring counties (Gladwin and Sage 1986): 35 at Dunstable SW in early April 1977, an increase at East Hyde during the last week of March and the first week of April 1977, and a flock of 100+ at Harrold GP on 23 April 1986 may support this, but such movements are not fully understood yet.

Corn Bunting

Miliaria calandra

A locally common resident (**Map 113**).

Steele-Elliott (1904) mentions this species as being fairly common in the agricultural areas in the east of the county, on the land bordering the River Ouse and the River Ivel, and more frequent in the chalk hill range in the south of the county. This is very much as it is now with it being noticeably absent from the wooded areas, particularly along the Greensand Ridge and on the Great Oolite Limestone in the north-west. Harding (1979) confirmed breeding in 51 tetrads (14%) and considered it probable in a further 129 (35%). The density of breeding pairs is much higher in the south of the county, particularly in the area to the north of Luton which includes Stopsley Common, Warden Hill, Galley Hill, and the farmland around Streatley. In 1971 the tetrad around New Farm, Streatley, was estimated to contain 35–40 pairs and 20 pairs were recorded on Stopsley Common in 1986.

Large flocks form during the winter months, most of which are composed of less than 50 birds, but larger flocks have occurred as follows: 50 near Luton Airport in second week of March 1974; 80 at Kempston Mill in November 1980; 100 at Kempston Mill 2 April 1981; 200 feeding on hay put out for sheep at Stevington in early January 1982; over 100 at Stewartby Turn at the end of January 1985; 150 near Tingley Woods from January to March 1987, and 250 buntings, mainly Corn, at Totternhoe on 26 January 1987.

4
The Breeding Birds Distribution Maps

In 1962 the Botanical Society of the British Isles published the *Atlas of the British Flora* which mapped the distribution of plants within each 10km square of the National Grid. This led the way for the British Trust for Ornithology in 1968 to commence a survey to map the distribution of breeding birds also based on the 10km square. Although the 10km square was suitable for a national survey the local variations within a county would not show up on this scale and so, taking a lead from J. G. Dony's *Bedfordshire Plant Atlas* (1976) which successfully used 2km × 2km squares (the tetrad), Bedfordshire Natural History Society again decided to use the same format. This fine grid system shows the distribution of birds much more accurately and enables the reader to relate distribution to quite small differences in habitat. For example it is easy to see which birds are restricted to the Greensand, the Chalk Downlands, or the river systems as well as throwing up certain anomalies which would benefit from further study.

The BTO survey took place over a five-year period 1968–72, and the Natural History Society's survey, coordinated by Nick Dymond, was closely connected during this period. The county survey continued for another five years with Pat Bonham director until 1974 and Barry Harding up to 1977.

In both surveys recorders made observations in order to classify birds as breeding (large dots), probably breeding (medium dots) and possibly breeding (the smallest dots) in all of the county's 371 tetrads. Further details of survey techniques can be found in the *Bedfordshire Bird Atlas* (Harding 1979).

The survey resulted in areas of the county being visited which had not normally been covered, being previously thought of as being ornithologically 'unattractive'. Interest was aroused in common species which had been for the most part ignored by many and even the local park or patch of rough ground was scrutinised in the hope of finding a new species for a particular tetrad. Above all it was great fun and gave an added purpose to the activities of the county's birdwatchers with the national and county atlases providing superb testaments to their efforts.

It would not be fair to publish this data without once again reiterating our thanks to those concerned with the publication of the *Bedfordshire Bird Atlas*: Nick Dymond and Pat Bonham who initiated the survey, Barry Harding who continued the work, John Dony who added his expertise and enthusiasm throughout, Derek Rands for producing the maps, A. J. Livett for coordinating the BTO survey, and to over 100 dedicated observers who made it all possible.

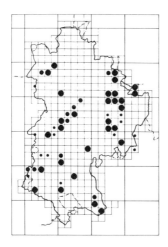

1 Little Grebe
Tachybaptus ruficollis

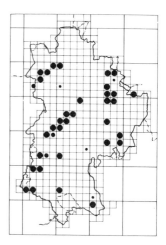

2 Great Crested Grebe
Podiceps cristatus

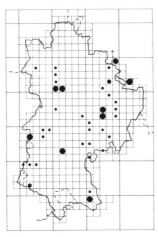

3 Grey Heron
Ardea cinerea

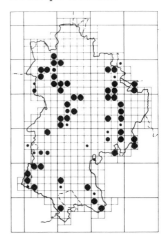

4 Mute Swan
Cygnus olor

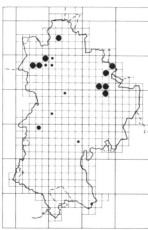

5 Greylag Goose
Anser anser

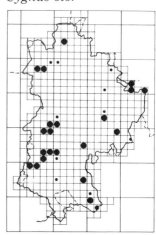

6 Canada Goose
Branta canadensis

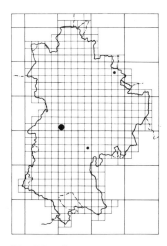

7 Shelduck
Tadorna tadorna

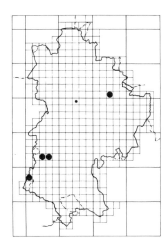

8 Mandarin
Aix galericulata

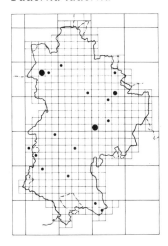

9 Teal
Anas crecca

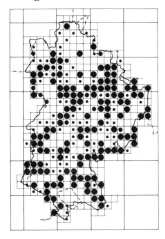

10 Mallard
Anas platyrhynchos

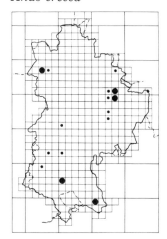

11 Shoveler
Anas clypeata

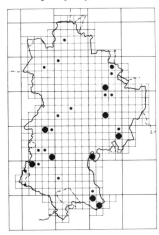

12 Pochard
Aythya ferina

307

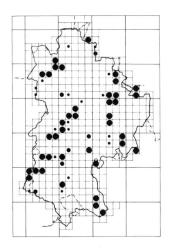

13 Tufted Duck
Aythya fuligula

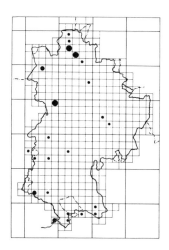

14 Sparrowhawk
Accipiter nisus

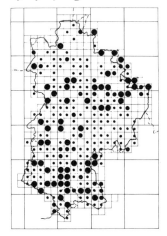

15 Kestrel
Falco tinnunculus

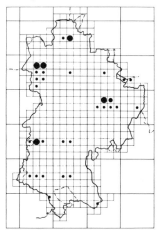

16 Hobby
Falco subbuteo

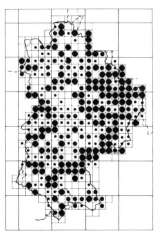

17 Red-legged Partridge
Alectoris rufa

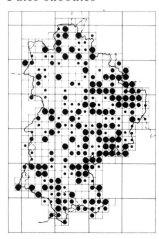

18 Grey Partridge
Perdix perdix

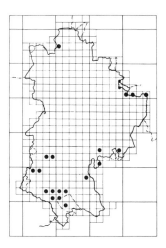

19 Quail
Coturnix coturnix

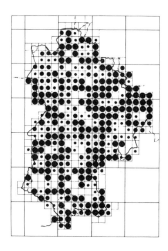

20 Pheasant
Phasianus colchicus

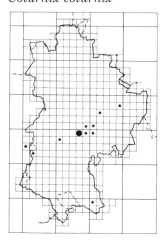

21 Golden Pheasant
Chrysolophus pictus

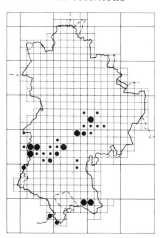

22 Lady Amherst's Pheasant
Chrysolophus amherstiae

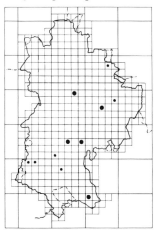

23 Water Rail
Rallus aquaticus

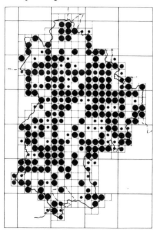

24 Moorhen
Gallinula chloropus

309

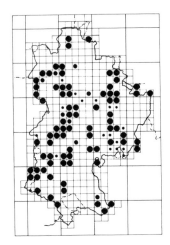

25 Coot
Fulica atra

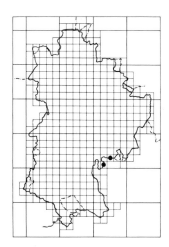

26 Stone Curlew
Burhinus oedicnemus

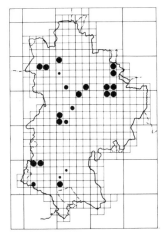

27 Little Ringed Plover
Charadrius dubius

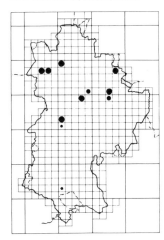

28 Ringed Plover
Charadrius hiaticula

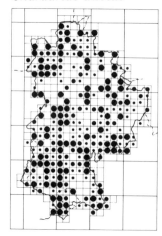

29 Lapwing
Vanellus vanellus

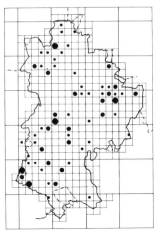

30 Common Snipe
Gallinago gallinago

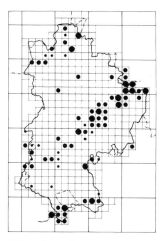

31 Woodcock
Scolopax rusticola

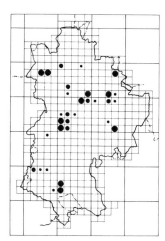

32 Redshank
Tringa totanus

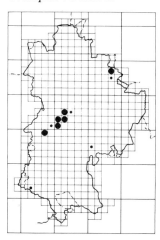

33 Black-headed Gull
Larus ridibundus

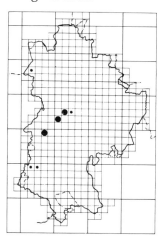

34 Lesser Black-backed Gull
Larus fuscus

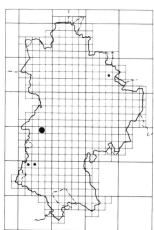

35 Herring Gull
Larus argentatus

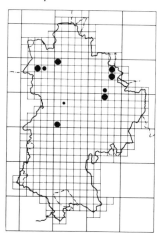

36 Common Tern
Sterna hirundo

311

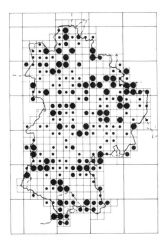

37 Stock Dove
Columba oenas

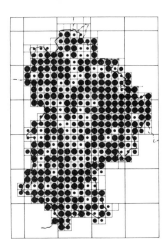

38 Woodpigeon
Columba palumbus

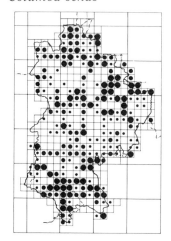

39 Collared Dove
Streptopelia decaocto

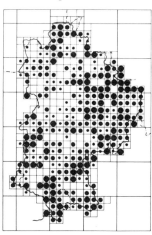

40 Turtle Dove
Streptopelia turtur

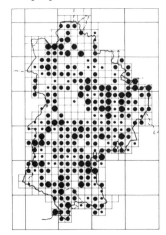

41 Cuckoo
Cuculus canorus

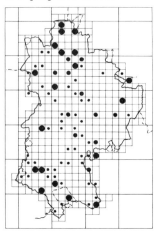

42 Barn Owl
Tyto alba

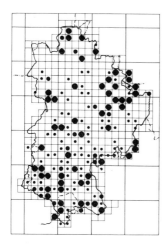

43 Little Owl
Athene noctua

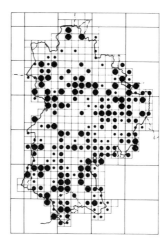

44 Tawny Owl
Strix aluco

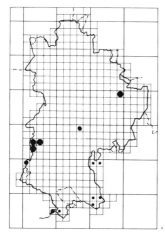

45 Long-eared Owl
Asio otus

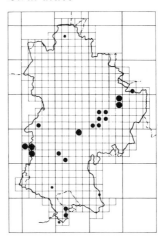

46 Nightjar
Caprimulgus europaeus

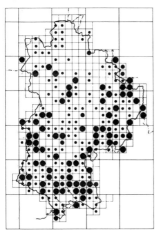

47 Swift
Apus apus

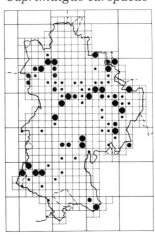

48 Kingfisher
Alcedo atthis

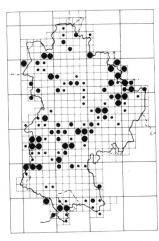

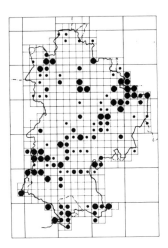

49 Green Woodpecker
Picus viridis

50 Great Spotted Woodpecker
Dendrocopos major

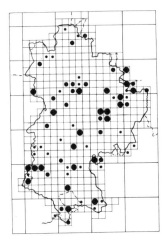

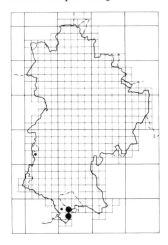

51 Lesser Spotted Woodpecker
Dendrocopos minor

52 Woodlark
Lullula arborea

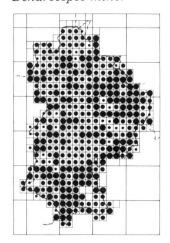

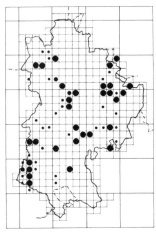

53 Skylark
Alauda arvensis

54 Sand Martin
Riparia riparia

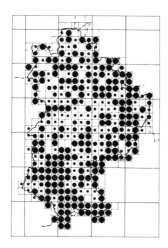

55 Swallow
Hirundo rustica

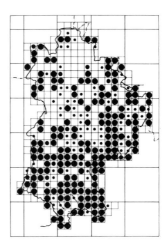

56 House Martin
Delichon urbica

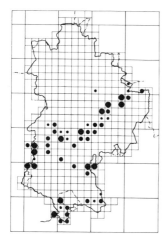

57 Tree Pipit
Anthus trivialis

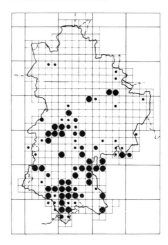

58 Meadow Pipit
Anthus pratensis

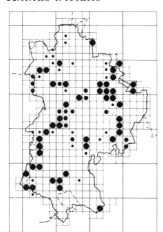

59 Yellow Wagtail
Motacilla flava

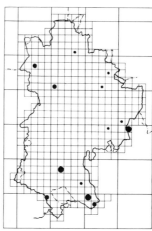

60 Grey Wagtail
Motacilla cinerea

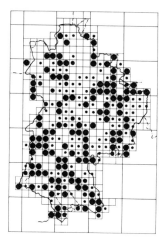

61 Pied Wagtail
Motacilla alba

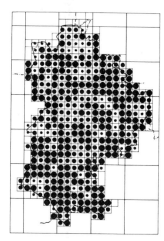

62 Wren
Troglodytes troglodytes

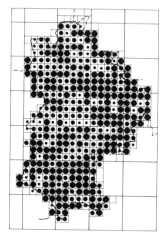

63 Dunnock
Prunella modularis

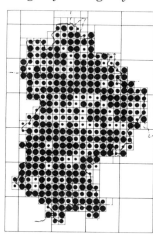

64 Robin
Erithacus rubecula

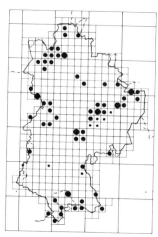

65 Nightingale
Luscinia megarhynchos

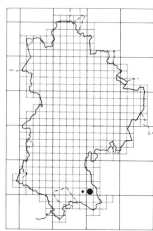

66 Black Redstart
Phoenicurus ochruros

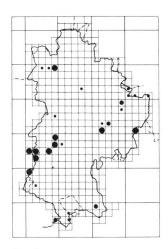

67 Redstart
Phoenicurus phoenicurus

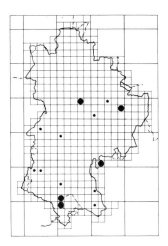

68 Whinchat
Saxicola rubetra

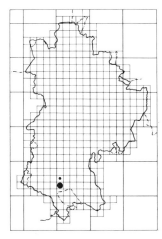

69 Stonechat
Saxicola torquata

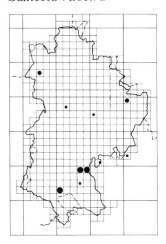

70 Wheatear
Oenanthe oenanthe

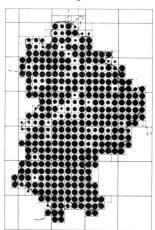

71 Blackbird
Turdus merula

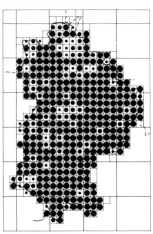

72 Song Thrush
Turdus philomelos

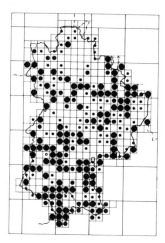

73 Mistle Thrush
Turdus viscivorus

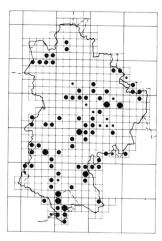

74 Grasshopper Warbler
Locustella naevia

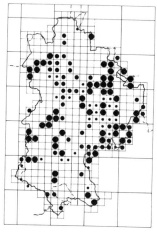

75 Sedge Warbler
Acrocephalus schoenobaenus

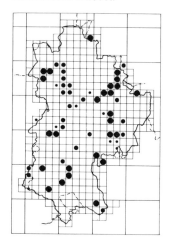

76 Reed Warbler
Acrocephalus scirpaceus

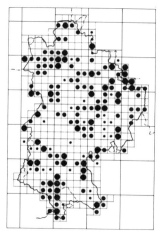

77 Lesser Whitethroat
Sylvia curruca

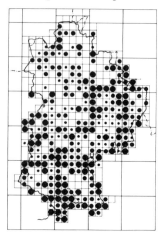

78 Whitethroat
Sylvia communis

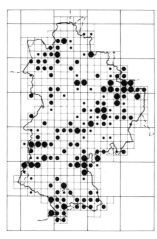

79 Garden Warbler
Sylvia borin

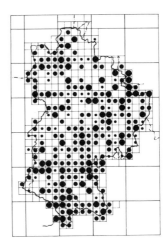

80 Blackcap
Sylvia atricapilla

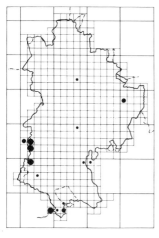

81 Wood Warbler
Phylloscopus sibilatrix

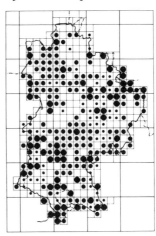

82 Chiffchaff
Phylloscopus collybita

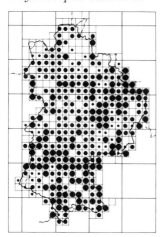

83 Willow Warbler
Phylloscopus trochilus

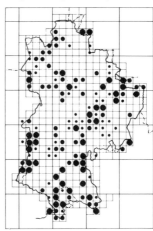

84 Goldcrest
Regulus regulus

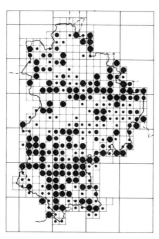

85 Spotted Flycatcher
Muscicapa striata

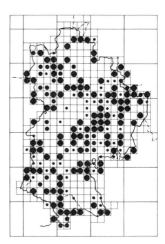

86 Long-tailed Tit
Aegithalos caudatus

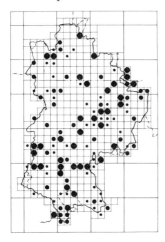

87 Marsh Tit
Parus palustris

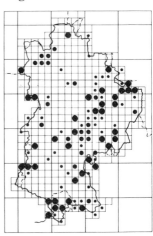

88 Willow Tit
Parus montanus

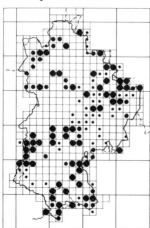

89 Coal Tit
Parus ater

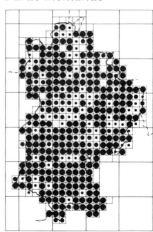

90 Blue Tit
Parus caeruleus

320

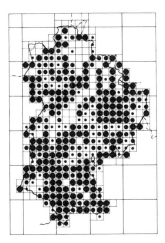

91 Great Tit
Parus major

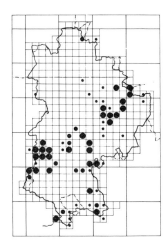

92 Nuthatch
Sitta europaea

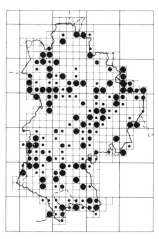

93 Treecreeper
Certhia familiaris

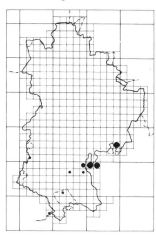

94 Red-backed Shrike
Lanius collurio

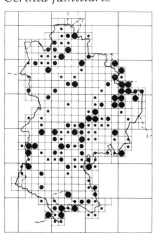

95 Jay
Garrulus glandarius

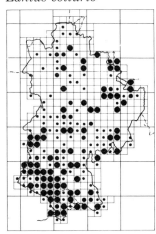

96 Magpie
Pica pica

321

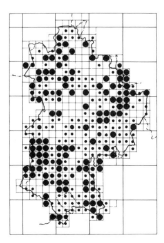

97 Jackdaw
Corvus monedula

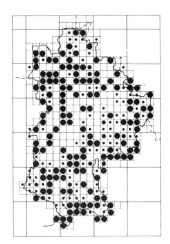

98 Rook
Corvus frugilegus

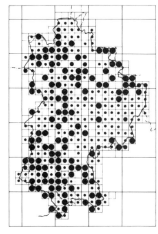

99 Carrion Crow
Corvus corone

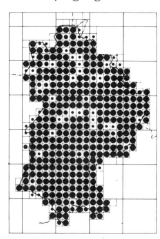

100 Starling
Sturnus vulgaris

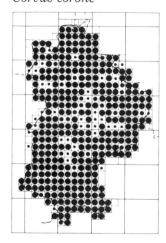

101 House Sparrow
Passer domesticus

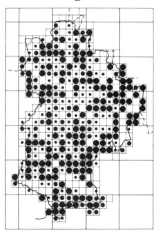

102 Tree Sparrow
Passer montanus

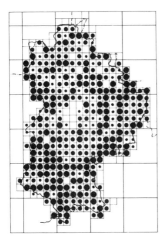

103 Chaffinch
Fringilla coelebs

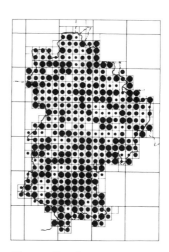

104 Greenfinch
Carduelis chloris

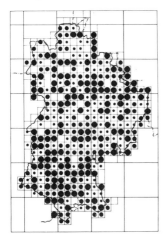

105 Goldfinch
Carduelis carduelis

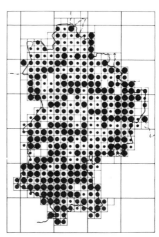

106 Linnet
Carduelis cannabina

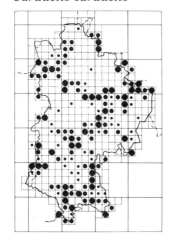

107 Redpoll
Carduelis flammea

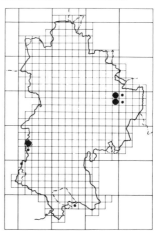

108 Common Crossbill
Loxia curvirostra

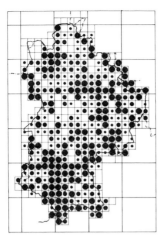

109 Bullfinch
Pyrrhula pyrrhula

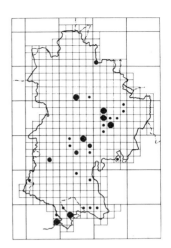

110 Hawfinch
Coccothraustes coccothraustes

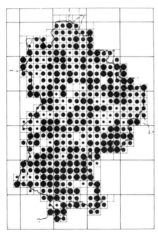

111 Yellowhammer
Emberiza citrinella

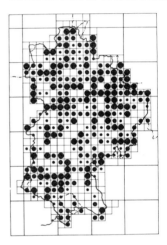

112 Reed Bunting
Emberiza schoeniclus

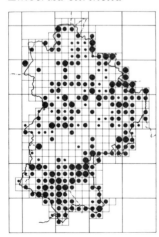

113 Corn Bunting
Miliaria calandra

Appendix A

The County List

By the turn of the century Steele-Elliott (1904) had recorded 214 species of birds in Bedfordshire of which three are now regarded as sub-species by today's taxonomic standards: White Wagtail, Hooded Crow, and Mealy Redpoll. He also omitted Mute Swan, which he did not consider to be wild. Several of the 214 species on this early list have not subsequently been recorded:

American Bittern
Little Bittern
Little Crake
Great Bustard
Red-necked Phalarope
Pallas's Sandgrouse
Dipper
Lesser Grey Shrike
Two-barred Crossbill

H. A. S. Key (1946) published a county list comprising 231 species which included Snowy Owl and Black Guillemot. Despite extensive enquiries and research no further information was discovered and therefore we decided to omit both species from the main list. We would of course be delighted if our scepticism was proven unfounded by future detective work! All the remaining species in section E of Key's list have been accounted for and are fully explained in the systematic list.

As the post-war boom in birdwatching continued, together with a more diverse landscape as the county's mineral wealth was exploited, the list steadily increased. By 1979 Barry Nightingale recorded a total of 257 species, although this list included Snowy Owl and Black Guillemot (Harding 1979).

By the end of 1987 the county bird list had moved to 267 (Trodd 1986), including Ring-necked Parakeet which is now given full Category C status as a species which has established a regular feral population, and the splitting of Water and Rock Pipit into separate species. In 1989 Black Kite and Ring-billed Gull were added to the list bringing the total at the end of the decade to 269 species. As the final chapters of this book are being written both Crane and Roller are under consideration for 1990. It remains to be seen what the ever-increasing band of rarity hunters or 'twitchers' can discover in the future, to push the county bird list beyond the inevitable 300 barrier.

Appendix B

Site Gazetteer

This appendix lists all the main sites, and many lesser known ones, of ornithological importance in Bedfordshire. Almost all are referred to at some point throughout the book and where a site is known by more than one name the alternatives are given. The naming of the county's still waters has varied over the years, particularly in the Marston Vale, although recently some degree of standardisation has been followed after B. Nightingale (*Beds Naturalist* 39: 73).

The site name is usually followed by the nearest town or village and National Grid reference. For a full description of the major localities see Clews *et al.* (1987).

The following abbreviations are used:

BCWT	Bedfordshire and Cambridgeshire Wildlife Trust
CP	Country Park
ChP	Chalk Pit
ClP	Clay Pit
FC	Forestry Commission
GP	Gravel Pit
NR	Local Nature Reserve
NNR	National Nature Reserve
RSPB	Royal Society for the Protection of Birds
SF	Sewage Farm
SW	Sewage Works
SP	Sand Pit
WT	Woodland Trust

A5 SPs. Collective name for a group of sand pits between Heath and Reach and the A5 trunk road.

AMPTHILL PARK, Ampthill — TL025384

AMPTHILL PARK WOOD, Ampthill — TL032385

ARNOLDS SP, Leighton Buzzard, formerly Pratts Pit — SP930242

ASPLEY HEATH. A general name for an area which includes the Wavendon Heaths and surrounding woodlands

ASPLEY WOOD, Aspley Guise — SP937350

BADGERDELL WOOD, Caddington — TL060212

BAKERS WOOD, Heath and Reach, now known more generally as part of Stockgrove CP — SP920290

BARKERS LANE GP, Bedford (BCWT), now a part of Priory CP — TL076493

BARTON HILLS, Barton (NNR) — TL090295

BATTLESDEN LAKE, Battlesden — SP957287

BEDFORD CLAY PITS. A general term for the excavations and flooded pits in the Marston Vale to the south-west of Bedford

BEDFORD PARK, Bedford — TL053511

BEDFORD SW, Bedford, formerly SF until the early 1960s — TL084496

BEESTON GP, Beeston   TL180475

BIGGLESWADE COMMON, Biggleswade   TL190474

BISON HILL, Whipsnade (NT). Also known by the general name Whipsnade Downs which also includes the downland inside the Zoological Park   SP999187

BLOWS DOWNS, Dunstable   TL033215

BLUE LAGOON, Arlesey, formerly Arlesey Pit   TL196343

BLUNHAM LAKE, Blunham, formerly Blunham GP   TL157512

BLUNHAM GPs, Blunham. A general name for a series of gravel pits between the river Ivel and the A1

BOULDER CLAY WOODS. A general term for a complex of mainly deciduous woodland in the Sharnbrook area

BRAMINGHAM WOOD, Luton (WT)   TL069258

BREAKHEART HILL, Millbrook, part of the Millbrook woodland complex   TL010378

BROGBOROUGH LAKE, Brogborough, formerly Brogborough ClP or No. 1 pit   SP975395

BROGBOROUGH No. 2 PIT, Brogborough, formerly Marston Thrift pit, now also known as Brogborough refuse tip   SP966405

BROMHAM HALL and PARK, Bromham   TL017513

BUSHMEAD PRIORY, Bushmead   TL118605

BUSH WOOD, Caddington   TL062210

CARDINGTON AIRFIELD, Cardington   TL085465

CASTLE MILL, Bedford   TL091510

CHALGRAVE MANOR, Toddington   TL017274

CHALTON SW, Chalton   TL026271

CHARLE WOOD, Woburn   SP930329

CHAWSTON GP, Wyboston   TL153565

CHICKSANDS WOOD (FC), Haynes   TL100400

CHIMNEY CORNER ClP, Kempston Hardwick, formerly known as Kempston Hardwick ClP. Today the two pits are generally known as north and south basins   TL037443

CITY FIELDS FARM GP, Henlow   TL185378

CLAPHAM PARK WOOD, Bedford   TL046532

CLAY-WITH-FLINT WOODS. A general name for the group of woodlands south of Luton and Dunstable on the Chiltern dip slope

COOPERS HILL (BCWT), Ampthill   TL027376

COPLE PIT (BCWT), Cople   TL100490

CORONATION ClP, Kempston Hardwick   TL030435

COWSLIP MEADOW, Luton   TL083248

CRANFIELD AIRFIELD, Cranfield   SP945420

CUCKOO BRIDGE GP, Great Barford, formerly known as Great Barford North Pit   TL120510

DAINTRY WOOD, Tingrith   SP998314

DEACON HILL, Pegsdon   TL127299

DEADMANSEY WOOD (FC), Studham   TL035165

DOUBLE ARCHES SP, Heath and Reach   SP940288

DUNGEE WOOD, Harrold   SP933595

DUNSTABLE DOWNS (NT), Dunstable   TL006195

DUNSTABLE SW, Thorn, formerly known as Dunstable SF   TL002243

EAST HYDE SW, Luton   TL120180

ELSTOW ClP, Elstow, includes reference to the adjacent refuse tip   TL045456

EXETER WOOD, Cotton End   TL100442

EVERSHOLT LAKE, Eversholt   SP979324

FELMERSHAM NR (BCWT), Felmersham,   SP990583

formerly Felmersham GPs

FENLAKE, Bedford — TL068488

FLITWICK MOOR (BCWT), Flitwick — TL046353

FLITWICK WOOD, Flitwick — TL023348

FORTY ACRE WOOD (FC), Harrold — SP945598

GALLEY HILL, Luton — TL092270

GIRTFORD GPs, Girtford — TL158503

GREAT BARFORD GP, Great Barford — TL130508

GREAT HAYES WOOD, Podington — SP965618

GREENSAND RIDGE WOODS. A general term for a collection of plantation woods on the lower Greensand stretching in a scattered band from Leighton Buzzard to Potton

GROVEBURY FARM SP, Leighton Buzzard — SP920231

GROVEBURY ROAD SP, Leighton Buzzard, formerly Rackley Hills Lagoon — SP919240

HALSEY WOOD, Souldrop — SP998613

HANGAR WOOD, Stagsden — SP998495

HARROLD CP, Harrold, formerly Harrold GPs — SP960570

HEATH and REACH SP, Heath and Reach, also known as Double Arches SP — SP940288

HENLOW LAGOON, Henlow — TL185382

HEXTON MANOR, Hexton, Herts — TL108304

HOME WOOD (FC), Northill — TL142463

HORSLEYS WOOD, Chiltern Green — TL132192

HOLCOTT WOOD, Cranfield — SP958403

HOUGHTON REGIS ChP, Houghton Regis — TL014235

HOUGHTON HALL, Houghton Regis — TL025235

ICKWELL BURY, Ickwell — TL144456

JONES SP, Heath and — SP939296

Reach, also known as the A5 Quarry

KEMPSTON HARWICK ClP, Kempston Hardwick, the former name for Chimney Corner ClP — TL037443

KENSWORTH ChP, Kensworth — TL017198

KIDNEY WOOD, Luton — TL094192

KINGS WOOD, Heath and Reach — SP925295

KINGS WOOD, Houghton Conquest — TL045400

KNOCKING HOE (NNR), Pegdon — TL130308

LANGFORD LAKES, Langford, formerly known as Henlow GPs — TL183397

LEAGRAVE MARSH, Luton, also known as Rotten Corner, Well Head, or Leagrave Common — TL059248

LEDBURN ROAD SP, Leighton Buzzard, also known as Mentmore Road SP — SP912235

LIDLINGTON ClP, Lidlington — TL000401

LOWES WOOD, Woburn — SP927325

LUTON HOO, Luton, including surrounding woodlands within the estate boundary — TL105185

MARKHAM'S HILL, Little Offly, mainly in Herts — TL130295

MARSTON THRIFT, Cranfield (FC) (BCWT) — TL973416

MAULDEN WOOD (FC), Maulden — TL070390

MELCHBOURNE PARK, Melchbourne — TL032650

MENTMORE ROAD SP, Leighton Buzzard, also known as Ledburn Road SP — SP912235

MILLBROOK ClP (BCWT), Marston Moretaine, also known as Millbrook Pillinge Pit and formerly as Marston Moretaine ClP — TL006413

MILLBROOK TEST TRACK, Millbrook — TL005395

MONEYPOT HILL, TL003375
Millbrook

NEWNHAM SF, Bedford, a TL070495
former SF now no more

NOON HILL, Pegsdon TL120292

ODELL GREAT WOOD, SP960590
Odell

ODELL LAKE, Odell SP953573

OLD WAVENDON HEATH, SP930345
Aspley Heath

OUZEL VALLEY SP,
Leighton Buzzard. A
collective name for a
complex of sand pits in
the Leighton Buzzard/-
Heath and Reach area.

PALMERS WOOD, Old TL130446
Warden

PARK WOOD, Harrold SP935583

PEDLEY WOOD (FC), Clo- TL095300
phill

PEGSDON HILLS, Pegsdon TL125300

PENNYFATHER MOOR, TL073370
Water End

POTTON WOOD (FC), TL252502
Cockayne Hatley

PRIORY CP (BCWT), Bed- TL076493
ford

PUTNOE WOOD, Bedford TL067527

QUEST ClP, Stewartby TL030420

RAE THURLEIGH, Thur- TL040600
leigh

RADWELL GPs, Radwell TL010585

RADWELL MEADOWS, TL015580
Radwell

RAVENSDELL WOOD, Stu- TL010148
dham

ROOKERY ClP, Stewartby TL018415

ROWNEY WARREN (FC), TL120405
Shefford

ROXTON LAKE, Roxton, TL156536
formerly Roxton GPs

RUSHMERE PARK, Heath SP915279
and Reach

SANDY SW, Sandy TL162502

SANDY WARREN, Sandy TL188482

SEWELL CUTTING SP995228
(BCWT), Dunstable,
also the site of a former
chalk quarry, now
infilled

SHARPENHOE CLAPPERS TL065303
(NT), Sharpenhoe

SHEERHATCH WOOD, Mog- TL130475
erhanger

SKIMPOT ChP, Dunstable, TL040220
now exhausted and
part of the Blows
Downs complex

SOUTHILL PARK, Southill TL146422

SOUTHILL LAKE, Southill TL145428

SOUTH MILLS NR, TL154501
Blunham

STANFORD PIT, Stanford TL159408

STEWARTBY LAKE, Ste- TL005425
wartby, formerly Ste-
wartby ClP

STOCKGROVE CP, Heath SP919294
and Reach

STOPSLEY COMMON, TL095294
Luton

SUNDON ChP, Upper TL040275
Sundon

SUTTON FEN, Sutton, pre- TL205475
viously managed by
the RSPB

SUNDON HILLS, Upper TL050290
Sundon

SWINESHEAD WOOD, TL060668
Swineshead

TEMPSFORD HALL, Temps- TL168535
ford

THE LODGE (RSPB), TL189478
Sandy

THORN SPINNEY, Hough- TL005249
ton Regis

TIDDENFOOT CP, Leigh- SP915238
ton Buzzard, formerly
Tiddenfoot SP

TINGRITH LAKE, Tingrith TL005329

TODDINGTON MANOR, TL004299
Toddington

TOTTERNHOE KNOLLS, SP979221
Totternhoe (BCWT)

TOTTERNHOE MEAD, Tot- SP991208
ternhoe

TWIN BRIDGES GP, Blun- TL158517
ham, formerly Blun-
ham GPs

VICARAGE FARM ClP, TL015435
Stewartby, also known
as 'L' Field Pit

WARDEN HILL, Luton TL091261

WARDEN WARREN, Old TL140345
Warden

WARDEN WOODS, Old Warden, comprising two woods, Warden Great and Warden Little   TL110430 TL110438

WARDOWN PARK, Luton   TL088228

WARREN WOOD, Clophill   TL085371

WASHERS WOOD, Eversholt   SP992315

WATERLOO THORNS, Tempsford   TL181519

WAVENDON HEATH, Aspley Heath, a general name for two former heaths known as Old Wavendon and New Wavendon   SP928340

WEST WOOD (FC), Souldrop   SP992626

WHIPSNADE PARK ZOO, Whipsnade   TL005175

WHIPSNADE HEATH, Whipsnade   TL018180

WILLINGTON GP, Willington, including surrounding woodland   TL105505

WILSTEAD WOOD (FC), Wilstead   TL074425

WINSDON HILL, Luton   TL073215

WOBURN PARK, Woburn, including various lakes and surrounding woodlands   SP960330

WREST PARK, Silsoe   TL090350

WYBOSTON LAKES, Wyboston, formerly Wyboston GPs   TL175575

Appendix C

Selected Records for 1988

Red-throated Diver   An adult in full breeding plumage at Stewartby Lake on 9–10 May.

Red-necked Grebe   One at Priory CP on 17 November.

Slavonian Grebe   One at Stewartby Lake on 6 December.

Leach's Petrel   One at RAE Thurleigh on 12 September was released at Llandbedr, Wales on 13th.

Cormorant   Attempted breeding at Little Paxton, Cambridgeshire.

Night Heron   A sub-adult at Girtford GP on 17–20 June was only the second record since 1946 (*British Birds* 82: 510).

Grey Heron   Breeding details of the Bromham heronry (*Beds Naturalist* 43: 37).

White Stork   One near Biggleswade on 29 August was only the second county record.

Mute Swan   A pair reared a brood of 15 cygnets on the River Ivel at Henlow (*Beds Naturalist* 43: 37, 39).

Egyptian Goose   One at Bromham on 28 February.

Mandarin   Flitwick Moor had its first breeding record when a pair reared 10 ducklings.

Garganey   A pair seen intermittently from 15 April to 13 June in the Ivel valley.

Red-crested Pochard   A duck at Wyboston Lake on 11–23 April.

Common Scoter   A group of 11 at Brogborough Lake on 20 November.

Velvet Scoter   Three at Stewartby Lake on 20 November.

Red-crested Merganser   One at Chimney Corner ClP on 14 April and one at Brogborough Lake on 21 November.

Honey Buzzard   One over The Lodge, Sandy on 12 July.

Red Kite   One over Bromham on 19 March with another at South Mills NR on 18 April.

Marsh Harrier   One in the Wilstead area on 14 May with possibly the same bird near Colesden on 15th. One at Rookery ClP on 7–8 September.

Hobby   Evidence of breeding from nine localities.

Spotted Crake   One at South Mills NR on 23–5 August.

Corncrake   One at Eaton Bray on 23 June, had been present for two weeks.

Stone Curlew   One at Houghton Regis ChP on 14 May and one at Rookery ClP on 10 September.

Knot   One at South Mills NR on 10–11 June.

Sanderling   Singles at Rookery ClP on 9–10 May and on 16th and 18th, at Chimney Corner ClP on 25 May, and at South Mills NR on 23 July.

Curlew Sandpiper   Five at Chimney Corner CIP on 24 August followed by three to four from 3–15 September and eight on 16th, when presumably the same birds were noted intermittently at Bedford SW. Two at Rookery ClP on 15 September.

Pomarine Skua   An immature at Brogborough Lake/Tip on 20–8 November was only the second record since 1946.

Arctic Skua   One near Bison Hill on 4 September.

Mediterranean Gull   A first-winter at Brogborough Tip on 23 January followed by an adult at Rookery ClP on 15 July.

Iceland Gull   A second-winter bird at Brogborough Lake on 24 January.

Glaucous Gull   A first-winter at Brogborough Lake and Tip on 2–9 January followed by a second-winter on 19 March and a first-winter on 29–30 December.

Little Tern   One at Stewartby Lake on 17 August.

Nightjar   One at Old Wavendon Heath on 31 May to 1 June. One dead at Thurleigh on 23 September.

Hoopoe   One at Shillington on 14–16 April.

Waxwing   A second-winter period influx involved at least 18 individuals.

Firecrest   A pair at Millbrook in April; a male at Whipsnade Zoo on 28 April; one at The Lodge, Sandy on 27 May; and a male at Tiddenfoot SP on 26 November.

Bearded Tit   Six at Priory CP on 14 October with two to six until 28th.

Great Grey Shrike   One near Stotfold on 20 November.

Appendix D

Selected Records for 1989

Great Northern Diver   One at Priory CP on 16 December moved to Stewartby Lake/Rookery ClP on 17th and Millbrook ClP on 18th.

Fulmar   Singles at Brogborough Lake on 9 September and Priory CP on 12th.

Leach's Petrel   One at Brogborough Lake on 29 October.

Cormorant   A maximum of 69 at Brogborough Lake on 26 November was a county record. Breeding at Little Paxton, Cambs.

Shag   A December influx involved at least 19 birds.

Whooper Swan   Three over Radwell GP on 11 March.

Bean Goose   Two at Radwell GP on 4 February.

Brent Goose   Two near Wyboston on 11 March and one at Luton on 9th.

Garganey   A pair at South Mills NR on 27 March. A drake at Dunstable SW on 6–7 followed by an eclipse bird on 6–7 August. A drake at Millbrook ClP on 5 July and a drake at Blunham on 19 July.

Red-crested Pochard   One at Houghton Regis ChP on 12 May; one in the Ivel valley from 10 September to 18 November and a drake at Brogborough Lake from 1–14 October with a pair on 16–18 December.

Ring-necked Duck   A duck at Harrold CP on 1–2 January was relocated at Radwell GP on 12 February where it remained until 19 March.

Common Scoter   Seven at Stewartby Lake on 12 July and a drake at Brogborough Lake on 16–24 December.

Velvet Scoter   Four at Radwell GP on 23 April.

Smew   One at Priory CP on 6 March.

Red-breasted Merganser   One at Priory CP on 28 December.

Ruddy Duck   A pair bred at Rookery ClP.

Black Kite   An adult at Little Staughton on 7 June was a first for the county (*Beds Naturalist* 44: 49–50).

Montagu's Harrier   A 'ringtail' at South Mills NR on 17 July.

Hobby   Evidence of breeding from at least 10 localities.

Peregrine   One at Rookery ClP on 20–7 August and one at Kempston Hardwick on 11 October.

Quail   A 'quail' year with singing noted at Warden/Galley Hill, Stopsley Common, Houghton Regis ChP, Sewell, Totternhoe, Haynes, Marston Thrift, Knotting Green, Chalgrave, Blows Downs, and Whipsnade Downs.

Stone Curlew   One at Barton Hill Farm on 3 May.

Grey Plover   A party of 13 at Houghton Regis ChP on 26 September.

Sanderling   Singles at Rookery ClP on 27 May and at Stewartby Lake on 6 June.

Little Stint   At least nine at Rookery ClP from 26 August to 17 September.

Pectoral Sandpiper   One at South Mills NR on 22–3 October was the sixth county record.

Curlew Sandpiper   One at Rookery ClP on 3 June.

Mediterranean Gull   A first-winter at Chimney Corner ClP/Rookery ClP on 23 April followed by an adult at the latter site on 20 September. At Brogborough Lake two first-winters on 30 September, one on 29 October and 31 December, with a second-winter on 15 December.

Ring-billed Gull   A second-year bird at Brogborough Lake on 25 February was a first for the county (*Beds Naturalist* 45 (1990)).

Iceland Gull   An adult at Brogborough Lake on 4–11 March followed by a first-winter at Stewartby Lake/Rookery ClP on 19 March and a second-winter 19–28 March and 21 April. One at Brogborough Lake on 15 December.

Glaucous Gull   At Brogborough Lake/Tip an adult from 2 January to 5 February and 19 March; a second-winter 2 January to 4 March; two first-winters 8 January to 4 March; a third-winter on 29 October and 20–5 November; a first-winter from 29 December and a first-winter at Rookery ClP on 27 March.

Sandwich Tern   A flock of 34 at Priory CP on 8 September.

Nightjar   A pair bred at Wavendon Heath with one or two other 'churring' males nearby. Also recorded at The Lodge, Sandy and Moneypot Hill.

Hoopoe   One at Clapham on 1 May and one at Houghton Regis ChP 24–7 September.

Water Pipit   One or two at Cuckoo Bridge GP on 18 April.

Rock Pipit   One at South Mills NR on 15 January.

Waxwing   Two at Marston Moretaine on 9 January and one at Blows Downs on 15 April.

Golden Oriole   One near Millbrook station on 21 May.

Great Grey Shrike   One at Kempston on 26 January and at Stewartby Lake/Millbrook ClP until 4 February. One at Ampthill Park 29–31 March and one at Bolnhurst 4–22 April.

Appendix E

Mean Peak Wildfowl Counts 1983/4–1987/8

The National Wildfowl Counts take place on the second Sunday of each month, the first count taking place in September and the last in March. They are organised by the Wildfowl and Wetlands Trust and are funded by them and the Nature Conservancy.

Up to the end of 1987 National Wildfowl Counts have taken place at various times at 35 wetland sites in the county, the earliest being at Stewartby and Millbrook in 1960. Unfortunately coverage has been intermittent at 25 sites leaving only 10 sites where coverage has been continuous for a period of five years. Only six of these sites have been covered for the same five-year period. Counts over short periods of time have little meaning when trying to make comments concerning population trends in the county and become more useful when carried out for 10 years or more, preferably for 25 years. Average peak counts have been given below for the five-year period 1983/4–1987/8 at the six sites where this has taken place. Wildfowl counts have been on a firmer footing since 1983 and in future years it should be possible to make more use of them.

Mallard		*Tufted Duck*		*Gadwall*	
Brogborough L	108.2	Brogborough L	197.6	Brogborough L	1.2
Chimney Corner ClP	41.8	Chimney Corner ClP	63.0	Chimney Corner ClP	0.0
Dunstable SW	89.4	Dunstable SW	53.2	Dunstable SW	58.2
Luton Hoo L	197.0	Luton Hoo L	42.2	Luton Hoo L	18.2
Priory CP	144.2	Priory ClP	52.2	Priory CP	5.8
Stewartby L	104.2	Stewartby L	19.8	Stewartby L	6.4

Shoveler		*Coot*		*Wigeon*	
Brogborough L	1.0	Brogborough L	1278.0	Brogborough L	24.0
Chimney Corner ClP	0.0	Chimney Corner ClP	322.4	Chimney Corner ClP	0.0
Dunstable SW	55.2	Dunstable SW	178.4	Dunstable SW	7.2
Luton Hoo L	3.0	Luton Hoo L	119.0	Luton Hoo L	3.8
Priory CP	10.0	Priory CP	37.2	Priory CP	69.2
Stewartby L	4.6	Stewartby L	193.8	Stewartby L	66.8

Pochard		*Teal*		*Canada Goose*	
Brogborough L	327.8	Brogborough L	3.4	Brogborough L	102.2
Chimney Corner ClP	82.8	Chimney Corner ClP	14.6	Chimney Corner ClP	57.4
Dunstable SW	45.8	Dunstable SW	11.6	Dunstable SW	1.8
Luton Hoo L	32.8	Luton Hoo L	29.6	Luton Hoo L	249.6
Priory CP	95.4	Priory ClP	65.2	Priory CP	4.4
Stewartby L	85.4	Stewartby L	15.4	Stewartby L	86.0

Mute Swan		*Great Crested Grebe*	
Brogborough L	7.2	Brogborough L	17.0
Chimney Corner ClP	14.4	Chimney Corner ClP	4.0
Dunstable SW	6.8	Dunstable SW	0.0
Luton Hoo L	4.6	Luton Hoo L	12.2
Priory CP	8.0	Priory CP	19.6
Stewartby L	11.0	Stewartby L	98.4

Wader Frequency Chart

	J	F	M	A	M	J	Jy	A	S	O	N	D
Oystercatcher												
Little Ringed Plover												
Ringed Plover												
Grey Plover												
Knot												
Sanderling												
Little Stint												
Curlew Sandpiper												
Dunlin												
Ruff												
Black-tailed Godwit												
Bar-tailed Godwit												
Whimbrel												
Curlew												
Spotted Redshank												
Redshank												
Greenshank												
Green Sandpiper												
Wood Sandpiper												
Common Sandpiper												
Turnstone												

Legend:

- Frequently seen
- Fairly frequently seen
- Occasionally seen
- Scarcely seen
- Rarely seen

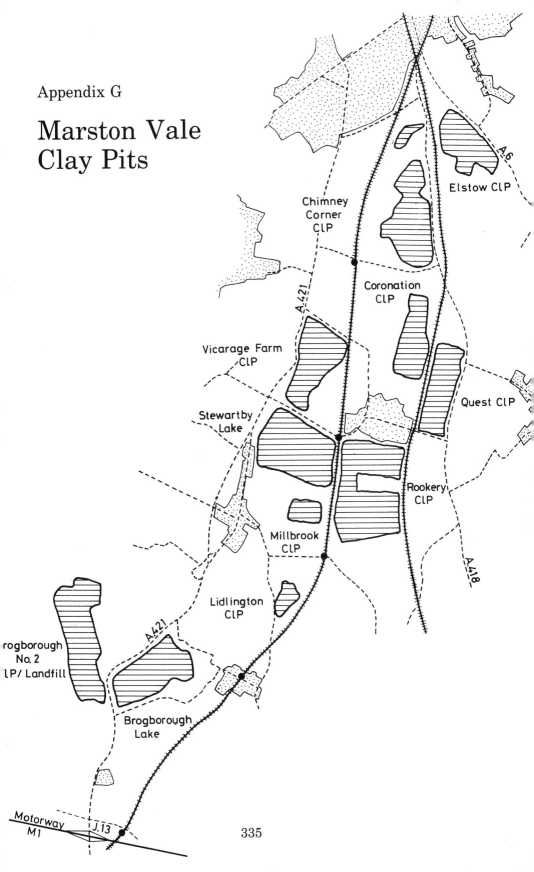

Appendix G

Marston Vale
Clay Pits

Chimney
Corner
CLP

Elstow CLP

A6

Coronation
CLP

Vicarage Farm
CLP

Quest CLP

Stewartby
Lake

Rookery
CLP

A421

A418

Millbrook
CLP

Lidlington
CLP

rogborough
No. 2
LP/ Landfill

A421

Brogborough
Lake

Motorway
M1

J.13

335

Bibliography

ALEXANDER, H. G. (1914–15) A report on the Land Rail enquiry. *British Birds* 8: 83.

ALEXANDER, W. B. (1943–4) Birds on Bedford Sewage Farm. *British Birds* 37: 117.

ALLSOPP, K. and DAWSON, I. K. (1987) Monthly Report. *British Birds* 80: 458.

ANON. (1929–30) Starlings using a roost in summer. *British Birds* 23: 273.

ANON. (1936–7) Obituary, The Duchess of Bedford 1865–1937. *British Birds* 30: 369.

ASH, J. S. (1970) Observations on a decreasing population of Red-backed Shrikes. *British Birds* 63: 185–205, 225–39.

ATCHISON, G. T. (1917–18) Large clutch of Little Owl eggs. *British Birds* 11: 93.

BALL, D. (1987) Birds new to Bedfordshire, Arctic Skua. *Beds Naturalist* 42: 46–7.

BATTEN, L. A. (1971) Firecrests breeding in Buckinghamshire. *British Birds* 64: 473–5.

—— (1973) The colonisation of England by the Firecrest. *British Birds* 66: 159–66.

BEDFORD, Mary Duchess of (1907–8) Statistics of breeding stock of Goldfinchs. *British Birds* 1: 178–9.

—— (1908–9) Goosander in Bedfordshire. *British Birds* 2: 384.

—— (1909–10) Irruption of Crossbills. *British Birds* 3: 303, 331, 373.

—— (1911–12a) Tufted Duck breeding in Bedfordshire. *British Birds* 5: 139.

—— (1911–12b) Sanderling and Goosander in Bedfordshire. *British Birds* 5: 248.

—— (1912–13) Crossbills breeding in Bedfordshire. *British Birds* 6: 342.

—— (1915–16) Firecrest in Bedfordshire. *British Birds* 9: 319.

—— (1919–20) Hobby in Bedfordshire. *British Birds* 13: 58.

—— (1920–1) Possible migration of Yellow Bunting in Bedfordshire. *British Birds* 14: 257.

—— (1924–5) Shelduck in Bedfordshire. *British Birds* 18: 30.

—— (1925–6a) Puffin at Woburn. *British Birds* 19: 155.

—— (1925–6b) Common Sandpiper wintering in Bedfordshire. *British Birds* 19: 255.

—— (1927–8a) Knot in Bedfordshire. *British Birds* 21: 205.

—— (1927–8b) White-tailed Eagle in Bedfordshire. *British Birds* 21: 283.

BEDFORD SCHOOL NATURAL HISTORY SOCIETY. Bird List, 1941–4.

BEDFORDSHIRE, COUNTY PLANNING DEPARTMENT (n.d.) *Bedfordshire, Landscape and Wildlife.*

—— (1982) *Bedfordshire, River Valleys*, Sector Study One.

BEDFORDSHIRE NATURAL HISTORY SOCIETY. Annual bird reports, 1946–89. *Beds Naturalist* 1–44.

—— (1979) *Bedfordshire Landscape and Wildlife*, Technical Volume.

BIBBY, C. (1973) The Red-backed Shrike; a vanishing British species. *Bird Study* 20: 103–10.

—— (1981) Wintering Bitterns in Britain. *British Birds* 74: 1–10.

BRAZIL, M. A. (1981) Whooper Swan migration and movements: a study using neck bands. Unpublished, University of Stirling.

BRITISH BIRDS (1984) *The British Bird Lists of the Western Palearctic.* Blunham, Beds.

BRITISH ORNITHOLOGISTS UNION (1971) *The Status of Birds in Britain and Ireland.* Blackwell, Oxford.

BRITISH TRUST FOR ORNITHOLOGY. Ringing data relevant to Bedfordshire until 1987.

BURTON J. F. (1956) Report on the national census of heronries, 1954. *Bird Study* 3: 42–73.

CAMPBELL, B. (1963) A Birds-nesting Jubilee. *Beds Naturalist* 18: 10–14.

CHANDLER, R. J. (1981) Influxes into Britain and Ireland of Red-necked Grebes and other waterbirds during winter 1978/79. *British Birds* 74: 55–81.

CLEWS, B., HERYET, A., and TRODD, P. (1987) *Where to Watch Birds in Bedfordshire, Berkshire, Buckinghamshire, Hertfordshire and Oxfordshire*. Helm, London.

COLE, H., WHITE, D. and R., and WORTLEY, M. (1955) Black-headed Gulls breeding in South Bedfordshire. *Beds Naturalist* 10: 16.

COLE, H. (1958) Wilson's Phalarope in Bedfordshire. *Beds Naturalist* 13: 46–7.

CORNWALLIS, R. K. and TOWNSEND, A. D. (1968) Waxwings in Britain and Europe during 1965/66. *British Birds* 61: 97–118.

COULSON, J. C. and BRAZENDALE, M. G. (1961) Movements and seasonal variation in mortality of Shags and Cormorants ringed in the Faroe Islands, Northumberland. *British Birds* 54: 225–35.

CRAMP, S. *et al.* (1977–) *Handbook of the Birds of the Western Palearctic*, Vols 1–5. Oxford.

DAVENPORT, D. L. (1982) Influxes into Britain of Hen Harriers, Long-eared Owls and Short-eared Owls in winter 1978/79. *British Birds* 75: 309–16.

DAVIS, F. (1855, 2nd edn 1874) *A History of Luton*.

DAVIS, P. G. (1982) Nightingales in Britain in 1980. *Bird Study* 29: 73–9.

DAZLEY, R. (1990) Blows Downs Spring Migration Watchpoint 1985–90. *Beds Naturalist* 45.

DELACOUR, J. (1951) *The Pheasants of the World*. London.

DURMAN, R. F. (1976) Ring Ouzel migration. *Bird Study* 23: 197–205.

DYMOND, J. N. (1963) Common Tern breeding in Bedfordshire. *Beds Naturalist* 18: 32.

DYMOND, J. N., FRASER, P. A., and GANTLETT, S. J. M. (1989) *Rare Birds in Britain and Ireland*. Poyser, Calton.

ELLWOOD, J. (1971) Annual yearbook. Wildfowl Association of Great Britain and Ireland.

FERGUSSON-LEES, I. J. (1944–5) Red-necked Grebe in Bedfordshire. *British Birds* 38: 57.

FINLINSON, H. W. (1928–9) Grey Phalarope in Bedfordshire. *British Birds* 22: 169.

FISHER, J. (1952) The wild birds of Whipsnade Park. *Zoo Life*. Summer edn 49–52.

FITTER, R. S. R. (1971) Black Redstarts breeding in Britain in 1964–68. *British Birds* 64: 117–24.

FLEET, L. (1911–12) Black Tern in Bedfordshire. *British Birds* 5: 54.

FOSTER, A. H. (1914) *The Birds of North Herts*.

—— (1917) A list of the birds which have occurred in North Herts., with notes on each species. *Trans. Herts Nat. Hist. Soc.* 16: 189–220.

FULLER, P. (1987) Study of Mandarin (*Aix galericulata*) in Bedfordshire. *Beds Naturalist* 42: 51–4.

GARDNER (1907–8) Lesser Grey Shrike in Bedfordshire. *British Birds* 1: 147.

GLADSTONE, H. S. (1924–5) Introduction of the Ring-necked Pheasant to Great Britain. *British Birds* 18: 84.

GLADWIN, T. W. and SAGE, B. L. (1986) *The Birds of Hertfordshire*. Castlemead, Ware.

GRIBBLE, F. C. (1951) The Little Ringed Plover in Bedfordshire, 1951. *Beds Naturalist* 6: 34.

—— (1955) The Purple Heron in Bedfordshire, *Beds Naturalist* 10: 29–30.

—— (1983) Nightingales in Britain and Ireland in 1981. *Bird Study* 30: 165–76.

HARDING, B. D. (1979) *Bedfordshire Bird Atlas*. Bedfordshire Natural History Society.

HARPER, W. G. (1958) The study of bird migration by radar. *Beds Naturalist* 13: 14–18.

—— (1959) Starling roosts observed from a radar site in South Beds. *Beds Naturalist* 14: 12–19.

HARRISON, T. H. and HOLLOM, P. A. D. (1932–3) The Great Crested Grebe enquiry, 1931. *British Birds* 26: 62–92.

HICKEY, M. P. and P. B. (1987) Birds new to Bedfordshire – Bluethroat. *Beds Naturalist* 42: 47.

HICKLING, R. A. O. (1967) The inland wintering of gulls in England, 1963. *Bird Study* 14: 104–13.

—— (1977) Inland wintering gulls in England and Wales, 1973. *Bird Study* 24: 79–88.

HINE, R. L. ed. (1934) *The Natural History of the Hitchin Region*.

HOLLOM, P. A. D. (1959) The Great Crested Grebe sample census, 1946–1955. *Bird Study* 6: 1–7.

HUDSON, R. (1976) Ruddy Ducks in Britain. *British Birds* 69: 132–43.

—— (1979) Nightingales in Britain in 1976. *Bird Study* 26: 204–12.

HUXLEY, J. S. (1936–7) Nests and broods in 1936 in Whipsnade bird sanctuary, Beds. *British Birds* 30: 224.

—— (1938–9) Nests and broods in the successive seasons at Whipsnade. *British Birds* 32: 40.

JACKSON, S. J. (1980) Hirundine and Swift arrival and departure dates. *Beds Naturalist* 35: 22–5.

JAMES, T. J. and SAWFORD, B. R. (1979) Rarer British birds in the collections of North Hertfordshire Museums Service and other local museums. *Trans. Herts. Nat. Hist. Soc.* 28(2): 29–44.

JENKINS, A. R. (1955) Migration of the Common Gull. *Beds Naturalist* 10: 29.

—— (1958) *The Birds of the Letchworth Region*. Letchworth Naturalists' Society.

—— (1959) Garganey breeding in Bedfordshire. *Beds Naturalist* 14: 44–5.

JOHN, A. W. G. and ROSKELL, J. (1985) Jay movements in autumn 1983. *British Birds* 78: 611–37.

KEY, H. A. S. (1946) The birds of Bedfordshire. *Beds Naturalist*. 1: 36–41.

—— (1947) The hard winter and its effect on birdlife. *Beds Naturalist* 2: 37–41.

—— (1953) The Rookery, St Peter's Green, Bedford. *Beds Naturalist* 8: 41.

—— (1950) Jannion Steele-Elliott (1871–1942). *Beds Naturalist* 5: 33–5.

—— (1956) Observations at a Starling roost. *Beds Naturalist* 11: 14–16.

—— (1958) Gravel and birds. *Beds Naturalist* 13: 10–13.

—— (1971) Birds in Bedfordshire; 25 years in retrospect. *Beds Naturalist*. 26: 58–66.

—— and GRIBBLE, F. C. (1950) Observations on a pair of Little Owls. *Beds Naturalist* 5: 29.

KITCHENER, P. G. (1963a) Observations of a pair of Blue Tits breeding in Bedfordshire – 1962. *Beds Naturalist*. 18: 30–1.

—— (1963b) Pheasant landing on water. *Beds Naturalist* 18: 33.

KRAMER, D. (1986) The effects of recreational activity on wintering wildfowl populations at Priory Park Lake, Bedford. *Beds Naturalist* 41: 21–6.

LACK, P. (1986) *The Atlas of Wintering Birds in Britain and Ireland.* Poyser, Calton.

LEVER, C. (1977) *Naturalised Animals of the British Isles.* Hutchinson, London.

—— (1985) *Naturalised Birds of the World.* Longman.

LEWIS, H. (1910–11) Goosanders and Cormorant in Bedfordshire. *British Birds* 4: 288.

LILFORD, Lord (1895) *Birds of Northamptonshire and Neighbourhood.*

LIVETT, A. J. (1975) A census of the Great Crested Grebe in Bedfordshire, 1975. *Beds Naturalist* 30: 33–8.

—— (1976) The decline of the Rook population in Bedfordshire. *Beds Naturalist* 31: 33–8.

—— (1978) Golden Plover survey in Bedfordshire. *Beds Naturalist* 33: 25–8.

LLOYD, P. N. (*c.* 1983) *Early Taxidermy in Bedford, 1860–1940.* Unpublished.

LLOYD, C. S., BIBBY, C. J., and EVERETT, M. J. (1975) Breeding terns in Britain and Ireland in 1969–74. *British Birds* 68: 221–37.

MANSHEAD ARCHAELOGICAL SOCIETY (1981) Remains of a second-century Roman cess pit in Dunstable. *Manshead Arch. J.* 15: 67.

MAURICE, H. G. (1948) Whipsnade's Bird Sanctuary. *Zoo Life*, Summer edn 39–40.

MEAD, C. J. (1973) Movements of British raptors. *Bird Study* 20: 259–86.

—— and HARRISON, J. D. (1979) Sand Martin movements within Britain and Ireland. *Bird Study* 26: 73–86.

MEAD, C. and SMITH, K. (1982) *Hertfordshire Bird Atlas.* Tring.

MEARNS, B. and R. (1988) *Biographies for Birdwatchers.* Academic Press, London.

MEIKLEJOHN, M. F. M. (1937–8) Willow Tit in Bedfordshire. *British Birds* 31: 238.

MILLER, J. A. (1939–40) Scaup in Bedfordshire. *British Birds* 33: 138.

—— (1943–4) Unusual birds in Bedfordshire. *British Birds* 37: 75.

—— (1944–5) Gadwall in Bedfordshire. *British Birds* 38: 56.

MILSOM, T. P. (1987) Aerial insect-hunting by Hobbies in relation to weather. *Bird Study* 34: 179–84.

MOREAU, R. E. (1951) The status of the Quail and some problems of its biology. *British Birds* 44: 257–76.

MORGAN, R. A. and GLUE, D. E. (1981) Breeding survey of Black Redstarts in Britain, 1977. *Bird Study* 28: 163.

MORRIS, F. O. (1895) *A History of British Birds*, Vol. 1, 4th edn (1st edn 1860).

MULLENS and SWANN (1917) *A Bibliography of British Ornithology.*

MARCHANT, J. H., HUDSON, R., CARTER, S. P., and WHITTINGTON, P. (1990) *Population Trends in British Breeding Birds.* Tring.

NAU, B. S. (1974) Bird population in relation to habitat in coniferous and deciduous woodland. *Beds Naturalist* 29: 56–62.

——, BOON, C. R., and KNOWLES, J. P. (1987) *Bedfordshire Wildlife.* Castlemead, Ware.

NEWTON, I. (1975) Movements and mortality of British Sparrowhawks. *Bird Study* 22: 33–45.

NICHOLSON, E. M. (1928–9) Heron census. *British Birds* 22: 270–323.

NIGHTINGALE, B. (1979) Arrival dates of regular summer migrants to Bedfordshire. *Beds Naturalist* 34: 33–4.

—— (1987) Birds new to Bedfordshire – Sabine's Gull. *Beds Naturalist* 42: 48.

—— and SHARROCK, J. T. R. (1982) Seabirds inland in Britain in late April 1981. *British Birds* 75: 558–66.

—— and SMITH, P. (1981) A summary of the wading birds recorded in Bedfordshire 1946–81. *Beds Naturalist* 36: 12–22.

NORTH, G. (1901–3) Unpublished diaries.

NYE, R. A. (1990) Birds new to Bedfordshire (1989) – Black Kite. *Beds Naturalist* 44: 49–50.

O'CONNOR, R. J. and SHRUBB, M. (1986) *Farming and Birds*. Cambridge University Press.

OLDFIELD, P. (1988) Pomarine Skua – short note. *Beds Naturalist* 43: 59–60.

OLDHAM, C. (1908–9) Cirl Bunting singing in October. *British Birds* 2: 204.

O'SULLIVAN, J. M. (1976) Bearded Tits in Britain and Ireland 1966–74. *British Birds* 69: 473–89.

OWEN, M., ATKINSON-WILES, G. L., and SALMON, D. G. (1986) *Wildfowl in Great Britain*. Cambridge University Press, 2nd edn.

PALMER, M. J. (1987) Birds new to Bedfordshire – Green-winged Teal. *Beds Naturalist* 42: 45.

—— (1989) Ring-necked Duck in Bedfordshire. *Beds Naturalist* 44: 51–2.

PATERSON, J. (1910–11) Black Tern in Bedfordshire. *British Birds* 4: 88.

PAYNE, C. S. (1949) Breeding of Short-eared Owl in Bedfordshire. *Beds Naturalist* 4: 51–3.

PEAKALL, D. B. (1962) The past and present status of the Red-backed Shrike in Great Britain. *Bird Study* 9: 198–216.

PERRINS, C. (1987) *Birds of Britain and Europe*. Collins, London.

PIERCY, W. E. K. (1947) Changes in bird populations. *Beds Naturalist* 2: 41–2.

—— (1951a) Heronries in Bedfordshire. *Beds Naturalist* 6: 34–5.

—— (1951b) Great Crested Grebes in Bedfordshire. *Beds Naturalist* 6: 35.

—— (1952) Herons in Bedfordshire. *Beds Naturalist* 6: 352.

PIKE, O. G. (1936–7) Blackbirds' large clutch of eggs. *British Birds* 30: 44.

PLAYER, G. and GOODALL, G. (1988) White Stork in Bedfordshire. *Beds Naturalist* 43: 58.

POTTS, G. R. (1970) Recent changes in the farmland fauna. *Bird Study* 17: 145–66.

—— (1980) The effect of modern agriculture, nest predation and game management on the population ecology of Partridges. *Advances in Ecology Research* 11: 1–82.

PRESTT, I. and MILLS, D. H. (1966) A census of the Great Crested Grebe in Britain, 1965. *Bird Study* 13: 163–203.

REAY, P. J. (1959) Nocturnal Redwing passage. *Beds Naturalist* 15: 38.

REYNOLDS, C. M. (1974) Census of Herons. *Bird Study* 21: 129–34.

RIDDIFORD, N. (1983) Recent declines of Grasshopper Warblers, *Locustella naevia*, at British bird observatories. *Bird Study* 30: 143–8.

ROWAN, W. (1913–14) Shorelark in Bedfordshire. *British Birds* 7: 228.

—— (1914–15) Incursion of Waxwings. *British Birds* 8: 49.

—— (1916–17) Blackbird's nest made of string. *British Birds* 10: 41.

SAGE, B. L. (1959) *A History of the Birds of Hertfordshire*. Barrie and Rockliff, London.

SALMON, D. G. *et al.* (1988) *Wildfowl and Wader Counts 1987–88*. WWT.

SAUNDERS, H. (1889) *An Illustrated Manual of British Birds*.

SAWFORD, B. R. (1984) Pied Flycatcher – confirmed breeding in Bedfordshire. *Beds Naturalist* 39: 14.

SETH-SMITH, D. (1929–30) Irruption of Crossbills. *British Birds* 23: 69.

—— (1931–2) Probable Red-breasted Flycatcher in Bedfordshire. *British Birds* 25: 54.

SHARMAN, F. (1911–12) Tufted Ducks breeding in Bedfordshire. *British Birds* 5: 114.

SHARROCK, J. T. R. (1976) *The Atlas of Breeding Birds in Britain and Ireland*. Poyser, Calton.

SITTERS, H. P. (1986) Woodlarks in Britain, 1968–83. *British Birds* 79: 105–16.

The Birds of Bedfordshire

SMITH, P. (1979) A summary of birds of prey in Bedfordshire, 1946–79. *Beds Naturalist* 34: 28–33.

—— (1982) A summary of Divers, Grebes, Swans, Geese and Ducks in Bedfordshire. *Beds Naturalist* 37: 12–23.

—— (1986) The first breeding record of Ruddy Duck in Bedfordshire. *Beds Naturalist* 41: 52–3.

SMITH, W. G. (1904) *Dunstable – its History and Surroundings.*

SNOW, D. W. (1948) The Willow Tit in Bedfordshire. *Beds Naturalist* 3: 45.

—— (1968) Movements and mortality of British Kestrels. *Bird Study* 15: 65–83.

—— (1969) Some vital statistics of British Mistle Thrushes. *Bird Study* 16: 34–44.

SOPER, F. and D. (1957) Migration of Redwings. *Beds Naturalist* 12: 42.

SPENCER, R. *et al.* (1988) *Rare Breeding Bird Reports*. British Birds.

STAFFORD, J. (1979) The national census of heronries in England and Wales in 1964. *Bird Study* 26: 3–6.

STEELE-ELLIOTT, J. (1897–1901) *The Vertebrate Fauna of Bedfordshire*. Birmingham.

—— (1904) *Victoria County History of Bedford*. Aves Section, 104–37. London.

—— (1909–10) Irruption of Crossbills. *British Birds* 3: 403.

—— (1910–11) Stone Curlew in Bedfordshire. *British Birds* 4: 94.

—— (1915–16) Rose-coloured Starling in Bedfordshire. *British Birds* 9: 29.

—— (1926–7) Spoonbill in Bedfordshire. *British Birds* 20: 202.

—— (1927–8) Peregrine Falcons in Bedfordshire. *British Birds* 21: 14–15.

—— (1928–9) Bitterns in Bedfordshire. *British Birds* 22: 91.

—— (1929–30) Two early records of Mute Swan in Bedfordshire. *British Birds* 23: 306–8.

—— (1930–1) Treecreeper nesting close to ground. *British Birds* 24: 75.

—— (1936) Bedfordshire 'Vermin' Payments, Luton Museum.

TEBUTT, C. F. (1931–2) Black Redstart in Bedfordshire. *British Birds* 25: 54.

TICEHURST, N. F. and JOURDAIN, F. C. R. (1911–12) The distribution of the Nightingale during the breeding season in Great Britain. *British Birds* 5: 2.

TOWLER, C. W. (1945–6) Lesser Whitethroat in Bedfordshire. *British Birds* 39: 94.

TRODD, P. (1986) Bedfordshire Bird List. *Beds Naturalist* 41: 49–51.

—— (1987a) Birds new to Bedfordshire – Blue-winged Teal. *Beds Naturalist* 42: 45–6.

—— (1987b) Spoonbills in Bedfordshire. *Beds Naturalist* 42: 49.

WESTELL, W. P. (1916–17) Rooks nesting in chimneys. *British Birds* 10: 137.

WHITE, D. and R. (1956) Pectoral Sandpiper in Bedfordshire. *Beds Naturalist* 11: 44.

WHITEMAN, R. (1936) Hexton Parish survey. Hexton Parish Council.

WILKINSON, P. J. (1962) The Lesser Whitethroat. *Beds Naturalist* 17: 37–9.

—— (1979) Sand Martin ringing in Bedfordshire. *Beds Naturalist* 34: 23–7.

WILLIAMSON, K. (1975) The breeding bird community of chalk grassland in the Chiltern Hills. *Bird Study* 22: 59–70.

WINSTANLEY, D., SPENCE, R., and WILLIAMSON, K. (1974) Where have all the Whitethroats gone? *Bird Study* 21: 1–14.

WITHERBY, H. F. and TICEHURST, N. F. (1907–8) The spread of the Little Owl from its chief centres of introduction. *British Birds* 1: 335.

WITHERBY, H. F., JOURDAIN, F. C. R., TICEHURST, N. F., and TUCKER, B. W. (1938–41) *The Handbook of British Birds*. Witherby, London.

342

Index of Bird Names

English vernacular names are indexed under the last word and are printed in Roman type. Scientific names are indexed under the genus and appear in italic type. The page numbers of the main species accounts are in bold type and of the *Breeding Bird Atlas* maps in italics. Commonly used English names of sub-species are also included.